Medicine for Ontario

MEDICINE FOR ONTARIO

A
History

by
Charles M. Godfrey, M.D.

Mika Publishing Company
Belleville, Ontario
1979

CONTENTS

Page

Acknowledgements   7
Foreword   9
Chapter I   - The New Century and the New Province   11
Chapter II   - To Turn a Penny   19
Chapter III   - A Doctor's Practice   27
Chapter IV   - King's Prelude   33
Chapter V   - The Father of Medical Education   40
Chapter VI   - From One to Trinity   46
Chapter VII   - Academic Immolation   59
Chapter VIII   - The Art of Being a Doctor   66
Chapter IX   - The Scalpel's Edge   73
Chapter X   - From Rose Hips to Medical Defense   83
Chapter XI   - Victoria Prospers and Passes   94
Chapter XII   - New Country - Old Medicine   143
Chapter XIII   - Bloody Flux, Pus and Miasma   149
Chapter XIV   - A Doomed Phoenix   163
Chapter XV   - From Alms to Grants   174
Chapter XVI   - The Distaff Doctors   186
Chapter XVII   - The Master-Words   191
Chapter XVIII   - Twentieth Century Prelude   209
Chapter XIX   - An Emerging Order   220
Chapter XX   - The Blooding of Medicine   231
Chapter XXI   - The Twentieth Century Promise   244
Tables   252
General Bibliography   257
Chapter Bibliography   258
List of Ontario Doctors   266
Index   293

ACKNOWLEDGEMENTS

During the past ten years, since beginning this project, many friends have helped me to choose the material, write the story and make the difficult decision of what should be omitted. In particular I wish to thank that ever-patient woman, Margaret, who has remained an interested audience and an unremitting, constructive critic. The Physician's Services Incorporated Fund aided by the provision of a research assistant. Others have given unselfish assistance, in particular Ms. Peggy Runacre, who organized the massive material at the Academy of Medicine library and did much of the proof-reading. And, in the background, giving counsel has been Albin T. Jousse — a truly gentle man and a wise doctor.

Toronto 1979   Charles M. Godfrey

FOREWORD

Medicine, like all knowledge, has a past as well as a present and a future ... wrote Alfred Stillé,* in 1884. The future is with us now, complete with current concerns over economics, ethics and empire. The seeds of our harvest were sown in the nineteenth century when Ontario was young and lusty.

To recount what happened in medical practice during that century without looking at other provincial events, means looking through a narrow window. Such a reduced field of vision might lead to a compacting of events and a reduction of variety so that the historian might see a blending of differences into a uniformly, bland, harmonious landscape. That is not the case. While it is common knowledge that doctors are confined by tradition, convention and the principles of self-protection which have maintained this oldest profession, there is ample room in the panorama for change and rebellion.

My bias is that the best doctors are rebels. They resist the conservatism which is the core of medical practice, generated by the Hippocratic injunction to do no harm. They rebel against the world as it is, in an attempt to relieve the pain and suffering of their patients. In doing so they may rebel against themselves, the medical establishment or the government. Given the tools by their training for incisive analysis and speedy execution, doctors have an advantage in that they can effect great changes in a short time. But this frequently demands a refusal to accept facts as they are or appear to be. The credo of Dr. R. Ian MacDonald, who was Head of the post-graduate courses at Sunnybrook Hospital in the 1950's (the finest flowering of Canadian medicine), was "where all think alike, no one thinks". Those words have been worn on the hearts of many Ontario physicians.

Those same physicians were not text-book heroes, virtuous paragons or Fidlesian prototypes. They grew old. They became petty. They were human.

This history shows the role of a few of those humans and that of hundreds of unnamed physicians during those formative years of the nineteenth century and the first quarter of the twentieth. At the end of that time the limits were set for present-day medicine. During those years the level of practice was equal to that in Great Britain, Europe and the United States as there was a constant stream of journals and visits across the borders. There were some differences. In Ontario the public general hospital was usual — in Great Britain the specialty hospital had greater development. In Ontario a provincially appointed licencing board meant that educational institutions could not grant the right to practise. Thus there was no "mushrooming" of medical schools, such as happened in the United States. However, even with the few medical schools which did operate, an enormous amount of energy was spent by many doctors on the educational system. Indeed, the story of medicine in Ontario is closely woven with the history of medical education, and this took place mainly in the capital city. Toronto set the pace, spent the money and was the political hub.

To some, medicine is a matter between a man and a physician. To others it is an arena where individuals, factions, movements and philosophies conflict or co-operate, regardless of pills or potions.

Medicine and doctors, like other social phenomena, change and develop.

> In medicine, perhaps more than in other fields, there is practical value in understanding the main outlines of one's lineage and the special contribution of its component parts.

wrote Dr. J. A. MacFarlane** in 1965. This outline traces some of the lineage to 1920. The developments since then are not yet complete and await an historian of the future.

* *Medical News*, 44:433, 1884.
** *Medical Education in Canada*. Queens Printer, Ottawa. p. 12, 1965.

Chapter I
The New Century and The New Province

*As the inoculation for the small-pox is this day com-
menced at Queenston, and the season of the year very
favourable, the subscribers propose inoculating immediately in the town of Newark, and throughout the
country of Lincoln, on the most reasonable terms. The
poor inoculated gratis.*

Robert Kerr
James Muirhead
Newark, January 25, 1797.

There was the land. Millions of rough, untamed, uninhabit-
ed acres which made up the Province of Upper Canada. Marshes,
bogs, bone-chilling winters, scorching summers, mosquitoes and
loneliness. In a narrow rim, clinging to the shores of the St.
Lawrence, Lake Ontario and Lake Erie, thirty thousand people
lived — mainly United Empire Loyalist settlers, disbanded soldiers,
garrison and officer personnel, and a sprinkling of immigrants who
were beginning to settle the land.

To provide medical care, there were a few active army
surgeons and physicians and those who had been discharged or
retired from the services. Most had received their medical education
in the United Kingdom. They were not wanting in knowledge or
desire to provide the best services in medicine to this hinterland, as
may be seen by the advertisement, signed by Dr. Kerr and Dr.
Muirhead, which appeared in *The Journal* of Newark. Both these
men were military surgeons. Muirhead was noted in the *Upper
Canada Gazette* of 1802, in his care of a man who had sustained a
chest injury affecting the lungs, to have "skillful applications in
care ... so much to this cure, much the greatest that has been effected
since the Province was established".

With the revolt of the thirteen British colonies in America,
thousands of British Americans sought asylum in Canada. The
majority entered Lower Canada and awaited the completion of a

land survey to secure an allotment in Upper Canada. Their names were recorded on a United Empire List (U.E. List) which entitled them, after the necessary legislation was passed, to take up their land grants, and also for their sons and daughters to acquire two hundred acres.

Physicians who adhered to the Crown in the U.S. were numerous and probably greater in proportion than any of their legal or clerical confreres. Most doctors remained in the States after the Revolution and pursued their calling unmolested, their persons and property generally respected, except perhaps in the larger cities. Those sympathizing doctors who openly cheered the Loyalist cause were driven out, ending in Canada. Many of these were numbered on the U.E. List, including Solomon Jones, Surgeon's Mate, Loyal Rangers; Dr. Sparham, Hospital Mate Reduced, who had served in the war of 1763; James Stewart, Surgeon's Mate; Dr. Charles Blake, Surgeon 34th Regiment; Dr. David Burns, Surgeon 71st Regiment; James Connor, Surgeon's Hospital Mate; Dr. Robert Guthrie, Surgeon, Butlers Rangers; Dr. George Smythe, Surgeon, Loyal Rangers; Dr. Thomas Wright, Surgeon, 1st battalion.

Now not all those who were listed were qualified physicians. Many were rough-and-ready military surgeons. The surgeon's mate was an assistant to the surgeon and might have had at best a little formal training. But, anyone offering his services as a doctor among the English-speaking people of Canada and who was able to show any evidence of qualification was welcomed. Most of them have passed into history without further note of their work.

After a while, more highly qualified physicians came, not out of love for the British institutions, but rather to earn a living. Some of them had a degree in medical education acquired in a United States medical school; some had diplomas from various institutions which were beginning to spring up in the United States. As the villages along the Ontario waterways formed and grew, so did the number of unproven practitioners.

John Graves Simcoe, Lieutenant-Governor of Upper Canada, realized that Newark (Niagara-on-the-Lake) was too close for comfort to the newly formed republic to the south. He established a new seat of government at York (now Toronto) and the legislative council met there for the first time in 1797. Twelve log houses had been hastily erected near the swampy outlet of the Don River in 1796, but settlement grew slowly and no physicians showed an interest in settling in an area that was still wilderness. By 1798 another dozen houses had sprung up — a dreary dismal place not even possessing the characteristics of a village. There was no church, no chapel, or schoolhouse. There was no inn. The Government House and the garrison were about a mile from York with a thick intervening woods. The census of 1801 gives a population of 336 which rose to 599 by 1809.

James MacAulay (1759-1822) was the first physician to be listed among the residents of York. He was an extensive land owner as well as an army surgeon. His long military service included being captured with Colonel Simcoe's regiment, the Queen's Rangers, at the surrender by General Cornwallis in 1781 at Yorktown to the Americans. He followed Simcoe to Upper Canada and became a member of the New Queen's Rangers. Among his duties, he was Senior Hospital Officer and Surgeon to the Forces and he was stationed in Quebec for several years. During the War of 1812, MacAulay moved to Kingston where he lived until the early part of 1817, when he was placed on half-pay and returned to York. His homestead was situated in the present Trinity Square and he held a patent of land which covered the area between Queen, Yonge, College and Chestnut Streets. The district between James St. and Queen St. was known as MacAulay Town. MacAulay did little private practice, being more involved in civic affairs and was a member of the Building Committee of St. James Parish Church. He was a senior member of the Upper Canada Medical Board from its formation until his death in 1822.

Dr. John Gamble, another early army surgeon in Upper Canada, was born in Ireland. He studied in Edinburgh and emigrated to America in 1779. He entered the King's service as assistant surgeon to the General Hospital in New York, and following the peace of 1783, he practised in Saint John, New Brunswick, and was later appointed assistant surgeon to the New Queen's Rangers. Transferring to the York Garrison, he remained until 1802 and then retired on half-pay to Kingston, where he practised until his death. Mrs. Simcoe reports in her diary that one of his more famous patients was Chief Joseph Brant of the Six Nations Indians. Gamble had four sons and nine daughters, and their descendants were prominent in the civil and military life of Canada — a common pattern with medical families. The eldest son, John William, married a daughter of Dr. James MacAulay and later became Colonel of the 2nd battalion in York Militia. A grandson served in the Afghan wars and died in the Khyber in 1879. A second son, William, built the "Old Mill" on the Humber River in 1848. He was a postmaster, merchant, woollen manufacturer, lumberman, and owned many other small businesses.

David Burns, another surgeon to the Queen's Rangers, was gazetted in 1791. However, in 1792 he was proclaimed Clerk of the Crown, a post he held until 1806. A mark of the erudition of this surgeon may be seen from a list of certain books advertised as "missing" from his library. The titles included Plutarch's Lives, 1st Volume; Voltaire's Works in French; Guthrie's History of Scotland; Swift's Works; and the Works of Molière. Burns never practised as a civilian, but carried on medical duties in his capacity as military surgeon.

Those duties frequently included protection against small-pox. Dr. Robert Kerr, Surgeon to the 2nd battalion of Sir John Johnson's Royal New Yorkers, came to Newark as surgeon to the Indian Department in 1788. He and Dr. James Muirhead, The Royal American Regiment of Foot, carried out what must have been the first incident of preventive medicine in Upper Canada. They are recorded as having inoculated Captain Brant and 160 men, women and children of Brant's tribe near Burlington Bay against smallpox. The native population was particularly susceptible to the pox and great efforts were made to protect them. Dr. MacAulay successfully inoculated 100 Mississaugan Indians, using material from active cases of smallpox. This method of prevention had been popularized early in the 18th century. It was called variolation and had many defects, the principal one being that it frequently caused smallpox rather than preventing it.

Another of the group of British army surgeons who was an important figure in Upper Canada was the Honourable Peter Russell. He arrived in Canada in 1792 with William Osgoode, who became Chief Justice of the Province. Russell held many administrative posts and acted as Lieutenant-Governor when Simcoe returned to England in 1796. But prior to his political appointments, he qualified for medical practice in Cambridge and was gazetted as surgeon to the 74th Foot in 1761. It is not known that he actually practised medicine in Upper Canada. Many doctors did not practise medicine. Thomas Stoyel who came to York from the U.S.A. in 1799, eschewed medicine and ran a hotel and brewery. In spite of this, he contributed largely to ministry missions and institutions of the Methodist church and when he died, he was noted in the *Christian Guardian* of February 29, 1832, as the "oldest inhabitant of the Town of York — a man of integrity and Christian propriety and one of the first Methodists in Toronto."

14

William Lee, a Surgeon's Mate to the 49th Regiment, was appointed to the Indian Department and moved to York in 1807. He cared for Indians who frequently visited York and usually encamped on the bank of the bay. Dr. H. Scadding, D.D., noted in his book *Toronto of Old* that Lee had comforted the Indians in their primitive wigwams administering from an ordinary tin cup "nauseous draughts" to the sick and convalescing squaws. Lee also visited settlements of Indians as far north as the Penetanguishene, travelling the trails with his medicines and instruments in saddlebags. In 1816, he received an appointment as Gentleman Usher of the Black Rod to the Legislative Council and was appointed Secretary of the Upper Canada Medical Board. So he, like many of his fellows, preferred to cure the country's ills by legislation, rather than prescription.

With the removal of the capital of Upper Canada to Newark from Kingston, that town returned to its status of a military and naval base. York, which in turn succeeded Newark, on the other hand, strove to play the part of the capital city. Realizing the lack of educational facilities, Parliament in the 1806 session in York voted £400 for the purchase of a collection of instruments suitable and proper for illustrating the principles of natural philosophy, geography, astronomy and mathematics. The resident physicians, who had had the benefit of some university education, gave a series of lectures and courses. These provided a social event to the small community, whose only alternative activities were going to church or to one of the six hotels. Dr. Robert Horne, Surgeon to the Glengarry Light Infantry Regiment, was prominent in these lectures. He was joined by the only civilian practitioner of medicine in York — William Warren Baldwin. Graduating as an M.D. in Edinburgh, Baldwin practised in Ireland before coming to York in 1798. He travelled with his family in an open boat to take up land in the Township of Clare where his family remained until 1812 when they moved to York to join him. Being an entrepreneur and finding that medicine was not sufficiently lucrative, he qualified for and was admitted to the Law Society of Upper Canada. In addition, he opened a classical school, in which to instruct "twelve boys in reading, writing, classics and arithmetic. The tariff for each boy, 8 Guineas per annum, 1 Guinea entrance and one quarter of it to be supplied by each of the boys on the opening of the school".

After his admission to the Bar, Baldwin divided his life between medicine and law. This pattern was not uncommon with many physicians qualified as lawyers. An even larger number who practised medicine took part in the Government at the same time. It was not uncommon for either of these groups to leave court or parliament in the middle of a process to repair a fractured leg or to attend a confinement.

In the early days of Upper Canada it was difficult to earn a living as a physician. The sparse population and the widely scattered settlements made it necessary for doctors to be circuit riders, and the general poverty of the population did not encourage physicians to settle. Robert Gourlay wrote: "Nobody above the rank of a common cow-herd would travel around a circle of 40 or 50 miles in the wilderness for the pittance which could be collected ...".

Even though there was a low incentive to practise medicine there was a firm legal basis for medical practice in Ontario, which was remarkable, and there was a great need for doctors. With the formation of the new province of Upper Canada in 1791, a physician could practise in Canada only under the terms of the statutes which had become law in 1788 and were a collection of Acts passed in the Parliament of Great Britain. These prevented persons from practising physic or surgery or midwifery without licence. Examination and approval of applicants was by the Governor or Commander-in-Chief. The Acts prove that a strong desire existed even then to protect the public and to prevent quackery. Penalty for violation of the Act was severe: £20 for the first offence; £50 for the second offence; and £100 plus three months for each subsequent offence.

This Act was the precursor of one passed in 1795 entitled "An Act to Regulate the Practice of Physic and Surgery" which again restricted the practice of the aforementioned skills to those licensed. The penalty for unauthorized practice was increased to £100. A licensing board, the Upper Canada Medical Board, was to be formed. The Act was repealed in 1806, as it exempted military doctors, those with a degree from the British Empire and those who had practised since 1791. There were few others. It had also become evident that people scattered in remote areas often had no medical aid upon which to rely; therefore, if a neighbour aided in delivery of a child, she ran the risk of a fine, notwithstanding the fact that she may have been the only help available. Obviously, the Act was unenforceable.

The 1818 Act (C.S.U.S., (1859) c. 40, at 436) was the first effective legislation concerning the medical profession. It authorized a Medical Board to "examine all persons desirous to apply for a licence to practise Physic, Surgery and Midwifery, or either of them" (Subsect. 2). This Act recognized the shortcomings of the previous legislation by establishing "that nothing in this Act shall extend to prevent any female from practising midwifery in this province, or to require such female to take out such licence". The penalty for practising without a licence was still to be £100 (Subsect. 3).

One of the earliest candidates to appear before the Board and to be found fit to practise was Dr. Pitkin Gross of Murray (now called Brighton). On receiving his licence, he returned to serve as doctor to an area of almost fifty square miles. When a call came from Carrying Place that a lumberman had sustained injury to his abdomen, Dr. Gross, without anaesthetic, incised the abdomen, removed a portion of the omentum and washed out the cavity, without sterile technique. The patient recovered. During his forty-five years of practice, he "made do" with only a few instruments. On one occasion, he performed amputation of the thigh, to save the patient's life, using a scythe blade as the amputation instrument.

During its first year, the Board, consisting of Drs. James MacAulay, Christopher Widmer, William Lyons and Grant Powell, established a high standard and failed eight of sixteen candidates. (One of the duties of the Board was to examine servicemen for pension rating, and during the following year it was necessary to extend the Board sessions to four times yearly.)

Many physicians who had been practising prior to the passage of the Act were exempted. One of these was Christopher Beswick. He was the only doctor north of Oak Ridges in the York area, and was remarkable in that when he settled in Newmarket, in 1809, he was 86 years of age! At that time, he was accompanied by Gabriel Lount, father of Samuel Lount, who was one of the leaders in the 1837 Rebellion. Dr. Beswick continued practising in that area, as far east as Stouffville, until 1837, when he died at the age of 118 years.

In 1827, "An Act to Amend the Laws Regulating the Practice of Physic, Surgery and Midwifery" in the province was passed. Section II set out that anyone showing a diploma from any University or from the Royal College of Physicians and Surgeons in London, or a commission or warrant as physician or surgeon in the services, could be granted the necessary licence to practise upon payment of two shillings and sixpence. Section IV established that anyone resident in Upper Canada prior to the War of 1812, practising in the profession, could upon presentation of a certificate from three licensed practitioners, receive a licence to practise. Section VI maintained that part of the 1818 legislation which exempted female midwives from requiring a licence. Section VII limited the penalty for unauthorized practice to no longer than six months and/or not more than £25. In spite of all these words, there are few records of any prosecutions for illegal practice, as cases would have been tried in local courts and were not recorded in any Law Registers. The colony, as did the mother country, made many efforts to suppress quackery with legislation, but found the same difficulty in enforcement of the law. It was cheaper and easier to self-dose or go to a friendly quack, than go to a licensed doctor, who had a monopoly over prescribing. The unlicensed continued to ply their trade.

As the population increased, so did the number of applicants for licence. Between 1830 and 1836, the Board awarded certificates to 100 to 164 candidates. One candidate, who was failed, claimed he had lost his course credits and could not remember what courses he had attended. Another reject failed "Pharmaceutical Chemistry." Jonathan Foot, who had graduated from Vermont Medical College, passed his licence examination in 1830. He set up his practice in Whitby and continued to practise medicine until his death at 81. He was joined in the area by George Low, who practised in Bowmanville and Darlington after immigrating to the country in 1833.

By the mid-30's the profession felt it was strong enough to govern itself, and several Bills aimed in that direction were proposed. This action was opposed by the Royal College of Surgeons of London on the basis that their Charter gave jurisdiction over the colony, and the basic Act of 1827 remained in force until 1865. In the intervening years, the emphasis changed from who should practise to attempts to control the study and practice of medicine. Homeopaths and eclectics, who were at constant odds with orthodox (allopathic) medicine finally achieved their own separate legislative authority in 1859 and 1861 respectively.

But for the first part of the century, a great amount of time was spent in examining and granting licences to those who could present adequate proof of competence — in spite of the fact there existed a large number of settlements in the remote areas where medical care was a luxury to be sought only after home and neighbours' remedies had failed. In addition, many competent doctors chose to go into government employment where they could help — or hinder — their medical colleagues.

Chapter II
To Turn a Penny

They came generally, not for attachment to the British flag but to turn a penny. Sometimes they had a degree of medical education which had been acquired in the United States medical schools; sometimes they knew a little about the use of drugs; but too frequently they only knew how to deceive the people by arrant quackery.

William Canniff, M.D.
The Medical Profession in Upper Canada

Many of the Loyalists coming to Canada had minimal education but were passed as doctors if they showed even the slimmest evidence of ability. Soon, quackery and poor medical practice stories appeared as news items in the newspapers with increasing frequency. A letter in the *Kingston Gazette* on March 3, 1812, complained of a doctor who inoculated his daughter with smallpox, thereby starting an epidemic which devastated the neighbourhood. The practitioner had used variolation, which had gone out of favor with the discovery by Edward Jenner that protection could be gained by vaccinating with cowpox, without the risk of causing smallpox, in 1800.

This matter was taken up by Reverend John Strachan. Arriving in Upper Canada, an impoverished teacher in 1791, this gritty, tough-minded Scot rapidly became a power in politics. Two credos dominated his life; the first: to maintain the preeminence of the Anglican Church, and the second: to found a school of medicine. He became the backbone of the Family Compact, as teacher and religious instructor to the children of the elite. The Family Compact — so branded by the editor-agitator William Lyon Mackenzie — was made up of the appointed ruling class and government officials in a province which was becoming full of "levellers and democrats". Strachan cultivated toryism in the sons of the local gentry and soon became a prominent figure in York and the province. With each of the succession of colonial governors, he addressed letters asking for a seat on the Legislative Council which functioned as advisor to the governor. He confessed, with frankness, that his "motives were not altogether disinterested", as with an appointment for himself and the political gains of his students in the Lower House of Parliament of the provinces, "I shall, by means of my pupils, possess a growing influence ...".

Strachan became a polemicist and wrote many letters to the editor about his major concern — health. He listed many horror stories of poor medical care he had seen as a minister for the congregation and charged:

> The welfare of the people calls aloud for some legislative provision that shall remedy this increasing evil; any examination, however slight, will terrify nine-tenths of the present race (of doctors).

The *Kingston Gazette* of June 2, 1812, carried a letter about a bill received from a "self-taught" physician of the province:

> The estates of Mrs. John Gould, debit. To Doctor, For Medsin and Attendants whene he was chokd with a large peas of Butter not of meat.

Strachan was outraged at such incompetence.

Unfortunately, the denseness of the forest often affected its inhabitants and the early pioneers were no exception to superstitions. Quacks "come and go from house to house like pedlars, dealing out their poisonous pills and herbs, and holding out to the gaping ignorant the advantages of a republican government", according to Canniff, eminent historian of medicine in Ontario.

Rather than seek a doctor's advice, or take it having sought it — "they go into the forest, search out a branch ... of last year's growth, fasten a thread ... then tie as many knots in it as they figure they'll have bouts of what ails them. They go home, convinced the charm will stop their illness."

But not all the unlicensed were unscrupulous. One — Samuel Thomson — began his practice in "an honest endeavour to be useful to his fellow creatures", with "nothing to guide him but his own experiences" (and a copy of Buchan's *Domestic Medicine*, which was a widely read popular home medical guide). While he admitted that he had read only one book to lift the veil of ignorance, he neatly premised that his ignorance "left his mind unshackled by the visionary theories and opinions of others." He is not known to have practised in Ontario, but his many disciples — Thomsonians

— read his book *New Guide to Health: or Botanic Family Physician,* which was published in Hamilton in 1832, and later in Belleville.

He declared that "all disease is caused by clogging the system, and all disease removed by restoring the digestive powers ...". Food fuelled the heat on which life depended — for heat was life, as cold was death.

Thomson and his followers took exception to the orthodox view of fighting fevers, the body's only mechanism — they said — for self-healing. "Fever is a friend, not an enemy," as regular doctors considered it. "No person ever died of fever", maintained their teacher, "for as death approaches the patient grows cold ...". His favorite prescription was steaming — described as water being heated by throwing it on red-hot stones.

He compounded his medicine from herbs and "natural" remedies and devised six special remedies. No. 1 — to cleanse the stomach ...; No. 2 — to retain the internal vital heat ... and cause free perspiration; No. 3 — to scour the stomach and bowels, and remove the canker; No. 4 — consisted of bitters to correct the bile and restore digestion; No. 5 — was syrup for dysentry, to strengthen ...; No. 6 — was rheumatic drops, to remove pain ... .

His medicine chest typically held:

> 1 oz. emetic herb (lobelia)
> 2 oz. cayenne
> ½ lb. Bayberry root bark in powder
> 1 lb. Poplar bark
> 1 lb. ginger
> 1 pt. "rheumatic drops" (principally wines or "fourth
>   proff brandy", gum myrrh, and cayenne)

The medical establishment of what Gourlay once termed "regular-bred doctors", considered Thomsonians a stomach canker to be removed. They tarred Thomsonians with the same brush as quacks, saying that any young man "disciplined to manual labour" could cast off his homespuns and don broadcloth to call himself a doctor. For many years, Thomsonians practised in open defiance of the law, without licences. Actually, Thomson solved the problem of licensure by simply printing a certification as the first page of each book. This "certificate" stated that the buyer, having paid $20.00, was given the right of preparing and using the system of medical practice devised by Samuel Thomson. This, therefore, constituted him as a member of the Friendly Botanic Society. The page was suitable for framing and could then be hung in the practitioner's office. Furthermore, if the buyer wished to buy a second volume of the *Botanic Family Physician*, the price was $10.00, if the original certificate had not been lost, given away — or sold. In this way the Society made sure that anyone who was going to practise the "System of Medicine" was qualified to do so through having read the book.

The botanical movement was a powerful force in the United States, particularly New England, where Thomson had farmed before becoming a "physician". There were Thomsonian Medical Societies in many cities and national conventions were held in the 1850's. The System included agents who sold rights to practise and a method of pre-payment for medical care. Naturally, the organization spread into Upper Canada and eventually commanded so much power that parliament granted them the right to licences and to practise. The Thomsonians called their system Botanic or Eclectic, the latter term deriving from the philosophy of H. Boerhaave (1668-1738), the Dutch teacher, who chose certain portions from each of several medical theories. There was a "regular" eclectic school of medical thoughts, which continued into the twentieth century, after absorbing the Thomsonians.

The fine line between quackery and doctory was blurred as much medical treatment was on an empirical basis. One doctor presented his bill to a father, and in all fairness, deducted the sum of £6 for "killing your son". It seemed the physician brought small-pox along with his black bag. It almost seemed as if the quality of doctoring was a self-fulfilling prophesy — people expected it to be bad — so they were never disappointed. Surgical techniques, in keeping with current knowledge, centered on amputation and tumor removal, with alcohol used to deaden the pain.

Medicinals used by "regular-breds" were prescribed ruthlessly, frequently with catastrophic effect. This pattern of practice was the best which medicine could offer. For marsh miasmata with its nausea, lassitude, and giddiness, or for remitting and intermitting fevers the treatment was massive doses of cinchona, bark of a tree in Peru.

Many children died from over-dosing with calomel, a standard pediatric medicine, or excess bleeding. Its effects were startling. The poor child would lie on her side "... for perhaps days, unable to swallow even liquids without torture, and with the tongue swollen to three or four times its usual size, protruded far beyond the lips, intensely sore, while from its tip a constant string of adhesive and stinking mucus was discharging". Thomson had a better treatment. "Come, come to me, ye afflicted ones! I use only God's holy herbs in treatment of your ailments", he wrote in his book.

Although Thomson built his system on "folk" medicine, using local herbs, its success was the result of many factors. It appeared about the time of "Jacksonian democracy", which emphasized the ability of anyone to do anything he desired. The ideas of self-treatment, and self-medication, were seized by the American public, who saw such actions as opposition to monopolistic legislation, which restricted the practice of medicine. Thomsonians actively proselytized workmen and frequently gave lectures at Mechanic's Institutes. (The first Mechanic's Institute in Ontario was established at York in 1830). In addition to speaking to the working man, the system relied heavily on the woman in the house, not only for helping in the preparation of the herbs, but also acting as a midwife. But in spite of its successes, the movement lost considerable impetus with the death of Thomson in 1843.

Thomsonians did not bleed patients, while a regular physician would no sooner go to see his patient without his bleeding lancet then he would go to church without his common prayer book. The blood-letting was frequently drastic, in keeping with the principles laid down by William Cullen (1710-1790), whose book *The Works of William Cullen* was reprinted many times with the last edition in 1827. But not all physicians agreed with his principles. Dr. James Hunter, of Niagara and later Whitby, was accused of leeching five quarts of blood from a girl in his care. She died.

"It was a d—d pity," said Dr. Cyrus Sumner, of Niagara, "they hadn't employed Granny Huff and two or three men, and then they might have killed her sooner ...".

"A devil of a case" (in Sumner's opinion) was that of a Peggy Berry to whom Dr. Hunter had given "some drops to make her sleep." She did, permanently. Hunter, who objected to such unsolicited remarks sued Sumner and was awarded £5 damages for slander. This was why the Thomsonians became popular — no amount of lobelia or mustard could ever wreak as much havoc as mercury or laudanum.

After a while medical science decreed that zinc was more fashionable, in pill form, as opposed to the usual powder form for mercury. For fevers, it was said to be equally effective but did not diminish the tremors. Science then switched to charcoal powders. They didn't work either.

This therapeutic triumph was succeeded by Fowler's Solution of Arsenic. Whether it was mercury, zinc, charcoal, or arsenic — the methods rarely varied. First, empty the stomach with an emetic (possibly mustard), then clear the bowels with senna pod tea (a gentle aperient), after which the prescription would be given. To round off the treatment the patient was blistered and bled, and given arsenic with opium added. And all of this was in keeping with the most advanced teachings.

By 1815 the *Kingston Gazette* urged that parliament act strongly against the number of quacks in medicine. Strachan wrote "The province is overrun with self-made physicians who have no pretension to knowledge of any kind". He thundered for a legal remedy to the "increasing evil" of the ignorant who tried to cure all diseases with opium or mercury.

With the new legislation of 1818, government tried to bring medicine under control in the province by a Medical Board which would issue licences to practise, after suitable examination.

The original Board members were Drs. James MacAulay, Christopher Widmer, Grant Powell and William Lyons. But although there was a Board, the problem remained that there were not sufficient candidates of reasonable standard to provide medical services which would take the place of the quackery and other medical horrors. It was becoming clear that the main problem was that there was no local source of doctor candidates. England was too far away and it was too expensive for the sons of Upper Canada residents to study there; and to send students to the United States resulted in candidates who as Strachan put it, "commonly learned little beyond anarchy in politics . . .". The obvious solution was to have Upper Canada train its own physicians.

This was a surprising conclusion, in view of a population of 300,000 most of whom were farmers and labourers. Yet the desire to teach and to have a medical school became and remained a driving force in the province for the next century. To many, a medical school was a source of nationalist pride. Dr. W. Henry wrote, during his stay in York:

> *One thing is much wanted here, a chartered Medical*
> *Institution; and as there are several able men; and good*

clinical facilities at the hospital, it is to be hoped that those parents who wish to train their children to the Healing Art, may not be much longer obliged to send them to the States for that purpose . . . Such Institutions being not only valuable to the community, considered with relation to health, but reflecting lustre on comparatively obscure places, and raising others, already of note to greater distinction.

To others it offered opportunity for self-satisfaction and moral gratification. Why else would individual practitioners have advertised for students? Teaching did not mean more income, and indeed, in many an instance during the growing period of medical schools, the fees from private practice were necessary to pay the school expenses — to buy the bonds and stocks which were necessary to fund needed expansion. Certainly John Rolph was not motivated by money, as is evidenced by Sir Francis Hincks' statement, ". . . never a man less likely influenced by pecuniary conditions". Even non-physicians were obsessed with the idea of having a medical school. Sir John A. Macdonald, when a young man just commencing law practice in Kingston, pointed out "am exceedingly anxious that my native city — practically — should have the honour of being a university city, a seat of learning".

Thus for Macdonald it was a matter of great satisfaction for the Presbyterian church and the former capital city to have a medical school. To others it became a mission to induct new members into an elitist group, who barely a century previously had stood in grace with God, who provided the holy power to heal. They now continued their Christian mission. To Rolph, Aikins, Geikie, Bovell, Canniff, Hodder and Barrett, it was a driving force which shaped medical practice in Ontario.

Strachan, by now a major force in the colony and the mother country, used his political powers to obtain a Royal Charter, to establish King's College, which included a medical faculty. In addition to receiving a large land endowment for the college, plus annual support from the taxes, Strachan, as Archdeacon of York, was named President.

But Strachan's success in securing this grant from the British government was overwhelming for others who led provincial affairs. The Canadian House of Assembly was by no means convinced that the Church of England was the best agency for King's College and with the arrival of a new Lieutenant-Governor, Sir

John Colborne, there was a change of direction and instead of building King's College, a school for classical education, Upper Canada College, was opened in Toronto.

It was well that John Strachan lived to a ripe old age, because he waited another fifteen years before seeing his burning desire for a medical college take substance and survive.

Chapter III

A Doctor's Practice

My father's practice was very laborious on account of the terrible state of the roads, especially in the Spring and Autumn.

History of Burford

Whether he took his half-pay from the military and retired or came as an emigrant, the doctor had little trouble finding work to do. From Bytown (now Ottawa) to Windsor, the early settlements offered opportunity to practise and to grow with the country. Dr. Archibald Chisholm practised in London about 1827 when there were 113 people recorded in the settlement, and as the town grew to 1,846 by 1840 he was joined by William J. Cornish, Elam Stimson and George Moore. Stimson, who had originally set up in St. Catharines and Galt, finally moved to London where he was coroner and physician to the jail. Of course, the doctor's practice extended over the whole countryside.

Farther west at Fort Malden, later to be called Windsor, Drs. George Anthony and William Harby, were the original garrison medical officers who also took care of civilians located near the fort. They were succeeded by Robert Richardson and Cyrus Sumner, the latter being an American-trained physician who had spent some time in Upper Canada. In their rounds of practice they encountered the common problems noted by other Canadians, and recorded in Robina and Kathleen Lizars' *In The Days of the Canada Company.*

Travellers in those days, if differing on most subjects, were one as to the mosquitoes; they travelled with torches, veils and lotions, and the Indian's terror of hell told of mosquitoes with probosces of brass.

More upsetting than the discomfort caused by the mosquito was the disease it carried. Bytown, in 1826, saw the beginning of the construction of the Rideau Canal, which resulted in an increase in population from two or three settlers to more than 2,000 within one year. The land was swampy and wet, and ague became prevalent in its most severe form. During the years of 1826-27-28 John McTaggart, an engineer, reported few could work because of the fever and ague — doctors and all were laid low together. One of these doctors was Alexander James Christie, who arrived in 1826. In addition to taking care of the sickness, he established *The Bytown Gazette,* the first newspaper published in the settlement. He also edited *The Canadian Magazine.*

James Stewart joined Christie in 1827 and continued practising in Bytown until 1848. He ministered to the settlers while Dr. John Edward Rankin, an army surgeon, took care of the workmen on the canal. Stewart returned to his army duties during the Crimean War and then came back to Canada and settled at Picton, Ontario in 1854. His partner was a fellow graduate, T.F. McQueen, who later was in charge of the cholera sheds from Cornwall to Brockville. In the latter town McQueen had contact with Dr. Solomon Jones of the U.E. List, who had settled close to Brockville in 1811. Jones was a rough-and-ready type of surgeon, who, it was reported, advised two farmers who had found the remains of a dead tramp in the corner of a fence, that they should not bother sending for a coroner to hold an inquest, but rather should make a cheap coffin and inter the remains. He contributed two dollars towards defraying the expenses. After he had left, the farmers searched the pockets of the corpse and found two dollars and fifty cents. The coffin was made and a religious service held, and when the burial rites were finished it was discovered that a balance of one dollar and fifty cents remained unspent — by mutual consent, it was invested in alcohol.

Actually Jones had been preceded by another American, James Schofield. The latter came to Canada in 1795 and in addition to practising medicine, built the first iron forge in Upper Canada. He served with the Canadian forces in the War of 1812 and was succeeded in his practice by his son, Peter, who was, ironically, a surgeon in the United States Army during the 1812 War.

Peter would not have had any contact whatsoever with Dr. Walter Henry but his father had several meetings with this redoubtable staff surgeon who was stationed at various times in York, Niagara, Quebec and Kingston. Henry wrote an account of his life *Trifles From My Port-folio By a Staff Surgeon* and in this he described life in the service, including the Napoleonic campaigns, the post-mortem examination he carried out on Napoleon, and his experiences in the Nepalese War in India in 1816-1817. He cared for many of the political leaders in Upper Canada as well as the garrison at Kingston during the cholera epidemic.

While not practising, he described the problems of wintering in Canada which faced his fellow practitioners:

> *An oppressive feeling of melancholy comes over one in passing through the gloomy recesses of a Canadian forest, seeing at every step the decay of vegetable matter ... all is cheerless, and unadorned, and monotonous, gloom and silence.*

One of his civilian colleagues was James Sampson. After service in the 1812 War, Sampson settled on half-pay in Kingston and remained in practice there over the next fifty years. During that time he served as mayor on three occasions and was a prime mover in the founding of the Kingston General Hospital and the Medical Faculty. Parts of his practice took him around the Bay of Quinte and Belleville. One of the earliest practitioners in this region was John Gilchrist, the first physician to be licensed to practise by the Upper Canada Medical Board in 1819. He was joined by brothers, John and Hiram, who practised in Port Hope and finally by Mathew, who practised in Colborne.

The settlement of Otonobee was given a great impetus with the Peter Robinson emigration from the south of Ireland in 1825 and 1826, when in 1826 more than 5,000 people were transported to the area. Before their arrival, all was wilderness north of the Newcastle district, far removed from the settlement tracts. The settlers addressed Sir Peregrine Maitland in 1826, and expressed thanks and gratitude to Dr. Reade for his active, skilful and unremitting care. G.H. Reade, the ship's surgeon in charge of the overseas passage, kept detailed records of the emigrant families, and noted:

Timothy Regan

> *came on board sickly, took fever on June 2, Died at Quebec Hospital. Wife took sick shortly after, produced a child in the 8th month. convalescent in Quebec, hurried off to Lachine. Arrived on Saturday evening. Took dangerously sick on Sunday and died at 12 o'clock on Tuesday — Child died and was buried in Kingston. Two boys and Two girls — very fine children are left orphans. I left eight dollars belonging to them in Mr. Reade's charge — their chest by some mistake had been left at Quebec. (This list compiled by John Thompson, Surgeon R.N.)*

At Prescott, Dr. W.J. Scott provided medical care to the immigrants from the 26th July to 19th August 1826, at 10 shillings per diem. He must have had great empathy for the immigrants as he himself had come from Dublin in 1814. Prior to setting up practice in Prescott, he had been employed by the North-West Company and spent a winter at Cumberland House.

Another Irish physician in the locality was Dr. James Haskins. He practised in Belleville and later at Trenton and Frankford. While Scott led an arduous life with the trading company, Haskins led a solitary and melancholy life contemplating the Trent River and other parts of the country. A posthumous publication *The Poetical Works of James Haskins* reflects how deeply moved he was by the country. Susanna Moodie, a noted early Canadian writer, recognized this:

> *neglected son of genius! Thou has past — in broken hearted loneliness — away.*

But for each withdrawn physician who led a reclusive life and devoted himself to medicine only, there was another one who was both a physician and a foremost member of the business community. William McGill of Oshawa was such a man. He was one of the first to practise in that area. McGill invested any profits from his practice in the industries of the town of Oshawa, including the Cabinet Factory, the Hall Works, the original Stove Company, the Masson Works and McGill Works. His biographer noted that "these investments proved more for the public good then his own benefit".

McGill was contemporary to R. Whichelo Clark, who reported to Canniff a "Munchhausen" episode on returning from an all-night confinement. On riding around the corner he saw eight large wolves drawn up in file right across the road:

> *My mare was at this sight all but unmanageable, and it was all I could do with spur and club to prevent her from turning and running back. Aided by my spurs and club and yelling with all the power of my lungs, I urged her to within twenty paces of the brutes, who were snarling and showing their lovely white teeth perfection ... I made a bee-line for the nearest settlement as tight as a hard gallop would allow. This was in 1834.*

Not so flamboyant was a letter William Allison of Brooklin sent to Dr. T.E. Kaiser who wrote *A History of The Medical Profession of The County of Ontario*. Kaiser in addition to practising in Oshawa was a member of the Legislature.

Allison reported:

> *there is nothing in my life worth noticing. I only tried to earn a living by my profession in the plainest manner possible. If I have succeeded or not, I leave my friends to judge. I have altogether retired from practice and live in obscurity; am 84 years of age in rather infirm health. Thank you for your kindness in taking notice of an old man, I hope you will succeed in your enterprise. It is a rather arduous undertaking; but there is plenty of material in the country to work upon.*

Some of that material was west of York. Dr. Joseph Adamson was the first applicant from Peel area to practise medicine in 1822, and many of his patients were Mississauga Indians. Some of the non-Indian patients had an agreement that they would give him two days work in a year to pay for services rendered, which was a common arrangement for payment of land taxes, and usually consisted of land clearance or road maintenance. One physician was summoned by the district to do his share of "stumpage" and to bring along the necessary tools. He appeared carrying his turnkey, an instrument used for tooth extraction. He pointed out, with logic, that his stumpage would consist of the necessary removal of teeth from those settlers, who would then reciprocate by doing the doctor's "stumpage" quota.

When Adamson began his practice, the Selkirk settlement near Chatham was well founded. The Earl of Selkirk had established Scottish crofters at Baldoon in 1804 and in a nearby settlement near Chatham, the Moravians had founded Fairfield. A malaria epidemic in 1804 decimated the settlers in the area and resulted in the dispatch of a Doctor Sims from Scotland as colony physician. He and Dr. Anselm Guthrie brought a higher level of medicine to the hardy pioneers who used brimstone or whiskey in the treatment of malarial fevers, but Guthrie was never able to get his licence from the Upper Canada Medical Board. An early Sydenham community in Kent provided a pharmacy and a general store from which Dr. Thomas Robert McInnis carried out a medical practice. He, Drs. Myers Davison, and Charles Tozer were among the original doctors of Kent county. McInnis later moved to British Columbia where he was appointed Lieutenant-Governor. While in that post a minority government impasse resulted in the entire House walking out on His Excellency. McInnis was dismissed by Sir Wilfrid Laurier, the Prime Minister.

Other massive land settlements in Canada West included the Huron tract, for which John Galt set up the Canada Company. The Lizars report that most of the medical care was given by Dr. William Dunlop and even though a Mr. Henry Ransford stated "military half-pay men and scholars were the cheapest and most useless things in the Canadian market", this type of doctor proved of great assistance in setting up the Talbot settlement, around London, St. Thomas and Port Talbot. Over the early years of its existence, Drs. Goodhue, J. Crouse and the Duncombe brothers were practising in that area. Ermatinger, a fur trader and writer who settled in St. Thomas in 1830, records that in the initial days of the settlement Peter McKellar was a self-taught doctor who was succeeded by a certain George Grow. Although neither of these men was qualified, they provided early medical care until a Dr. Travers located in Fingal.

Charles Duncombe lived in St. Thomas but travelled throughout the country as far as Burford. His daughter, Eliza, later wrote of an episode when he was sent for from Oxford to attend a child who was suffering from an egg shell which had lodged in the throat and which he removed successfully. On another occasion he was called to Ingersoll to treat a military rider who had dislocated his neck during a fall. She described the journey:

> My father had to dismount to feel for the road, as there was a road that led down to the River Thames quite out of the way. Frequently our horses were frightened by the wild animals running through the woods and cracking the limbs of the trees.

In addition to travelling to visit patients, some doctors found time to attempt the establishment of medical societies. In 1832 a Dr. Gilbert of the village of Vienna arranged a meeting at which Crouse, Stimson, Duncombe, Goodhue and Bowman formed themselves into a society which had as its aims the improvement of medical knowledge.

Dr. Allison was correct — there was much material.

Chapter IV

King's Prelude

... nor are we aware that the people of this northern climate are likely to die off from epidemics, should there be no public institutions for the special purpose of educating physicians ...

Christian Guardian October 1, 1831

With the small population in Upper Canada there were not many university graduates who could launch plans for medical education. But a number of brilliant and forceful men tried. Some acted for personal gain, some for political aims, some for the good of the profession and welfare of the people. Some were caught up in academic enterprises because they offered a fascinating opportunity to wield power beyond that offered in a normal medical practice.

Dr. John Rolph was a man who acted from many motives. Born in Gloucestershire in 1793, the son of a doctor, Rolph finished his schooling in England rather than emigrating to Canada with his family. He joined them in 1812, in time to sign up as paymaster of the London District Militia.

The Rolph home at St. Thomas in the early years of the century was an attractive household for bachelors. Two pretty and accomplished daughters were visited on many occasions by the local gentry, one of whom was William Talbot, the brother of Colonel Thomas Talbot. Col. Talbot had been given the task of settling an area of 5,000 acres on the north shore of Lake Erie. Thus, John Rolph grew to know the Talbot family and undertook to organize a celebration of the anniversary of the founding of the Talbot settlement in 1817. Opinions differ regarding Rolph's personality. Ermatinger states Rolph "... ingratiated himself ... he was a young man of smooth and persuasive tongue and manner ... and a reverence either real or assumed for Talbot ...".

In so doing, Rolph successfully rubbed the sitting M.P.

Colonel Burwell the wrong way. Despite Talbot's friendship and support, this angry old Member of Parliament wrote a scathing address to the settlers opposing the celebration. However, it was a success with great credit to Rolph.

Rolph returned to England and between 1818 and 1821 studied law and medicine at St. John's College, Cambridge. He was welcomed back to the Talbot settlement on his return and lost little time in addressing a letter to Talbot suggesting the establishment of a medical school at St. Thomas. This, although he had been qualified for only three years. The letter proposed that Rolph and Dr. Charles Duncombe, a colleague, would establish an institution for the instruction of candidates in medicine and surgery at St. Thomas under Talbot's patronage. Rolph pointed out "... no school of that description has yet been formed in any part of the province ...". It was proposed to have a weekly dispensary where students could be instructed and a library made up of books from the two doctors and a collection of anatomical preparations, the product of Rolph's work when a pupil of Sir Astley Cooper (1768-1841).

Following the proposal for the school, an advertisement appeared in the *Colonial Advocate*, August 19, 1824, announcing its opening. Every student before admission was expected to have complete knowledge of the Latin language or to give satisfactory assurance of immediately acquiring it. Duncombe was to give a series of lectures on the theory and practice of medicine and Rolph was to give the first course of lectures and demonstration of the anatomy and physiology of the human body.

The medical school was in a building at the foot of Old Talbot Hill. There is record of only one pupil having attended, Hiram David Lee; who qualified as a physician, and commenced practice around London. The school does not seem to have operated for more than two years.

While teaching the courses Rolph ran successfully against Burwell and took his place in parliament. In addition to being a physician, teacher and parliamentarian, Rolph also practised law. Rolph lore is replete with stories of eleventh-hour legal reprieves, carrying saddlebags into court — one side full of law books, the other side filled with surgical instruments. Reputedly, he'd plead a case in court, pluck up his saddle bag and race down the courthouse steps to his waiting horse to make his rounds.

But his legal career came to an abrupt end in 1828. At that time Justice Sherwood sternly rebuked Reform Judge John Walpole Willis for "using the bench as a pulpit," with the result that Willis was "amoved" by Attorney-General John Beverly Robinson. Rolph and the two Baldwins threw off their gowns and stormed out of the courtroom in protest. Rolph never returned to the court but continued to protest Willis's dismissal in the House of Assembly.

Since much of his Middlesex County constituency was American-born, Rolph was greatly concerned with "the Alien question", a backlash issue that stemmed from the anti-American sentiment of the War of 1812. The Yankees who had emigrated since 1783 were branded aliens, which affected their citizenship as no machinery existed to naturalize settlers. Their political status and property titles were in limbo. Rolph spoke strongly for giving the "aliens" a just hearing and in this was joined by Francis Collins, Editor of *The Canadian Freeman*. Rolph's main thrust denounced the prejudice of the conservative members towards the American settlers, and eventually, he was successful in helping to pass a bill which permitted naturalization.

Although Rolph was re-elected to the House in 1828, for some reason he did not seek re-election in 1830 when it was dissolved. Possibly he felt that he could not continue as a good doctor and a good politician. He moved first to Dundas, then to York in 1831 and re-established his medical practice.

In York he was in close contact with Strachan, who was hard at work trying to build King's College. A College Council was appointed with Lieutenant-Governor Sir Peregrine Maitland as Chancellor, and funding for the college was to come from the Clergy Reserves.

The Imperial Act of 1774 had conceded to the Gallican Clergy the right to collect tithes, which provided support of a "Protestant Clergy". In 1791, one-seventh of the lands of Upper Canada was set apart for that purpose under the name of Clergy Reserves. There was dispute as to which sects constituted the Protestant clergy and in 1819 the Presbyterians of Niagara petitioned Maitland for a grant of one hundred pounds to support a Scottish church ministry. In a decision handed down by Earl Bathurst, the Colonial Secretary, it was pointed out that the reserves were intended for the established churches of England and Scotland and not for "denominations". This decision formed the basis of the further decision that King's College was to be essentially an Anglican university. In the four faculties, all the professors were to be members of the Established United Church of England and Ireland and were required to sign and subscribe to the Thirty-nine Articles. However, the charter had a liberal provision in that there was an exemption from any religious test on the part of students and graduates in faculties other than that of divinity.

The first meeting of the College Council was held in January of 1828 and at a subsequent meeting in May of the same year the question of a site for the College buildings was considered. A major factor in the choice of a suitable location was its proximity to the town in order that students might attend upon medical practices and lectures in the General Hospital.

But Maitland left Upper Canada in 1828 and was replaced by Sir John Colborne, who did not put as much weight on Strachan's advice as had Maitland. Colborne observed that the House of Assembly on March 30, 1828, expressed appreciation of the government's intention to establish the university, but at the same time pointed out that the majority of residents in the province were not members of the Church of England. The House deplored this as:

> ... having a tendency to build up one particular church, to the prejudice of others, ...

Colborne agreed that the anglicanism of King's College made it unacceptable to the province as a whole. He felt it would be:

> ... madness to proceed with the university while there is no tolerable seminary in the province to prepare boys for it ...

The result of this was that in January of 1830, Upper Canada College was opened in York, with funds for the establishment and maintenance of the school being taken from the grant for the Crown Reserve lands which had originally been scheduled for King's College.

At the same time Colborne was strongly advised that the Charter of King's College should be surrendered and replaced with a new one on more liberal terms.

However, the House of Assembly continued to disagree with the Lieutenant-Governor. If they could not have King's College as a new building they were willing to take it as an add-on to existing buildings. In December, 1833 the House strongly urged that the buildings erected for Upper Canada College be expanded to make up the University of King's College and the original plan for the establishment of the university and all its departments be reinstituted.

While all this was going on in the upper levels of government, John Rolph in 1831, established an office on Lot Street and in continuance of his previous school advertised for medical students. They came from various parts of the country. Rolph was, apparently, a good teacher:

> ... He loved the medical profession dearly, and was never happier nor more at home than when teaching its various branches to young men whose good fortune it was to have so eager and interesting a teacher ...

wrote Dr. W. Geikie, one of his students.

This sentiment was corroborated by Dr. Norman Gwyn, the descendant of another early pupil, who stated "where Rolph was, there was medicine to be taught".

Rolph was appointed a member of the Upper Canada Medical Board in 1832 and for many years pressed for the opening of a medical department in the projected King's College.

Since 1818 The Medical Board had continued to examine candidates to certify their ability to practise medicine. It also advised the government on various matters such as the General Hospital, and on control of health during epidemics. It was the sole government medical agency and only the most respected physicians were appointed.

In August of 1837 the Medical Board sent to the Chancellor of the University of King's College an expression of the

> ... anxiety with which the members of the medical profession throughout the province are waiting for the development of an effective plan of medical instruction.

The letter was signed by Christopher Widmer, president of the Board. But the message received a discouraging reply. The Chancellor was not aware that any arrangements for the establishment of the medical department had been made and invited the Board to advise him on the matter. So, ten years and three lieutenant-governors after it had been approved, Upper Canada was no closer to the establishment of a medical school.

The Medical Board convened a special meeting and requested

an audience with the lieutenant-governor to make out a case sufficiently strong to convince him of the necessity of establishing, at once, a medical faculty in King's College. They despatched a letter to him pointing out there was an urgent need to satisfy the general interest of the community, and that medical education was totally disregarded in the Province. The fact was that some medical gentlemen gave instruction to their own pupils which was not adequate because of:

> ... *deficiency of adequate means, means beyond their reach, and which nothing can supply but the appropriate institution of a university* ...

The message also mentioned rumours that a medical department in the proposed King's College might be concentrated in one chair to be filled by a professor of chemistry. To counter this, the Medical Board strongly advised the formation of a faculty with six professors who would give instruction in Anatomy, Materia Medica and Pharmacy, Practice of Physic and Medical Pathology, Chemistry, Principles and Practice of Surgery and Surgical Pathology and Midwifery and Diseases of Women and Children.

To bolster their case, the Board reported that in the seven years between 1830 and 1837 during the examination of candidates for medical practice, of 164 who had presented themselves, 64 were rejected. Of these, seven were rejected twice and one was rejected three times. Of the 100 who had passed, 64 were members of Colleges of Dublin, Edinburgh, Glasgow or of foreign universities; 36 were Canadians. Of the 36 Canadians, not one had been educated totally in the province. It had been necessary to go to foreign institutions.

The Medical Board said it was surprised that it was being called upon at this time to make out a case sufficiently strong, as it presumed that this case was common knowledge. By the tone of the letter, it appeared the Board was a little miffed that they were being called upon to repeat the case "as if private interest alone dictated their interference." A rapid reply, from Lieutenant-Governor Colborne, was in order. There was no way he could tolerate a chastisement from this group of doctors!

> ...*His Excellency, however, desires me to inform you that, should the scientific matter of the report be divested of the un-called-for observations to which I have alluded, His Excellency will be happy to bring the suggestion of the Medical Board under the immediate consideration of the College Council.*

In a meeting on the 24th day of November 1837, the Medical Board answered with an apology but added they could not understand the objection to the "un-called-for observations."

This meeting was attended by Widmer, Baldwin, John King, Peter Deihl, and John Rolph. Read reports that William Lyon Mackenzie left Dr. Rolph's house on the 24th of November to rouse the "disaffected in Stouffville, Lloydtown, Newmarket and other hotbeds of revolution in the County of York to strike for liberty and independence." The rebellion broke out on December 7, 1837.

Chapter V
The Father of Medical Education

£500 REWARD
PROCLAMATION

By His Excellency Sir Francis Bond Head, Baronet etc.
Whereas it appears that Doctor John Rolph of Toronto,
absconded hastily from his residence on the breaking out
of the insurrection.

And whereas ... it appears that he has been concerned in
the traitorous attempt, which has happily been defeated,
to subvert the Government of this Province, the above
award of five hundred pounds is hereby offered to anyone
who will apprehend the said John Rolph, and deliver him
to justice, in the city of Toronto.

In spite of a very successful medical practice and a seat on the city of Toronto council in 1834, Rolph continued to have greater political ambitions. These seemed to be fired by a burning desire to correct the wrongs he saw in the government. When Colborne was replaced by Sir Francis Bond Head, Rolph volunteered to sit on the Executive Council of the province, an appointed group of senior advisors, but in doing so he gave firm notice that he was not there as a figurehead and demanded to be consulted in the affairs of the province. Within a short time he disagreed violently with the new lieutenant-governor and was invited to resign. Later in the year he contested and won a seat in the Assembly, where he spoke out firmly against Compact platforms and in particular challenged the establishment of a University under Anglican domination and the exclusive use of the Clergy Reserves by the Anglican Church — the two most cherished concepts of John Strachan. In a speech acknowledged to be a masterpiece of parliamentary eloquence, Rolph declaimed:

> ... I am happy the claims of the English church are
> vindicated by so able and eloquent an advocate as the
> learned solicitor-general ... Contemplate the learned

*gentleman (to whom I give every meed of praise) in his
elevated place as its champion, see him surrounded with
all the clergy reserves and their rents and profits; confess
the worth of bishops, archdeacons, priests and deacons in
their extended diocese; multiply, if you please, the 57
rectories with their endowments and their exclusive
ecclesiastical and spiritual rights and privileges; view
about the learned gentleman in concentrated perspective
all the wealth and glory of our provincial hierarchy, lately
gilded too, with 70,000 pounds, a fractional product of a
fraction of their vast estates, besides the most wealthy
congregations yielding revenues unknown. Amidst all
this ecclesiastical splendor and aggrandizement, the
learned gentleman is approached with a humble request.
He is prayed to recover his sight from the glare about him,
and to condescendingly cast a glance into the surrounding
distance. There he is shown numerous other churches
formed of Christian groups about pious pastors, with no
wealth but the Bible, and no distinction save the cross.
Behold those fellow labourers in vineyard; — will you be
pleased Sir, out of your abundance, to share a portion of it
among them? — Will you? — What is the answer — Not
one jot ...*

Rolph's party of Reformers was in the minority. For a man
who enjoyed victory, it was irksome to sit in opposition, able only to
fulminate and attack Head and the Tory Family Compact with
impassioned speeches. There is conjecture that he was actively allied
with William Lyon Mackenzie in plotting the rebellion, but this is
based only on Mackenzie's assertion — with no tangible evidence.
However, he certainly knew of some of Mackenzie's plans and seems
to have approved of a bloodless take-over of the government.

Even as late as December, 1837, while the rebels were
gathering at Montgomery's Tavern north of Toronto, and the
loyalists were beginning to flock to the city, Rolph remained an
enigma and had not openly declared his loyalty. Head later wrote:

*... Dr. Rolph has been proved to have been the most
insidious, the most crafty, the most bloodthirsty, the most
treacherous, the most cowardly, and taking his character
altogether, the most infamous of the traitors who lately
assailed us ...*

Before he reached that opinion, Head entrusted Rolph and
Robert Baldwin to go to the rebels under a flag of truce, to
discourage them from moving on the city. It was a stalling tactic on

the part of the Government — and Mackenzie seemed to be taken in by it, or perhaps he was beginning to realize that he too needed more time to gather his supporters.

According to testimony given by one of the rebel leaders, Samuel Lount, who later was hanged, Rolph pulled him aside on the first "peace parley", and told him to hurry the rebel advance before the loyalists arrived in droves. This version Rolph publicly denied, "it impugns my honour as a gentleman". It was all he ever said on the subject. He prepared, but never published, a repudiation of Mackenzie's version of the rebellion which maintained that Rolph, as "executive" of the state of Upper Canada, had been active as a planner of the insurrection and acted as a rebel during the truce talks.

There is a thin line between sympathizing and sharing Mackenzie's aims and actively plotting an armed take-over, but when Rolph heard, through his medical student (later a doctor), H.H. Wright, that there was a warrant for his arrest, he carefully and coolly rode out of town to the west. He was stopped at Port Credit but managed to persuade the picket that he was visiting a sick aunt. Part of the persuasion consisted of pointing out that he had been the government bearer of a flag of truce on the previous day and part was a character reference support given to him by Dr. James Mitchell of Dundas, who had been gazetted surgeon to the 7th regiment. Rolph made good his escape to Rochester, where he established himself as a physician and began, once again, to take students.

His opening lecture to medical students, which he repeated for many years, reflected his political philosophy, although it was couched in scientific illustrations drawn from the current interest in astronomy and the world scene:

> *May not our world be a miniature of vaster worlds affording a like theatre for brighter creative displays, and for similar, loftier beings?*

Part of the Reform rhetoric before 1837 was that Upper Canada was a microcosm of England, and as such, it should be subject to the same laws — but also the same privileges. Back home, they had elected responsible government; why shouldn't the same rules apply in Upper Canada? This was reiterated in:

> *Such new ratios of chemical combination would burst upon our view a new order of things, excluded by the present irrefrangible law ...*

Reputedly, Rolph was convinced to go along with the uprising by Mackenzie's assurances of 5,000 men and arms — backed up by list upon list of names, members of the various townships' "vigilance committees". In his unpublished counter-attack, Rolph blamed Mackenzie for keeping and publishing these lists, thereby warning the governor. This was alluded to in:

> *A revolution is accomplished in the display of the whole world of matter — simply by altering the numerical order of the series ...*

And finally, in explanation (and expiation) of his position, he added in his lecture:

> *mind may, like matter, have its recondite modes of impulse ...*

Wright was not able to warn Dr. Thomas Morrison of impending arrest. Morrison, another member of the Reform Party, was a popular Toronto physician who had been mayor in 1835. He, Rolph and other leading radicals had drafted a Declaration which set forth the principal grievances of the Reform Party and declared the time had arrived for the assertion of rights and redress of wrongs. However, at a later meeting, when Mackenzie proposed an armed uprising and proclamation of a provisional government, Morrison refused to have anything to do with such a treasonable proposal. During the tense day of the approach of the rebels from Montgomery's Tavern and the flag of truce parleys, Morrison carried out his normal medical practice. The next day he was arrested on a charge of high treason as he entered a patient's house. He was jailed until April 24, at which time he was brought to trial and found innocent of the charge. Hearing that the Attorney-General was preparing another indictment, he moved quickly to Rochester. With the general pardon in 1843, he returned to Toronto.

The main thrust of the government in pressing charges of treason was that Morrison had signed the Declaration. But a Dr. O'Grady who had also signed the document, was not arrested and similarly Dr. John A. Tims, who was vice-president of the "Toronto Political Union Society" and had represented St. Patrick's ward as alderman in 1834, was not charged. Tims had been a member of the cholera board during the first epidemics and died of that disease in 1839.

Rolph was also joined, for a short time, by Charles Duncombe, who was elected to parliament several times and joined

Rolph and the others in criticism of the Family Compact. However, Duncombe broke with the radicals in his censure of Mackenzie and his intemperate journalism.

During the 1835 session Duncombe, Morrison and William Bruce were appointed to make recommendations to plan a lunatic asylum and to investigate the school system.

Duncombe's report led eventually to the construction of an asylum in Toronto. His recommendations for the operation of a penitentiary along the lines of the Auburn Prison in New York resulted in the construction of Kingston Penitentiary, and his report on education became the basis of the provincial educational policy in Ontario under the administration of Egerton Ryerson.

The gist of the report was that the populace must be educated, which would lead to a reduction of intemperance and crime and would be the only way to make the people capable of governing themselves.

During the 1836 elections, Duncombe and his fellow reformers were shocked at what they considered corruption and interference by Lieutenant-Governor Head. Duncombe was chosen to make a trip to London to lodge complaints, but to his disgust, he was refused an audience with the Colonial Secretary and returned to Canada sharply disillusioned with the British system of rule.

It is reported that Mackenzie put Duncombe in charge of a division of the rebels which was to assemble in the town of Scotland and march through Brampton to Hamilton. When word of Mackenzie's defeat in Toronto was received, Duncombe dispersed the force and escaped to the United States. While there, he took part in some of the invasion planning; however, he eventually moved to the west coast where he was elected to the state's legislature.

He showed considerable brilliance and ingenuity while in Rochester, in planning a "Republican Bank" which sought in part to finance the patriot forces and also to democratize banking in the United States.

Dr. Duncombe was able to escape because of his popularity in the area where he was renowned for readiness to take any trouble in the care of his patient. Dr. John Wilson, of Sparta, was not quite as fortunate. Although Wilson escaped to the U.S. during the first phase of the rebellion, he was a member of a force which re-invaded Hamilton in March of 1838. This campaign was organized by the

Hunter Lodges which sprang up in several of the American cities. These lodges were founded on the proposition that there should be an actual conquest of Canada leading to a severance from the Mother Country. A solemn oath was taken by the many American members to the advancement of that cause. Some historians attribute the founding of the lodges to Dr. James Hunter of Whitby, who eluded government forces at Montgomery's Tavern but was eventually arrested by the Cobourg Militia in his home in Whitby on December 10. He was released on December 21, and escaped to Vermont. Hunter, vehement in his hatred of the government in Canada, swore "never to rest until all the rulers of Britain ceased to have any dominion in North America." The Hunter Lodges launched several expeditions against Canada, including Prescott (Battle of the Windmill), Windsor and Hamilton.

Wilson was part of the Hamilton expedition, but returned to the United States without fighting when it was realized Hamilton would resist an invasion. He returned to Canada again crossing at Chippewa in June 1838. This group was captured by the militia and Wilson was transported to London. He was soon rescued by fellow patriots, but only to be recaptured at Norwich and transported to Toronto for trial.

One of the government forces which were active in searching for the rebels was the St. Thomas Calvary Troop, including Dr. Andrew Mackenzie.

Chief Justice John W. MacAulay drew up a list of Upper Canadians who were arrested and imprisoned during the troublous times. He noted that most of the rebels had nothing to lose — and seemed to ignore that the list included some farmers and land owners. The list points out that eight doctors were arrested (and three medical quacks). While the loyal doctors far out-numbered the "patriot" ones, there were powerful figures in the latter group. They had deep roots and firm convictions, and it is not surprising that most of them returned to Canada and resumed their careers after pardon. One of these was Dr. Thomas Henry, who, although he had served as a surgeon in the Royal Navy, when he took up practice in Sandhill in 1835, rapidly became involved in the cause of the Reformers. Following his pardon, he returned to his practice in Peel, which lasted for another 39 years. Unlike their rebellious colleagues in Lower Canada, Dr. Wolfred Nelson and Edward Theller, the Upper Canada doctors, while politically active, did not bear arms against the Queen.

Chapter VI
From One To Trinity

... and in this department at least public necessity would
have prevailed over senseless bigotry ...

J. Macara
Origin, history and Management of the
University of King's College, Tor. 1844

During the troublous times at the end of 1837 and the
beginning of 1838, the main activity of the province was to repair its
defences and rally its citizens. There was little time for any new
medical developments. In October of 1838, the Upper Canada
Medical Board was reconstituted by the new Lieutenant-Governor,
Sir George Arthur, to consist of Widmer, Baldwin, Robert C. Horne,
James Samson, Peter Deihl, John King, George Neville Ridley,
Samuel John Stratford, Robert Hornby, Lucius O'Brien Durie,
Joseph Hamilton, Walter Telford, James Hamilton, W.C. Gwynne
and Robert D. Hamilton.

Hamilton practised at Queenston Heights and was well
known for the high quality of his farms. He also achieved some
notoriety through a duel he fought (on the American side of the
river) in 1840. Later he worked in the emigrant Fever Hospital and
died of typhus, during the 1847 epidemic.

The Medical Board lost little time in returning to the
problem of medical education, as this was still considered the
highest priority for the country. It pointed out that the council at
King's College had no representation for a medical faculty, and
circulated a petition to be signed by the medical practitioners of the
area to press for the medical faculty.

To give greater strength to their request, and at the same time
make the medical profession self-governing, the Medical Board was
superseded by the Provincial Act in 1839, which incorporated a
College of Physicians and Surgeons of Upper Canada, vested with
the authority to examine candidates for a provincial licence. The
College had the same composition as had made up the Board. The
members, once again, lost no time in petitioning the Lieutenant-
Governor to establish a school of medicine. By the end of the month

of May, a petition was sent to the president of King's College that it:

... proposes the propriety of meeting the wants of the medical youth of the Province, by conjointly establishing a school of medicine ...

The proposal outlined that there was ample precedent for such a step, as seen in the University of Dublin. By August of 1839, King's College replied that while being impressed with the importance of the proposition, it did not feel justified in extending assistance to any other corporation.

The College of Physicians and Surgeons sent another letter to King's College retracing all the activities that had taken place in the twelve years since the charter had been given, and suggested that "if the proposition put forward was not given approval, then King's College should suggest another plan to establish a school of medicine without further delay." It was obvious that growing frustration was leading to a demand for action of any kind.

This had no result. Accordingly, the College of Physicians petitioned the Legislative Assembly to ask that certain members of the medical faculty be appointed to the King's College Council so they might have a voice in its deliberations.

Once again, this had no effect. By now, there was a new Governor General, Charles Poulett. He was duly petitioned. This time there was a clear note of impatience in the letter:

We have waited in patient but anxious expectation that the intentions of our Sovereign and of the Legislature of the country would be carried into execution by the Honourable the council of King's College, ... for the establishment of a medical school.

On December 28, the College of Physicians and Surgeons was told that a ruling had been received from the Colonial Office that the Act establishing the College had been passed improperly. The legal interpretation held that Royal Charter of the College of Surgeons in London conferred on that body the right to practise freely and without restraint in all of Her Majesty's Dominions and that any act passed counter to this infringed the rights of the charter of the London College.

The Upper Canada Medical Board was reformed. One of their first acts was to welcome a new Governor General, Sir Charles Bagot. Once again, the Board put forward the case for the need of a Faculty of Medicine in the University of King's College and early attentive consideration from His Excellency was promised.

In 1842, work began on refurbishing the Parliament Buildings which had occupied an area originally slated for King's College. The President of King's College, Bishop Strachan, and his staff were appointed. This included Dr. John McCaul (Rhetoric); Professor H. Croft (Chemistry); Professor Nicol (Materia Medica); Professor W. C. Gwynne (Anatomy and Physiology); Professor G. Herrick (Obstetrics); Professor J. King (Medicine); Professor Henry Sullivan (Practical Anatomy); and Professor W.R. Beaumont (Surgery).

At a meeting of the Council of King's College on September 25, 1843, a committee was appointed for the establishment of the medical school.

At long last, there was to be a Medical School in Upper Canada. Many felt this was not too soon. Already coming events were throwing their shadows and it was clear Upper Canada was beginning to fall behind in its medical knowledge. Dr. Crawford Long (1815-1878), in Georgia, was beginning to use ether, and he was followed in short order by Horace Wells (1815-1848) with the introduction of nitrous oxide. Dr. J. Marion Sims (1813-1883) was enthusiastically expanding the work of Ephraim McDowell (1771-1830) in female surgery. News of the many advances in medicine spread quickly throughout the province among the regular doctors giving confidence to the patients, but serving also to emphasize the urgency for a medical school, where the new knowledge could be taught.

There was a sad irony in the announcement of the new school, in that Rolph and Duncombe, who had urged a medical school for so long, could not be part of the planning group, since they were in exile.

During the first phase of planning for medical education in Upper Canada, only one school was foreseen. On the basis of the money that was made available through the Crown Reserves the proposal was to locate that one school in Toronto. This was not unreasonable. In 1839, the Home District (including Toronto) had a large population (57,799 of the 386,285 Upper Canada residents), the only large hospital and a predominance of doctors for the teaching staff. This centralization of medical education with a preponderance of students and graduates remained until the twentieth century. What was thought and taught in Toronto was soon spread throughout the province and the education of the capital city doctors shaped the future of medicine.

It is difficult and confusing to follow events over the forty years from 1845-1885, since teachers moved back and forth from one school to another, schools changed names or locations or simply went out of existence only to be revived again. (See Table 1). In addition, new personalities began to shape events. Christopher Widmer, who had been a major medical force in the first half of the century, had less influence by the 1850's. He had taken over the practice of Dr. Grant Powell in 1815 and remained as the only qualified physician in a "settled practice". His surgical skill was legendary (as was his vocabulary) and Canniff reported he had witnessed the completion "of an operation with tact and precision over which another, although skilful, had become embarrassed". When Lord Sydenham broke a leg in Kingston, Widmer, a slight autocratic man, rode a relay of horses 150 miles to set the limb. He was founding member of the Toronto General Hospital, The Upper Canada Medical Board, and was President of the University of Toronto.

But in the 50's Widmer's vitality was waning and Egerton Ryerson, Aikins and Bovell were assuming more importance in medical matters.

Ryerson was born in 1803 in Norfolk County, the son of a retired British Army officer who had married a Methodist wife. Five of their six sons, including Egerton, became Methodist ministers. But Egerton spoke on far more than ecclesiastical matters and was especially concerned with university education. In this he encountered John Strachan. When Strachan attacked the Methodist sect, Ryerson defended with a reply publication which "produced a sensation scarely less violent in general than a Fenian invasion". When he edited *The Guardian* one of his strongest editorial messages concerned public education for all of the children in Canada. He petitioned the imperial government for funds to help the Upper Canada Academy at Cobourg which was for the education of the Methodist ministry, and in 1842 this academy was upgraded to Victoria College with Ryerson named as principal.

He campaigned actively for the income from the Clergy Reserves to be given to other than the Anglican Church. His credo for education was enunciated at Victoria College in 1841:

> ... *education must be useful and suited to the intended pursuits of the educated ... is not a licence for idleness, but a means of active honourable and mutual enterprise* ...

Ryerson's special interest was the education of mechanics and tradesmen, rather than of doctors, and to reach these aims he was instrumental in the founding of a Normal School for teacher training. He had constant budget problems wanting to expand the Normal School to provide more and more educational opportunities yet being limited by the funds that were voted to him. During the "University Question" hearings in 1860 he specifically attacked the university expenditures as being lavish.

Another major figure who appeared on the scene was William Thomas Aikins. Born in Upper Canada, he took his medical training at the Toronto School of Medicine and Jefferson College, Philadelphia. He became Dean of the University of Toronto Medical School on its formation in 1887 and continued as such until 1893. As well as occupying the chair of Surgery, and being on the staff of the Toronto School of Medicine, he was involved with nearly all the important medico-legal cases of his day. An expert surgeon, he introduced the hoop-iron splint for fractures of the femur, rubber tubing for the continuous application of cold, circular tourniquets or blood savers, elevation of the extremities in treatment of haemorrhage, osteoplastic amputation at the knee joint (some years before Gritti, 1828-1920) and he was one of the first to adopt the Listerian antiseptic views.

James Bovell, M.D., studied in London, Edinburgh and Dublin. Beginning his medical career in Barbados, he came to Toronto in 1848 and took part in the establishment of the Upper Canada Medical School. He was Dean of Trinity College until 1856 and lectured in physiology and pathology in the Toronto School of Medicine until 1870.

In October, 1843, the Medical Committee, appointed by the Council of King's College, reported with a curriculum, a request for hospital affiliation and a resolution to start the school in the east wing of the Parliament buildings, which had recently been vacated. At that time the Parliament buildings were on King Street between John and Peter Streets. The original plan for King's College called for six divisions, the last one being medicine, and in November, 1843, it was decided there should be six professors in the Faculty of Medicine each carrying a salary of £200 sterling with an extra £50 sterling to the Chief Professor (Anatomy).

Requisites for the degree of M.D. included a degree in Arts, attainment of the age of 21 and certification of medical studies of not less than four years. The four years included two courses of six months' duration each, in practical anatomy with dissection, anatomy and physiology, principles and practices of medicine and principles and practices of surgery. One course of six months was required in materia medica and pharmacy, chemistry, midwifery and diseases of women and children and medical jurisprudence, and a three-month course in practical chemisty. In addition, the student was required to attend the medical and surgical practice of a recognized hospital for eighteen months and medical and surgical clinical lectures during six months of the above time. Written and oral examinations were conducted in all subjects, and the candidate was required to submit a thesis on a medical subject chosen by himself and approved by the Dean of the Faculty. He was required to have performed upon a dead subject such capital operations as might be required by the examiners.

Fees were set at £4 sterling per subject for anatomy, medicine, surgery and physiology, and £2 sterling for materia medica and midwifery. Hospital attendance cost was £15 sterling for eighteen months.

The inaugural lectures took place in the public hall of the Parliament Buildings, which had been fitted up along with the University Chapel in the best possible manner at a cost of £4,800 sterling. Newspapers noted that the chapel had been fitted with solid walnut stalls for the professors.

An anatomy building was constructed to the west, adjacent to the Parliament buildings. The first regular lectures were delivered in this building, which was designed by Dr. William Gwynne, who had first come to York to fight the cholera epidemic in 1832. Prior to 1843 there were no provisions for obtaining subjects for dissection, but by Act 7 Vic. c.5, the bodies of those found dead publicly exposed or who immediately before their death had been supported by or were in any public institution should — unless the person so dying should otherwise direct — be delivered to the teachers of anatomy or surgery, such as Gwynne. However, in 1860 it is noted that dissection cadavers cost £20 each and according to Dr. W.W. Ogden there were still some incidents of body-snatching, that is stealing bodies from graves. Perkins Bull reports that Dr. Thomas Deazley of Grahamsville, ''borrowed'' a cadaver from the Toronto General Hospital in the early 1850's. The theft was discovered and two constables were sent in pursuit, but Deazley hid the corpse in a barn and avoided arrest. This initiative to enhance his knowledge may have been a factor in his appointment to the chair of surgery at Trinity in 1853.

By 1863, patients dying in a provincial lunatic asylum were excepted from the Act. This legislation may have arisen from a report in 1851 of an order from Dr. King, a city coroner, to the Toronto Lunatic Asylum for an inquest. Apparently a coffin was to be interred when the sexton became suspicious of the lightness of the coffin. On opening the box, the body of a man was discovered lacking the head, neck, right arm and leg. Three days later the missing portions arrived in another box. On examining the parts it was obvious they had been used for anatomical study.

Further legal changes by the end of the century maintained the rights of medical schools to corpses, if they were unclaimed within 24 hours by friends or relatives. The law required proper burial following dissection, although sometimes the cadaver was used for grisly humour while in limbo. In 1890 a fashionable meat store on Parliament Street in Toronto unwittingly displayed a freshly pickled cadaver on one of its meat hooks, by courtesy of the adjacent Trinity Medical students. It was reported "business was rather dead for the next few weeks".

Students were accepted as matriculated students proceeding to a degree; or as occasional students, who might be qualified to practise by the Medical Board of Upper Canada on completion of a suitable course of studies. During the 1843-4 session there were two regular students, James H. Richardson and a Mr. Lyons, plus a few occasional students. Richardson who was the sole regular student at the medical lectures given by Dr. Charles Beaumont, wrote, "At his kind suggestion I would draw up my chair beside his, in front of the fireplace, while he read his carefully prepared lecture." Of course, both teacher and pupil wore academic dress. While Beaumont would have been required to attend chapel, Richardson, who was not a member of the Church of England was excused attendance under a special dispensation from John McCaul, President of the College. The undergraduate was kept busy with a full timetable which kept him employed throughout the whole day.

The Medical Committee had recommended that clinical facilities be secured in the General Hospital where the professors of the medical faculty should either have the exclusive medical superintendence, or a certain number of wards would be set aside for their sole use. Widmer, Chairman of the Board of Trustees of the Toronto hospital, made an offer to surrender the whole of the upper floor of the hospital to the medical faculty for their exclusive use on the payment of £100 sterling plus 3 shillings per diem to be paid monthly for each student in the medical faculty. However, the faculty did not feel it could stand the financial strain and were forced to turn down the offer.

The Church of England's influence in the affairs of King's College had prevented the establishment of the College for many years by evoking opposition from the non-Church members. By the Amended Act of Legislature in 1837, the religious distinctions and tests were abolished, but there was still considerable concern by those outside King's College that preference would be given to Church of England members. This concern was heightened by suspicions that public funds were being used improperly.

John Macara, who reported for *The Globe* and was called to the Bar in 1848, was an outspoken critic of King's College and wrote:

> *an alarming extent the effects of this mismanagement ... it might be expected that every means should have been adopted to render the education of practitioners easily accessible, and in this department at least public necessity would have prevailed over senseless bigotry ...*

"Mismanagement" applied, according to Macara, to the conditions of admission and also to the financial management of the College. The High Church candidates were given admission preference, and the endowment which had been given originally to King's College had been used exclusively for the Provincial University and other sectarian universities were given little aid. He claimed that the endowment was being dissipated at a fast rate in building domestic accommodations for the students and staff, and suggested that if and when the time came for a reorganization of King's College these new buildings would remain in the hands of the High Church. From a rising chorus of protest, led by Egerton Ryerson, George Brown of *The Globe* and others, it was obvious that a radical change was in store for the governing body of the College.

Although Macara may have been motivated politically to such outspoken criticism, Gwynne was not. In "A Document Respecting King's College" laid before the Legislative Assembly on May 7, 1846, Gwynne and Croft

> *... perceived with alarm and regret the system pursued of alienating the extensive estates ... and using capital proceeds to meet current expenditures ...*

The signatories maintained the charter of King's College did not give express power to use up the capital as Strachan was doing.

Strachan was furious at the action of two of his staff and appointed a special committee, with John McCaul presiding, to investigate the charges. McCaul did not question the motives of the signatories but felt that such a course was highly injurious to the college, as no institution could be well conducted if the officers would not be satisfied to yield to the opinion of the majority. Bishop Strachan was a little stronger in his opinion — "a contoomaashus sleight of our authority", he stormed.

Gwynne stuck to his guns and eventually caused a full-scale inquiry into the use of King's College funds with subsequent censure of the bursar, Dr. Henry Boys. Boys had practised previously in Whitby and was famous for his collection of butterflies and insects, which formed the nucleus of the University museum, but somehow had allowed large sums of public money to slip through his net.

In addition to these internal problems, there was outside pressure. Brown of *The Globe* pointed out that the university question remained virtually the only active political issue in the western section of the Province. In February of 1846, some reformers held a "Great King's College meeting" in the Congregational Chapel in Toronto with the new Pastor of Knox College, Dr. Burns among the speakers. The meeting passed resolutions which opposed the continued church control of King's College and proposed the division of its endowments between various church colleges. At the same time there was obvious support for one non-sectarian Provincial university (a plan put forward by Baldwin).

In June of 1847, John A. Macdonald introduced another university bill which would divide the state endowment between the church colleges, the lion's share going to the Anglican King's College. This was not accepted.

In spite of these difficulties, there continued to be a good enrolment at King's. By 1849 there were 18 students in the anatomy class and by 1852 there were 53 names registered in the calendar, although not all were proceeding to a university degree. However, the gap between home-trained and imported practitioners remained great. Of the 260 doctors from 1783 to 1850 whose biographies appear in Canniff's history, Scottish Universities had graduated 17, English 43, U.S. 40, 28 were from Ireland, 39 had taken apprenticeship training, 10 were graduates of McGill, 11 of Royal College of Physicians and a few were from King's College.

But the handwriting was on the wall with regard to continued Anglican domination of King's College. Strachan resigned his presidency in 1848 and in 1849 the school became non-denominational by the "Baldwin Act" (12 Vic., c.82). By this legislation King's College ceased to exist and became the University of Toronto.

The medical school continued and to meet an increasing demand, Moss Hall (as it was known beginning in 1879) was constructed on the site of the present medical building by the architect of the original King's College Building. The new building was two storeys of white brick, and was described as "a gloomy old structure". The basement at the west contained apartments for the resident porter; the ground floor had rooms for the professors, the porter's room, the dissection room and a theatre — the two latter on the north side being the entire height of the building. Notwithstanding the increased University facilities, the majority of students continued to take training as occasional students and gain qualification before the Upper Canada Medical Board. In its entire lifetime, King's College awarded the M.D. degree to 19 students; one C.M. degree was awarded to Dr. Hodder.

In 1843, when King's College had begun the business of educating doctors, it was evident that there was hard feeling in the community that the school was under the charge of the Anglican Church. Brown, through his newspaper, had supported the Bill of 1843 which separated public higher education from church authority. At that time, he had printed, "Electors, never forget that King's College will be only a hotbed of sectarianism unless you return Liberal members to the Parliament."

And a hotbed of sectarianism it appeared to be to other spokesmen, who remembered the Family Compact and its religious bonds. Rolph had returned from exile in 1843, and had once again started a private medical school. It was in opposition to King's College and a bitter rivalry rapidly developed between the two schools, which was made even hotter by the fact that McGill University in Montreal accepted attendance at Rolph's school on an equivalent basis. The pressure continued to build until the reform government took office and passed the Baldwin Act.

Strachan, realizing he had lost his battle for the control of university education in Upper Canada, made a hurried trip to England in the spring of 1850 to collect funds to establish in Upper Canada a Church of England university. On his return to Toronto, he was met by a deputation consisting of Drs. Hodder, Bovell, Badgley, Halliwell, Bethune and Melville who proposed the establishment of a new medical school — The Upper Canada School of Medicine. Advertisements for this school appeared in the *Toronto Patriot* on October 22, 1850.

So in 1850, there were three medical schools in Toronto. The University of Toronto continued the work of King's College with the same staff. The Upper Canada Medical School was advertising for students, and the Toronto School of Medicine (Rolph's) was active with Drs. Workman, Morrison and Wright as lecturers. The latter school boasted that it was "a self-supporting institution, and as it draws nothing from the public resources or from the education resources of the country ... the lecturers confidently rely upon the continued patronage of a liberal and enlightened community ...".

The school, in Rolph's old house on Lot Street (now Queen), was located in one end of a frame building. W. Geikie, one of the first students, wrote:

> ... *One part of this room had plain pine seats in it, arranged one above the other, while the table behind which Dr. Rolph and the other lecturers sat when they lectured, was that used for anatomical purposes. The rest of the room was provided with dissecting tables on trestles and this constituted the dissecting room where a great deal of good dissection was done for a number of years. Only a thin wooden partition separated this medical college part of the building from the rest of it, in which were comfortably housed Dr. Rolph's horse and cow. So thin was this partition that while the medical students were drinking in their scientific knowledge as they listened to the lecturers, working at their dissections, the four-legged occupants of the very adjacent stalls, who cared little and thought less about anatomy, medicine and surgery, could be distinctly heard heartily enjoying their more substantial material aliment.*
>
> *Humble as this building was, and small as such a beginning may appear when compared with the finely-built and well-equipped medical school of today, teaching of a very high order was given in it, and with a punctuality, earnestness, ability and fullness, not to be surpassed, and which is not now surpassed anywhere in Canada ...*

By 1850, Rolph's school of medicine was expanding and gaining repute. As the number of students increased, the accommodation became inadequate, requiring a new adjoining brick building. The upper part was reached by a stairway leading directly from the street, and consisted of two large rooms, one of these intended as a lecture room and the other as a museum.

> *... The latter had on its walls and on both sides of a special arrangement which extended from one end of the room to the other, a very large number of carefully prepared anatomical specimens ...*

Although Rolph's school was gaining in reputation, the University of Toronto Medical School controlled the U.C. Medical Board by virtue of its established representation over previous years. Rolph objected strongly to the graduates of his school being examined by a Medical Board on which he had no representation and which included his "rivals".

In 1851, he returned to politics and accepted a seat in the cabinet of the Hon. Francis Hincks. He used his position to place his own nominees on the Medical Board, as may be seen in a letter to Aikins, May 21, 1852:

> *... You perhaps think I was not over-moderate in putting on the board so many of my own pupils; but really I looked around in vain for pupils from the University that could be recommended to the Crown and no one came to my recollection ...*

Although the Medical Board was becoming more inclined to Rolph, he was having a good deal of difficulty in another arena — the Toronto General Hospital. The University of Toronto professors held the chief positions which led, naturally, to charges being made of discrimination against students of Rolph's school. There were constant quarrels with respect to the privileges of visiting patients by the Toronto School of Medicine men.

By January, 1853 the next course of action was clear. In a letter of the 24th of that month, Rolph suggested to Aikins:

> *... You may advantageously suggest from yourself, a series of articles on the confinement of University instructions and expenditure to all knowledge which is the foundation on which professional students rest — the languages — chemistry — botany and the natural sciences, which are preliminary to medicine, law and divinity. But if, in addition to these fundamental elements, the professions are taught, so ought every other occupation. We may next have socialism and all in common. You must get*

Workman to draw up his abundant resources for showing why medicine is best left to itself and its independent colleges — you can get the opinion of professional men, and get them to write to me and Hincks on the subject protesting against the medical faculty being fastened on the college and on the public ...

Richardson, who had graduated from King's College and was appointed to the chair of anatomy in 1849 of that school, states in a letter dated 1899 to University of Toronto President Loudon that

... When the Honourable Mr. Hincks introduced his Grand Trunk scheme, he found it necessary to consolidate the sections of the Reform Party, and accordingly took the Honourable Mr. Cameron and Dr. Rolph into his government ... Dr. Rolph was induced to enter his government by the promise that he should have control of the Toronto General Hospital, the lunatic asylum, and the University of Toronto question ...

All of Rolph's complaints were answered by the Hincks Act which made drastic changes in the constitution of the University of Toronto. The University was no longer to teach any subjects, but was to be purely an examining body. Lectures in arts were to be given in the University College; law and medicine were to be taught at other institutions. The populist basis for this decision was that students who were being trained to enter lucrative professions ought not to be educated at public expense!

Now the three medical schools which were present in 1850 had been reduced to two.

Chapter VII
Academic Immolation

Be it ever so brilliant, his fate may be doomed when it is whispered that he did not attend "our" school and his examinations cannot be begun without first discovering whose classes he followed ...
Medical Chronicle (Montreal 1855)

The Baldwin Act of 1849 finished King's College. It left many Anglicans in the Province incensed as a result of having lost control of their sons' education and led to a resolve that under no circumstances would they permit their progeny to study within the walls of the University of Toronto — the "godless" university. Strachan had little difficulty in raising funds in England for the establishment of a Church College. In a letter to the laity of the Diocese of Toronto on February 7, 1850, he wrote:

> *... deprived of a university, what is the church to do?... it is the bounden duty of the Church, of every one of her baptized children, as the value of the gifts conferred upon them, any that holds sacraments to come forward at this crisis in the name of God, the Saviour to stay the plague which exists, as it has done other ... and to honour His Holy Name ...*

When he returned from England to be met by representatives from the Upper Canada School of Medicine, he eagerly expressed his willingness to take the medical school under his protecting wing in the new Church University. In November, 1850 the inaugural lectures were held in the hall of the Mechanics Institute at which time the Lord Bishop explained the terms under which he had incorporated the medical faculty and declared this the commencement of the university.

It was agreed by the staffs of the Upper Canada Medical College and the Church University that the faculty should be under the control of the Lord Bishop for the time being; that the medical faculty of the Church University would consist of six professorships;

that these would receive their commissions from the Lord Bishop and that the medical faculty would have the power to make, alter or amend their own by-laws for the government of the students of medicine; that these by-laws would be in accordance with the spirit of the constitution and that they would not be considered valid until they had received the sanction of the Lord Bishop of Toronto or the governing body of the university.

Regular lectures began in the building previously used as a jail (north-east corner of King and Toronto Streets) and ten students were enrolled. Courses included:

Materia Medica and Therapeutics including Pharmaceutical Chemistry, by Dr. W. Halliwell

Anatomy and Physiology with Anatomical Demonstrations, by Dr. N. Bethune

Principles and Practices of Medicine, by Dr. J. Bovell

Midwifery and Diseases of Women and Children, by Dr. E.M. Hodder

Principles and Practices of Surgery, by Dr. H. Melville

Medical Jurisprudence, by Dr. F. Badgley

Clinical instruction was available at the Toronto General Dispensary (corner of Richmond and Victoria Streets) and at the Burnside lying-in hospital, as well as The General Hospital.

In 1851 the medical department moved to a large house on the west side of Spadina Avenue and the following year, work began on a building to house the college on Queen Street. This building was designed for classes in Divinity, Arts, Medicine, Chemistry and Natural History.

By January 5, 1852, Hodder presented to the corporation the statutes constituting the Upper Canada Medical School as the Faculty of Medicine of the University of Trinity College. They were adopted and the medical faculty came into its formal and recognized existence. Trinity was founded with the express purpose of maintaining the Anglican traditions and teachings in opposition to the "godless institution" of the University of Toronto. Knowing the story of its foundation, it is most unlikely that any student began his studies of medicine without knowing that he would be required to take an oath of Allegiance to the Queen before receiving a degree at Trinity. The candidate also subscribed to the following declaration:

I do willingly and heartily declare that I am truly and sincerely a member of the United Church of England and Ireland.

No degree could be granted by Trinity College under different circumstance, and consequently many students went elsewhere. But, at a later date, the Trinity Medical Faculty advertised in the papers that a degree in medicine would be granted to students who might not conform to the religious requirement. Dispute over this advertisement was one of the causes of the breakup of this first medical faculty of Trinity.

By the 1854-55 term, the Faculty of Medicine consisted of Drs. Hodder, Bovell, Badgley, Bell, Bethune, Halliwell and Cornelius James Philbrick, Professor of the Principles and Practice of Surgery; Henry Y. Hind, Professor of Chemistry; Francis M. Russell, Lecturer on Medical Jurisprudence. The calendar published for that year stated that the course of medical instruction would be six months. Fees for attendance were the same for all students, occasional or matriculating. Occasional students were not subjected to a preliminary or matriculation examination and were not required to subscribe to a declaration. Two medical scholarships of £25 and £35 were founded in Trinity College. Candidates for a scholarship had to pass the matriculation examination and an examination in General Anatomy, Practical Anatomy, General and Organic Chemistry, and Materia Medica.

Trinity University granted two degrees in Medicine, those of Bachelor and Doctor. For an M.B., four years of Professional studies and pass examination in Divinity, Classics, Mathematics, Euclid and Algebra were required. Particular attention was paid to grammatical accuracy and the entire examination was written.

The faculty of Trinity prospered. The brains and social standing of Bovell and Hodder, plus the active support of the Anglican community, soon pushed the school into prominence. The University of Toronto faculty had disappeared, and at the same time, Rolph was by no means in good repute.

Hodder achieved a considerable reputation as a surgeon. In 1852 he published an article in the *Upper Canada Journal* describing a Caesarian operation performed after the death of the mother, but which saved the infant's life. He remarked on first being called and making preparations to bleed the patient, but permission was refused by the family because they had always heard that taking blood from a person after the sun had gone down "was invariably fatal".

Bovell was most likely the best trained medical man in Canada. He read widely in all the medical journals and is believed to have owned the second microscope in Canada with which, on the basis of his observations, he pioneered the microscopic observation of tissues.

In a matter of a few years, the Trinity Medical Faculty gained the controlling influence in the one real place of clinical instruction — the Toronto General Hospital — and became the leader in matters of medical education in the little world of Toronto. The Trinity Medical faculty's influence in the hospital is evident in a letter to Dr. W. Aikins from Dr. A. Fisher, of Amherstburg, dated June 8, 1854. This letter concerned the fact that the

> ... Trinity professors announced that they would consider any student who was not a member of their school an intruder at their hospital, and that they would refund the fee to any students who would not join their class ...

It was argued that this was one scheme used by Trinity College to obtain more students. In another letter written by Dr. M. Lavell, of Kingston, to Aikins, the problem was presented that Canadian students were obliged to seek clinical instruction in foreign hospitals due to difficulties in the General Hospital.

In the next years, however, the Trinity Medical Faculty grew careless in the matter of their relationship to the Corporation as a whole. In 1855, the Government of the Province proposed the repeal of Hincks' bill which had abolished the University medical school. The Trinity Faculty feared for their future if the University of Toronto School should be re-established and some members actively considered relinquishing their appointments in preparation for appointment to the "new" school. There were those who submitted to the Inspector General of the Province a draft of a document entitled, "A plan to amend the laws relating to the University of Toronto and to give increased power to the said foregoing University". But others felt, as before, that the public purse should not be used to support the University and consequently countered with another document:

> ... with the view to inform him of the injustice and undesirability of Government giving its whole support to an institution richly endowed thereby ...

At the close of the last session at Trinity, the Attorney-General John A. Macdonald stated in answer to questions in the House that the government intended to reinstitute the faculties of medicine and law at University College. This statement caused strong opposition because it meant spending more public money on the University. *The Christian Guardian* printed a series of letters which stated that spending $40,000 annually to educate twenty-eight students at the University constituted a failure on the part of the University, and was a waste of public funds; and now the government was proposing to add another $30,000 in waste to educate lawyers and doctors.

Trinity Council was upset by the independence of thought and action shown by the Medical Faculty over the amendment of Hincks' Bill. The Council minutes, which were passed on to the Medical Faculty stated:

> ... Any open attempt to prevent the re-establishment of a school of medicine in the University College would have been, in the opinion of the Council, ridiculous; any covert attempt to effect the same would have been dishonourable.

The Medical Faculty apologized to the Council, explaining to them that their whole object in the move had been to further Trinity's progess, but unfortunately this apology was not enough to promote kindly feelings between the Faculty and Council.

Nevertheless, teaching and activities resumed. Trinity's position should have been secure to a degree since the repeal of Hincks' Bill did not take place and Rolph's school was having troubles. The affair about the Hincks' Bill eventually blew over, and was not renewed because the government was put out of office. (Ironically, Rolph and Aikins in the Toronto School of Medicine had been fighting just as hard against the reinstitution of the University of Toronto Medical School and the two enemies, Trinity and Toronto School of Medicine, had combined forces involuntarily.)

In spite of problems of this type, Trinity continued to gain strength. Aikins, writing to Rolph who was at a parliamentary session in Quebec, said:

> ... Trinity is not failing but is gathering strength every day. Bovell lives on an income ... Bovell and Bethune spend a great deal of time in the dissecting room — the former with the microscope ...

The 1851 calendar shows ten students in the first year. By the 1853-54 session, there were fifty-two, and in the 1854-55 session, there were thirty-eight.

In addition to attracting students, the faculty received much admiration from colleagues outside the school. Dr. E. Clark, superintendent of the Toronto General Hospital, wrote:

> ...I consider the Medical staff of Trinity College the most efficient in Upper Canada for this reason; every chair is filled by a professor who is admitted by the students of all schools to be an able man ...

Although enrolment was increasing, there were still many who could not qualify as full-time students, since they could not sign the Thirty-Nine Articles. But there was a way around this. Part-time or occasional students could take the course and, having satisfied the faculty of the University of Toronto, could receive the degree from that institution. Obviously, this means of subverting the intention of the founders of the Church College was condoned by both the Council and the Medical Faculty of the College. It meant that more students could be received into the classes, thus raising the fees which the professors received and which constituted the bulk of payment for their teaching duties.

While this covert arrangement could be overlooked by the Council, overt evidence of the philosophy could not. On October 18, 1856, an advertisement appeared in *The Toronto Leader* under the heading of "Trinity College Medical Faculty" which read:

> The Lectures in this Department will commence on Wednesday, 18th of October, 1856. No Religious Test Required of Students attending these Lectures. Gentlemen not being members of the Church of England may obtain their degree of M.D. at the University of Toronto on complying with the requirements of that Institution. (signed) N. Bethune, Dean, Richmond Street.

Five days later, the Council of Trinity University met and fired off a resolution to the Medical Faculty to the effect

> ... that the attention of the Medical Faculty be again drawn to the Order in Council (sic) that no advertisement was to be inserted in newspapers relating to Trinity College except through the Bursar who is instructed to submit all such advertisements to the Council for their approval; and that the present objectionable advertisement be immediately withdrawn.

On November 2, in a letter signed by Hodder, Bovell, Bethune, Hallowell and Russell, the Council was informed that the "objectionable" advertisement had been withdrawn. However, the signees were unaware of what the Council termed "objectionable", and, being convinced that all their efforts to advance the interest of Trinity College met with repeated rebuffs from the constituted authorities of the College, the faculty resigned.

This action seems to have been precipitated, when reading the bare correspondence in the University archives. But it must be realized that both sides were tense. Trinity University had secured a charter, but its finances were shaky. It had been threatened by the possibility of the reinstitution of teaching at the University of Toronto. In order to preserve its identity as a Church University, it was necessary to be firm in compliance with the founding terms.

And the Medical Faculty had difficulties. Compensation derived mainly from the fees paid by students was at its upper limit, and was insufficient. It would not be possible to enrol more Anglicans, as there was only a limited number who would be interested in joining the school. Rolph's school was taking those who could not enrol at Trinity.

In addition, there was a problem of communications between Council and the Medical Faculty. The Medical Faculty did not have a seat on the Council. All communications were second-hand. Furthermore, the first letter which went out with the complaint of "objectionable" advertising from the Council was passed by a very small attendance, which may not have fully represented the Council's feelings. In any case, the Faculty was dispersed, some leaving the city, others going to the Toronto School of Medicine. The students did likewise; among them Drs. R.J. Johnston going to Thorold, W.P. Gilmon to Penetanguishene and David Burdett to Belleville.

So the powerful, leading Medical Faculty of the 1850's succumbed to iatrogenic disorders, and not to the machinations of rival medical schools or sectarian activities.

Chapter VIII
The Art of Being a Doctor

... it was agreed that Dr. Dowding should retract the
words, "liar scoundrel and coward" applied to Dr. — ...

To the protagonists in these greatly significant events, it must have seemed that Toronto was the hub of the medical universe. Each momentous decision was bound to reverberate throughout the province. But life — and doctoring — went on. Formal medicine sat cheek-by-jowl with the art of medicine. Dr. John Hutchison settled in 1818 at Port Hope. From 1822-27 he practised in Cavan and Monaghan. Having moved to Peterborough, he was persuaded to stay there by the local townspeople who rallied to provide a suitable dwelling place when he contemplated moving to Toronto. The house still stands.

Hutchison, like other practitioners, frequently used bleeding and in some cases of pneumonia it was a difficult matter to decide what quantity of blood should be let. In order to "resolve the inflammation" and "resolve the disease" usually bleeding of eight to ten pounds of blood was required, but in extraordinary cases it was recorded that sixteen pounds were removed. Cinchona, or Peruvian bark which contained quinine, was a successful remedy for fevers, but because of gastric irritation, its use was frequently limited. If such irritation occurred, tonic medicines were commonly used. Zinc was administered in the form of a pill and charcoal powder was employed, as recommended by Dr. Calcagno of Palermo. However, Hutchison found charcoal powder proved serviceable only in a few cases, which were not of long standing, so he used Fowler's solution of arsenic, but only after emptying the stomach with an emetic. In the course of four or five days many of the most obstinate cases of the disease began to yield to this medicine. The arsenical solution, though in some cases given in conjunction with opium, could not be continued with safety on account of the irritable state of the stomach and bowels. It was, therefore, not employed by all doctors.

Hutchison knew and loved his new country. When he visited his birthplace in Scotland in 1842, he gave glowing accounts of the new land and induced many families to emigrate, including his nephew Sandford Fleming. During the 1847 typhus fever epidemic, Hutchison was infected and died.

Hutchison had watched with great interest the struggle between Dr. John Gilchrist and M.L.A. Colonel Alexander McDonell in the 1841 election in the Colborne District. As the election progressed and it became evident that Gilchrist would be elected, a plot was hatched to break up the election and to prevent his legal return. It was arranged that the constable and doorkeeper of the room in which the poll was being held, would make a show of resistance and be knocked down by a group of conspirators and in the melee which followed, the poll book was to be seized and destroyed thus depriving the opposing party of the only legal evidence of the election of their candidate. The room was full of people. The guardian of peace rolled over as if "smitten by a thunder bolt". The books of the clerks and other papers were speedily seized. But the presence of mind of the returning officer defeated the design when he slipped the poll book under his coat, where it remained secure. Gilchrist, after receiving a blow on the head, was delighted to hear he had been elected as member of parliament for the new Colborne district by a large majority.

Many of the doctors of the nineteenth century were involved in politics at the local, provincial or federal level. Dr. James Alexander Grant, K.C.M.G., practised in Ottawa for many years and represented the county of Russell in the Dominion Parliament for eight years. Others were mayors, magistrates or contenders. The stormy life of medical politics was often mirrored in the political arena.

However, for the students of medicine, such as Rolph's class in 1843, there was little time for discussion of political matters, only time for action in a solitary practice. Graduates like Edward Bull practised in Lloyd Town. John Rolph Graham moved to Tillsonburg. Henry Hansen went to St. Thomas in London. John W. Montgomery, who had escaped to the U.S. during the Mackenzie Rebellion, returned to Canada in 1843, took his classes with Rolph and then practised in Sutton. William Henry Browse after his qualification, moved to Prescott. All of these, including young men like Dr. Robert Edmonson, lived a life of service.

Edmonson settled in Brockville in 1829 and for the next forty years practised his profession, was an elder in the Presbyterian Church, President of the Bible Society and "a sympathizing friend of the young men beginning life". He used sassafras, the bark of a tree, as a blood purifier when his patient complained of tiredness and might prescribe butternut bark to cleanse the system. Calomel, whiskey and port were some of his frequent prescriptions, and suturing was done with hairs pulled from the tail of his own horse.

The gentle physician was as common as the curmudgeon. Dr. Thomas Rolph (not related to John) practised in Ancaster in the 1830's. He visited different parts of the province collecting facts related to the character of the land and what inducements existed for emigrants from the old country. He became well known in his promotion of emigration following publication of *A Statistical Account of Upper Canada,* and was appointed Emigration Agent for the Government of Canada. He continued his medical practice but apparently dissatisfied one family. As a result of this a tombstone was erected by the family of the patient with the indictment "sacred to the memory of the beloved wife of (deleted), who was killed by Dr. Thomas Rolph". Canniff reports that Rolph saw the inscription and went home "prostrated and within a short time died, the victim of malice".

Such Christian virtue might not have been displayed by all of his colleagues. Dr. Gerald O'Reilly, who qualified in Dublin, commenced practice in Hamilton in the mid 30's. He became known as "the young Irish Surgeon" and had a large lucrative practice extending to St. Catharines, Brantford and Oakville. He never bothered with the niceties of legalities when he felt he had sustained a social or professional insult. If he sensed an affront, he lost little time in demanding satisfaction and getting it, at the cost of a meeting on a field of honour. One such duel was avoided as is shown by an advertisement in the *Hamilton Argus* of 1843:

> ... I, Richard Howell, having on the 21st January last published a statement reflecting on the professional character of Dr. Gerald O'Reilly of Hamilton, inasmuch as I accused him of extortion in charging me with a sum of £1.1.6 for one visit ... now declare that the whole of that statement was made by me was totally without foundation ... and now express my deep regret in having been the cause in any way of injuring Dr. O'Reilly ...

Howell may have got off easily in toying with a medical man. Dr. Alexander Thom of Niagara was more taken with the "code of Honour". As a military surgeon he saw many of the cases described by Dr. John Douglas in his book *Medical Topography of Upper Canada (1819)* and he described the common occurrence of pneumonia and catarrh:

> ... *Catarrh seemed to depend on the changeableness of the weather; pneumonia on the great and sudden transitions of temperature. The soldier was a likely subject to an attack of pneumonia, since it was produced in some by exposure to cold while on picquet; in others by acts of intemperance and sleeping out of doors under night ... Men who were transported in batteaux from one part of the country to another, and whose clothes were constantly wet as the oars, suffered severely from its attacks.*

It was believed that the practice of blood-letting made manifest the symptoms of a disease, because the theory of disease bound the illness to spontaneous congestion of the blood. To reduce the congestion and relieve the disease it was necessary to bleed the vein, using a lancet.

However, Thom used other means to draw blood. It was reported that he engaged in a duel with Alexander McMillan to decide an affair of honour and that after exchanging shots the matter was terminated amicably. Thom shed a little of his own blood from a contusion of the leg.

Duelling was not uncommon at the beginning of the century. In 1812 Dr. Warren Baldwin fought a duel with Colonel MacDonell on the Toronto Island. However, being friends, MacDonell refused to fire and Baldwin fired his piece into the air. A year later, in Newark, Dr. Shumate lost his life after challenging a Lieutenant Smith of the 16th Regiment.

Whatever the causes of duelling, professional disagreements were the most explosive and sometimes they were disastrous. Dr. John Dowding who practised at Ancaster and later at Brantford was called to attend a lady in Brantford during her confinement. He decided it would be advisable to call Dr. Alfred Digby of that town in consultation. That doctors differ in their opinions is an old adage but apparently in this instance a greater than usual difference of opinion arose as to the treatment of the patient which escalated into a demand for satisfaction. Letters were exchanged and a challenge thrown by Dowding and accepted by Digby. He was an Irishman who had established a successful practice and had been elected reeve. One of his historical motions in Council was:

> *If any councillor arrives drunk, be it resolved that he not be listened to.*

With the proper etiquette a notice appeared in the *Dundas Weekly Post* on February 27, 1836, which stated that after an exchange of two shots each between the parties, the seconds interfered, and although a reconciliation was not effected between them, it was agreed that Dr. Dowding should retract the words, "liar, scoundrel and coward" and that his opponent should in a like manner retract the words, "liar, villain, scoundrel and fool".

Intemperate language and unbridled emotions were common in all levels of life in the frontier psychology which still marked the growing province. In the case of a doctor it is quite possible that the practice of medicine with its intrinsic frustrations through the ineffectiveness of treatment, led to more frequent outbursts. Certainly the physician was exposed to multiple levels of visual, auditory and olfactory trauma as he proceeded from the genteelness of Upper Canada society, law courts and government salons to the grossness of hospitals and hovels.

After Duncombe had visited asylums in the U.S. in preparation for his report, Dr. James Macdonald of New York in turn made a visit to Canada. He recorded his observations of hospitals in Montreal:

> *Hotel Dieu — upon entering the hospital of this notorious establishment a case of smallpox presented itself — it so alarmed some of our party that we immediately bent a retreat and sought for vaccine matter ...*
>
> *Montreal General Hospital ... fever treated simply with calcium and anti-mercurials followed by "cough infusion". Some with anti-mercurial solution and laudanum — and others by starvation and cold sponging only. Chronic gastroenteritis/diarrhea by blistering over the abdomen and the application of strong mercurial ointment which relieves so soon that ptyalism does not ensue.*
>
> *The General Hospital where the infirm, idiotic, paralytic and insane are seen. Found at the latter eleven males shut up in narrow cells and six females. The cells about seven by eight feet — lined with planks, each having a coarse opening place for going to stool and a stone basin in the wall, unmovable, for putting in drink, no beds — dirty wretched — the inmates never allowed to come out — the room doors seldom open not once a week — the straw changed once or twice a month ...*

Each of the vignettes quoted serves to show a small portion of the life of a doctor. The diary of Jonathan Woolverton, as documented by C.G. Roland, traces the life of that country physician who lived in Grimsby for many years. Dr. Woolverton begins his diary in 1832, at which time he was on the Faculty of Medicine at McGill. Upon graduation he went to Philadelphia and graduated from the University of Pennsylvania in 1834. During his undergraduate years he had considerable trouble with his eyes, which retarded his studies. His eye problem was treated with bleeding, local and general, and blistering. He qualified before the Upper Canada Medical Board and began practice. One of his early entries concerns a number of children who contracted bloody flux and

> *after enduring much pain and distress for several days,*
> *died in great agony and convulsions, some were taken off*
> *as early as the third day, others that had it in less severe*
> *form lingered on for nearly a fortnight.*

Treatment for this disease consisted of astringents, sedatives, alteratives, vermifuges, counter-irritants, antiseptics, none of which seem to be effective in preventing that "the little sufferer would sink in the arms of death".

Woolverton tells of the family of Peter Mitchell, three or four of whose children had scarlatina:

> *... they passed through the fever very well, became quite*
> *smart so that I left them, but owing to want of proper food*
> *and clothing, together with an impure and tainted*
> *atmosphere in the home in which they lived they became*
> *debilitated, or rather did not regain the proper tone of*
> *their systems in consequence of which dropsical symp-*
> *toms set in, and when I was again called to see them, ...*
> *they were entirely out of the reach of medicine.*

Describing a stage coach ride to Toronto when the coach was upset on Burlington Heights, en route to observe the cholera epidemics in 1835, he says: "... a dozen bodies mangled and dissected by James Mitchell and myself".

In 1835 he notes the death of Samuel Jackson:

> *... through life he had given an unlicensed sway to his*
> *carnal desires and sinful appetites, but being arrested by*
> *the hand of disease he was mercifully led to consider his*
> *ways and to seek after the one thing needful ...*

But death came to the doctor's family as well, when his first son was seized with scarlatina and "sunk sweetly in the arms of death".

> How mysterious are the dealings of Providence. He gave us a son in His own good time. He felt proper to take from us, and whose so good a right to take, is he who gave . . .

The Woolvertons went on to have six more sons and the diarist duly recorded episodes of dysentery, disaster and death. The doctor died in 1862, after a lifetime of service to his community. His last entry in his diary states:

> I can both trust and trace the hand of My heavenly Father and all his dealings with me; and, although I felt that chastisment for the present is not joyous but grievous, yet in the end I have found the promise verified that all things work together for good to all that are exercised thereby; to all that love God.

Possibly Dr. J.W. Kermott of London was not as pious. He was more direct. *The People's Guide to Health, Prosperity and Good Old Age* which was published in London, 1855, advertises and prints testimonials for Dr. Kermott's Vegetable Tonic Mixture and Mandrake Pills — "a mild and powerful tonic communicating vigor to the stomach . . .". The author was lavish in his praise of the medication, and put it simply to the public:

> We leave to you to determine which is the quack, he who restores you to health by simple remedies, or the college bred tyro who salivates your life away by rule, but under the immediate protection of the license law. To him all is quackery except that which emanates from college avenues where he listlessly smokes his cigar, leans back upon his lineage and spends a few years in pursuit of the best method by which he shall be able to gull an unsophisticated populous.

Chapter IX

The Scalpel's Edge

... truly, he was a one-man power established in all its purity ...

The Medical Chronicle, 1855

Rolph was the heart whose pulse throbbed through the Toronto School of Medicine. His school attracted students for several reasons: they could attend as day students and were not required to "live in", which meant it was cheaper; there were several outstanding members of the staff, including Drs. Joseph Workman, George Park, M. Barrett, H.H. Wright and W. Aikins. But Rolph provided the major drive. Workman had graduated at McGill in 1835 and moved to Toronto the following year to take over the family hardware business. He felt it incongruous to practise medicine at the same time, and did not return to medicine until 1846, when he became a teaching member of the Toronto School of Medicine. The task of running the school fell on Aikins, who was named Dean. He carefully directed the courses, kept the accounts, provided the backbone of the lectures and brought in new lecturers. Rolph directed from afar. His wife, Grace Haines of Kingston, took a keen interest in the finances of the school, and shared in some of the profits and she, with Aikins, made many arrangements whereby supplies and expenses were kept at a reasonable figure. While Rolph was the official partner, Mrs. Rolph was the business person.

The lecturers in 1850, when the school opened on the last Monday in October, included Aikins, Workman, T. Morrison and James Langstaff. The latter had studied medicine with Rolph for two years and had obtained his medical degree at Guys Hospital, England. He pioneered his practice in Unionville and Thornhill.

What was taught in the classrooms of Toronto affected the health of all residents of the province as young men graduated and started their practices.

In addition to lectures, students had access to the latest medical journals. *The Upper Canada Journal,* 1851-2, Vol. 1, reported that Dr. Simpson of Edinburg had used Indian hemp (cannabis) in several cases of prolonged labour. Another article reported the effectiveness of colchicum for reducing uric acid in the urine of a patient.

Rolph, in announcing the opening of the eighth session in 1851, pointed out that the General Hospital was open to all students who obtained a ticket of admission. In addition, he noted that the Samaritan Hospital, a four-bed lying-in hospital, to which was attached a general dispensary, could also be visited by students. He announced with pride:

> ... *The Degrees of the Toronto School of Medicine are now received on equal terms by the University of McGill College, Montreal and by the most distinguished medical colleges in the United States ...*

But government responsibilities caused Rolph to be absent. Although the school kept up its enrolment with thirty-one students in 1851 (only one had failed to return from the previous year), by the following March, Workman was not as satisfied:

> ... *The school is as yet in fair repute but next winter we will see it in a lower state. There is a time for dying both in physical and public life and my belief is that it is wise to leave the stage while our fame is yet fresh ...*

However, Aikins was full of ideas for expansion of the school. A letter on March 24, proposed that Michael Barrett, who would be going before the Medical Board in July, should be taken on to teach chemistry. Dr. Russell, Aikins reported, "takes but little interest in the school and only brings reproach upon us, we propose throwing him overboard ...". Workman was to take the Medicine and Midwifery for the 1853 session, Eastwood Materia Medica, and Aikins would continue with Surgery. In the same letter Aikins notes that some of the Toronto School of Medicine pupils were concerned whether the University would recognize their "tickets". He went on to say, "... I do not like the ideas of our school being a feeder to the University ...".

The status of the school was a worry to its founders over the next two years. Although the school had been incorporated, it was not directly associated with any university, which led to some very practical problems. If the University could offer a degree and a licence to practise at the same time, then obviously the majority of students would pass by the Toronto School of Medicine. In effect this happened, for most of the University of Toronto staff was on the Upper Canada Medical Board and at the same time comprised a minor part of the Trinity College staff. This situation was rectified by Rolph, through his position in government, by arranging the appointment of sympathizers from his school to the Board.

But this did not solve the situation. It became apparent that examiners for the University of Toronto (the degree-granting agency), were excessively searching when examining candidates from the Toronto School of Medicine, whereas those from Trinity seemed to pass through quite readily. The situation came to a head, as reported in a letter from Aikins to Rolph, when Dr. Beaumont insisted on examining one of his own pupils, and giving him a pass. According to Aikins, a complaint to Widmer, the Chairman of the Board, had resulted in a ruling that Beaumont was quite entitled to examine his own students!

Aikins reacted strongly to this and dispatched a protest to the newspapers entitled "Good doctors and safe people". In it, he charged that the Toronto School of Medicine professors had, by their unfair influence in the proceedings of the Medical Board, tempted students from rival medical schools by:

> ... reduction offers ... benefit of a sort of discount in the shape of a private examination by them on the Medical Board for licence ... a hint of the set examination ensured success from the five pounds voluntary fee, given by a student and taken by an examiner for a few private grindings preparatory thereto ...

None of this endeared Aikins to the establishment.

The emnity which was being generated spilled over into the General Hospital. It was used as a clinical site by all the medical schools. Widmer, Hodder and Beaumont were the Chiefs of Staff but the Toronto School of Medicine professors were permitted to walk the rounds. In June 1852, Trinity attempted to restrict the medical attendance in the hospital to two men from each school, and some independent men of the city. These independent men would be drawn from the Trinity establishment. But this project was not put through and there continued to be considerable friction between the various staff men with regard to patient care and teaching. The situation was finally settled by the passage of the Hincks Act and the appointment of a new Board of Trustees at the Toronto General Hospital which permitted eight visiting physicians to walk the hospital, including Drs. Aikins and Wright from the Toronto School of Medicine, and Drs. Bovell and Hodder from Trinity. In addition, it was "... thought proper not to leave unrepresented the University as it might establish an independent medical school". Accordingly, Drs. Herrick and Beaumont were appointed visiting physicians with Drs. Wooder and Telfer appointed as the non-medical school representatives.

To balance this preponderance against his school, Rolph decided to apply for affiliation with the University and he urged Aikins to put an application to the Chancellor by July 23, 1853. Aikins acknowledged the letter, but did not move quickly. He did, however, report in a letter of November 5:

> ... we have suffered much this season from want of affiliation — the professors of University College are anxious for it also ...

Rolph, on November 14, noted that he had received from others as well as Aikins the comment that medical students were discouraged and apprehensive with enrolment in the Toronto School of Medicine. He felt that the application to the Senate, which was to be reorganized, would be successful and that the Toronto School of Medicine would be formally associated with the University of Toronto and as happened with Trinity College, examine its own pupils and issue the degree subsequent to the examination. He pointed out this happened at McGill in Montreal.

But, the affiliation did not proceed quickly. By December 9, Rolph was sending anxious letters to Aikins inquiring why there was no progress and on February 21, he complained to Aikins about the delay. Obviously, the Senate of the University felt that affiliation would mean considerable financial gain to the Toronto School of Medicine. Also, the name Rolph, coupled with affiliation, aroused suspicion. He wrote on February 21:

> ... The whole delay is no doubt to prevent your affiliation in the restoration of the old state of things. I have discovered this and presume upon a prejudice against the school and against me as an enemy ...

Aikins came up with a different strategy than joining with Toronto. Using the larger university powers of the Charter of Victoria College in Cobourg, which permitted it to increase its faculties, he approached President W. Nelles and, after speedy negotiations, affiliation of the Toronto School of Medicine with Victoria College was ratified in 1854.

Victoria, like Queen's, felt a medical faculty provided a good academic enterprise and undoubtedly would reflect glory on the school. Rolph was delighted, and in a letter of September 23, pointed out:

> ... having the affiliation to the University is an additional
> "feather in our cap" to justify and embolden us ...

In the same letter, Rolph was looking forward to returning to Toronto. For a time, there had been rumours and speculations that he had fallen out with Hincks and that his resignation was imminent. In the early part of 1853, Rolph had written to Aikins asking him to conduct a discreet search for a dwelling and by September, 1854, he was formulating plans for the return. For the 1854 session, he outlined the following staff: Anatomy and Physiology, Aikins; Surgery and Surgical Anatomy, Wright; Medicine and Pathology, Rolph; Chemistry and Materia Medica, Barrett; Midwifery, Workman. In addition, Professor Croft might be used for Chemistry. He inquired about physical arrangements for the lecture room and noted:

> ... Appearances are not to be despised as the age grows
> more aristocratic and the competition greater ... Are you
> fortifying yourself with subjects? You see, I am at the
> Collegiate again ...

And so he was, on his return to Toronto in October 1854, after leaving the government. Attendance at schools of medicine for the session 1853-54 showed 50 registered students in Trinity, and 37 in the Toronto School of Medicine.

Having left an unruly House in Quebec, Rolph was ready to step back into the fire in Toronto. The General Hospital was the hot spot. Aikins, in a letter to Rolph earlier in 1854 had pointed out:

> ... Trinity is not failing but is gathering strength every
> day ... at the Hospital Herrick, who is an attendant
> physician, gives over all his patients to Hodder and Bovell,
> the two Trinity men attending — and until we get our
> anatomical inspector, Beaumont and Telfer will have not
> questions as to what becomes of their dead friendless
> patients. But it is quietly arranged that they may go to
> Trinity ... please remember that Trinity has all expenses

> *paid by the Bishop and receives all the influence of a sect,*
> *the most wealthy and learned, if not the most numerous in*
> *Canada — while up to the present we draw our students by*
> *the reputation you have earned for the school.*
>
> *Your presence here would turn the scale at once, —*
> *it would do everything — Napoleon's presence was not the*
> *assistance of ten thousand, it was victory ...*

Rolph's presence brought things to a boil. He had no status at the hospital, as the eight attending physicians had been specified in 1853. However, visit the hospital he did. In a diary kept by Aikins, it was noted that on July 6, 1855:

> *... Rolph visits the hospital — Richardson is admitting —*
> *when Dr. Rolph walked into the hall Richardson ordered*
> *Burns to shut and lock the door — door was shut but not*
> *locked — Dr. Rolph soon walked in again — to see a case*
> *of testicular disease examined by Richardson ...*

Such actions by the Toronto School of Medicine men constituted a great threat to the other hospital doctors. Aikins kept a list of what he considered malpractice procedures and, in particular, was concerned with Beaumont's failures. These are listed on the January 13 page as:

1. Ligature of the vein as well as the artery.

2. The polyp case and forceps.

3. Lithotomy cases.

4. Fistula of perineum — operation unsuccessful — death.

5. The case of empyema — treated as psoas abscess — dislocation of shoulder — the ignorance and cruelty.

Aikins, who was a good surgeon, pushed even further. He noted on the June 30 page:

> *... Beaumont comes at 1/4 afternoon, five minutes later*
> *went slying along to visit a lithotomy case — I followed,*
> *he saw me and shut the door in my face. I opened it and*
> *went in — he was not (illegible) enough to speak — order*
> *the mother and nurse not to allow anyone to see him*
> *except Dr. Widmer or Dr. Clark ...*

This professional warfare was aided and abetted by charges against the hospital. In the *Toronto Leader,* March 20, 1844, an editorial pointed out that serious charges had been raised regarding mismanagement of patient care at the Toronto General Hospital.

Apparently Rolph's student, Dixon, had claimed that there was cruelty and relentless heartlessness throughout the hospital. He was quoted in a letter as saying:

> ... it is impossible in one letter to give even a faint exposition of the corruption which exists and stalks forth in open day in this house of sin ...

A public inquiry was demanded and this was instituted by the Board of Trustees. Throughout the inquiry, charges were made that the letter had been written at the instigation of the Toronto School of Medicine and was due to the rivalry between this school and Trinity; that the doctors on the hospital staff failed to come to the hospital when they were supposed to, and as a result the medical students received little teaching; that it was often some weeks after they had seen a patient before they were able to establish what was the diagnosis.

The inquiry was quickly concluded. *The Church*, April 12, 1855, reported:

> ... it is sufficient for our purpose to state that the charges generally, and especially those which attacked our respected townsman, Dr. Hodder, and the indefatigable Dr. Clark (House Surgeon) had been completely refuted ... there seems to be little doubt that the whole affair was brought up by a party spirit and to serve a party purpose ...

However, *The Christian Guardian* took another view. On April 18, 1855, it stated:

> ... We have no hesitation in stating that ample proof was given of the gross mismanagement on the part of two of the principal servants in the hospital, such as should induce the trustees to dismiss them forthwith and we cannot believe from the evidence given, as well as from his own declaration that the resident surgeon is free from blame for his evident partiality towards the professors and students of Trinity College, while his duty in that institution demanded that all medical attendants of the hospital should be treated with respect. There has obviously been a design and effort to deprive the professors and students of Victoria College, of the advantages which the attendance at the hospital was intended to confer ...

The surgeons were now using their scalpels on each other as well as on their patients. Postmortems became political events as each school sought to gain over the other. In 1854 a patient was overdosed with morphine. The student doctor, a Trinity man, was jailed on a charge of manslaughter. After hearing evidence the Coroner's jury declared him innocent, with a verdict — drunkenness, hastened by a drink of cold water. Toronto School of Medicine men testified too much morphine had been used but Trinity witnesses said: Not so.

The following year the other edge of the scalpel drew blood and Trinity got its chance. Dixon, a student of Rolph, had killed a patient with an overdose. Bovell, who the year before had sworn that 7 grains of morphia repeated once in three hours was good practise, now swore 6 grains given once was too much. The rest of Trinity agreed. Their opinion was published in a pamphlet and distributed to the Coroner's jury. Dixon was found guilty. A trial jury freed him.

By this time George Brown of *The Globe* was exasperated with the constant bickering among medical men. He editorialized that the respectable medical practitioners of the province (and he excluded Trinity and Toronto School of Medicine men) should urge that the province re-establish the University of Toronto Medical School and take medical education out of proprietary schools.

It is difficult to determine how many students were in the various colleges at this time because of the unsettled state of affairs of the university. Between 1853 and 1856, only seven Doctor of Medicine degrees were conferred, with one Bachelor of Medicine degree.

This continuous warfare between the schools was noted in other areas. *The Medical Chronicle* of Montreal in 1855 stated:

> ... Be ye ever so brilliant, his fate may be doomed when it is whispered that he did not attend "our" school and his examinations cannot be begun without first discovering whose classes he followed ...

But by then Rolph was back and in full charge, being appointed Dean in 1855. Things had changed since he last personally directed a school. In June, 1855, the Board of the Presbyterian Church (of Scotland), representing Queen's University, Kingston, had resolved that a medical faculty should now be permanently established in that University. Toronto was no longer the sole centre of teaching. In addition, Rolph was no longer the one-man school of the King's College days as he now had highly qualified staff who had been accustomed to working without him for many years. And the fact was that Aikins was the main reason the Toronto School of Medicine had survived through all those years.

Rolph made a serious miscalculation which resulted in disaster. *The Medical Chronicle,* 1855, reports:

> ... *Dr. Rolph, whose energy and talents are generally known and acknowledged throughout the province was appointed in our opinion justly, Dean of the Medical Faculty of Victoria College ... a more irresponsible Dean, however, never before held place, and in making him such a serious evil was committed. A power of managing solely and without reference to his colleagues, all matters connected with the school, pecuniary or otherwise, was conferred on him with the simple proviso that he must submit, whatever he determined on, to the said Board before it become law. The medical faculty were to do the will of Dr. Rolph, be good boys, in fact do their work and ask no questions and at the end of the session they would get what money was coming to them after the funds had been well drained by expenses of management by an irresponsible Dean. Truly he was a one-man power established in all its purity ...*

The result of this was that his six-man staff resigned on the day before the course was due to commence in 1856.

The course was scheduled to open in a building formerly used as a church on Little Jarvis St., Yorkville (subsequently 10 Bismarck Avenue, subsequently Asquith Avenue), which had been purchased and fitted up for the newly-formed medical department. The Victoria Board supported Dr. Rolph and he responded with his typical vitality and ability and, during the first two weeks, lectured four or five times daily on all subjects on the curriculum. At that time, he was joined by Dr. W. Geikie, a former student, who was appointed Professor of Materia Medica and Therapeutics, although he had barely been in practice a few years. Fifty-one students attended lectures during that year, and 20 completed the prescribed course of study and were admitted to the degree of Doctor of Medicine.

Meanwhile, those professors who had resigned lost no time in renting a building from the University, in which they established themselves under the name of "The Toronto School of Medicine". Rolph continued to advertise his course as "Medical Department of Victoria College — The Toronto School of Medicine". Aikins and his colleagues took Rolph to court after filing an injunction restraining Victoria College from using the title of the school. The Judge decided, after hearing Rolph plead his own case, against Victoria College. The Toronto School of Medicine was no longer associated with Rolph. Rolph was now with the Medical Department of Victoria College.

Chapter X

From Rose Hips to Medical Defense

... asserting the rights and duties of every man to investigate and choose for himself in relation to the philosophy and the means of health ...

The Unfettered Canadian, 1849

At the time of Confederation there were approximately 760 licenced physicians in Ontario. They were outnumbered at least 2 to 1 by the unlicenced, who were referred to in such terms as healers, steamers and quacks. But in addition to these battalions, a great deal of medicine was practised in the home, usually through the wife and mother who used her herb garden to great effect. It was the housewife's work to grow, gather and prepare different medicinal plants for tisanes, poultices, and liniments. Many of these recipes were drawn from different parts of Europe, brought to Ontario by the new immigrants with the result that the brew on the kitchen stoves in most settlements was a melting pot of varied remedies. The leaves, petals, flowers and hips of native roses were used to make medicines. The petals produced a soothing lotion for application to inflamed eyelids; rose honey could be applied to ulcers or wounds, and a tea of rose hips was useful for indigestion. Feverfew, a wild flower, was used commonly in the treatment of marsh fever and a tea from the bark of the slippery elm was effective for rheumatism. Sage, boral, mint, phlox or nasturtium all had an important part in home remedies, and one could read all about them in a broadsheet distributed by a Mrs. Palmer. She claimed that "gravel" could be cured with wild lettuce, warts killed with the oil from angle worms and lung disease treated successfully with hoarhound, camomile, sassafras, sarsparilla, black cherry and comfrey root. When boiled in rain water, strained clear and one pint of honey added with one quart of black currant wine, a potent medicine was as close as the kitchen range.

One of the heirlooms in the family of Jessy Trull of the Township of Darlington was the small iron pot in which herbs were mixed to serve all the medicinal requirements of the first settlers. With a rare skill used in the preparation of herbs and fortified by a book of directions in midwifery and healing of the sick, grandmother Trull was an important assistant to doctors such as R. Whichelo Clark who had studied in Edinburgh and Glasgow and migrated to Canada in 1833, settling in the Township of Percy. During the 1837 rebellion he moved to Whitby and continued his surgical practice. Later he became one of the surgeons to the Protestant hospitals in Ottawa.

During his practice he would have seen cases such as reported by Dr. George Buchanan in the *Canada Medical Journal* of 1864. A three year old child showed signs of being ill for a few days before it was seen that the whole posterior part of the throat was covered with diphtheritic exudation. Treatment in the home was started using chlorate of potash and dilute mineral acids. There were signs of laryngeal and tracheal effusion and finally the good doctor had to perform a tracheotomy to relieve harsh rattling breath sounds caused by obstruction. Three days later the tube was removed and the child was lively and playing on the bed. About midday he said he felt chokey, became pale and died shortly after.

Diphtheritis in those days was a constant problem. Dr. W.S. Christoe of Flesherton reported a case in a male aged 40 which puzzled him. He used the gargles, the potash, the tonics and the stimulants. However, the pulse denoted weakness, with a rate of 90. After three weeks the patient complained of inability to swallow and had a sense of numbness at the tips of his fingers, and a paralysis gradually extending to both hands and the lower extremities forced him to bed. He was treated with iron, quinine, strychnine and electricity. Five months after the first attack of diphtheria, he was able to walk and do light labour — such as feeding his cattle and other farm work.

This scrupulous observation of patients was practised by many physicians. Dr. Archibald Leitch, who practised initially in St. Catharines and later in St. Thomas, kept a diary of all his patients. Before he went for a walk up town he consulted the diary and the first persons he encountered were apt to be informed of what day they were born and what they were doing 20 years ago. Other doctors did "diarizing" in a more professional style. Alexander James Christie, for example who practised in Bytown, established *The Bytown Gazette,* the town's first newspaper, and he edited the first *Canadian Magazine.*

Some doctors did their writing in the Ontario or Canadian journals which were beginning to appear. The first medical magazine published in Toronto was *The Upper Canada Journal of Medicine Surgical and Physical Science,* which appeared between April 1851 to about the middle of the year 1854 and was edited by Dr. S.J. Stratford. Among its original communications were articles from William Beaumont, Norman Bethune, John G. Bethune, Charles Covernton, John Dixon and Edward Hodder. During the time of its publication a wide range of articles were published including treatment of bilateral fractures of forearms, successful treatment of puerperal convulsion, aneurisms of the innominate and functional derangement of the spine. Hodder, in spite of his surgical prowess, was called upon to treat cases such as diabetes. One case report in the first volume of the *Canada Medical Journal* in 1864 records that the treatment for this was dietetical, with bran bread, celery, tea, four eggs per day and two ozs. of whiskey, medical tincture of iron and cod liver oil. The case was followed and it was noted that the patient stopped passing glucose in the urine.

Speaking of early journals, *The Upper Canada Journal* had been preceded by *The Unfettered Canadian,* a journal of the Thomsonites in 1849, edited by Dr. R. Dick, which continued to publish for a few years. It carried as its slogan a devotion "to medical reform, asserting the rights and duties of every man to investigate and choose for himself in relation to the philosophy and means of health". Another short-lived journal was *The Canadian Medical Times,* published by Dr. James Neish in Kingston for the first half of 1873. *The Canadian Lancet* was more successful and, under the editorship of Dr. John Fulton for 15 years, remained in publication from 1862 to 1922. It was co-edited by Uzziel Odgen and John Rolph. One of its advertisements concerned the text book *Canniff's Principle of Surgery.*

In a leading editorial in 1870 the *Lancet* queried why there were so many deaths from chloroform and pointed out that Boston used ether which did not have the dangers associated with the former.

Actually the first Canadian use of an anaesthetic-ether had been reported in the *Dominion Medical Journal,* published in Montreal in 1847. Chloroform came into use the following year. Montreal had the first anaesthetic death in 1858, although the *Upper Canada Journal* noted a case of death by chloroform in England in 1854. In 1868 *The Dominion Medical Journal* reported more deaths which were felt due to the action of chloroform causing a direct poisoning of the central nervous system. In that year Dr. Rosebrugh read a paper before the Canadian Institute in which he pointed out a safe use was to gauge the amount of chloroform used by administering it by drops over a stated time period. Professor Simpson (1811-1870), of Edinburgh, had already suggested the drop method (but not against a time basis) and had added that instead of dropping chloroform onto a napkin, a gauze-covered wire mesh should be used.

But neither ether nor chloroform was required for a case of amputation surgery reported by Dr. R.B. Nevitt in 1871. His patient was a veteran who, following amputation at his hip at the Battle of Trafalgar, suffered the most horrible attacks of sciatica. He spent most of his time under the trees in front of The Toronto General Hospital, with a long clay pipe in his mouth, and he developed cancer of the tongue. Nevitt prepared to operate and remove part of the tongue. The old sea dog refused an anaesthetic. He said that, with a nail between his teeth, he had stood the amputation of his leg and so could stand this. And so he did, giving a responsive groan at each tightening twist of the ecraseur.

While scientific medicine continued the march of progress in the big hospitals and the university, the country doctor still used many herbals. Possibly his diagnostic skills were not as keen, but his patient had a reasonable chance to survive. The doctor's ability was validated early in Ontario medical history by the performance of postmortems. "At postmortem it was found that both layers of the pericardium were universally adherent, and separable with difficulty by dissections; the membrane was also much thickened. The heart was dilated and hypertrophied", reported *The Canada Medical Journal* in 1852.

Although postmortems were an every-day event in most hospitals by that time, one examination that might have been most revealing was missed. Dr. James M. Barry, who had arrived in 1857 as Inspector General of Hospitals for Upper and Lower Canada, contracted pneumonia in 1859. Dr. Barry had received many promotions throughout the Empire in recognition of skilled medical services and as a result of an incisive manner in dealing with the administrative departments in the British Army. On his arrival at Quebec, orders were immediately given for the installation of better sewage and drainage in the hospital barracks. Similar clean-ups were ordered in Kingston and Toronto before it became necessary to ship the Inspector General back to England with severe diarrhea. Dr. Barry eventually succumbed to the disease. The staff surgeon, Major McKinnon, does not appear to have examined Dr. Barry's body thoroughly, for it was not until a charwoman made the startling observation that Dr. Barry had a body which looked perfectly female, that the truth became known. Dr. James (Miranda) Barry, masquerading all these years as a man, had been the first female doctor in Upper Canada or, for that matter, in the British Empire. No autopsy was performed and she had taken her secret with her to her grave.

Such was not the case with Miss Sofia Burnham of Brockville, Ontario. In 1874 Dr. Eric Benzel Sparham, a well known physician and one of the oldest practitioners in the town, was charged with a criminal attempt at abortion resulting in the death of the patient. During the subsequent trial testimony revealed that the putative father, a ticket agent, had applied to Dr. Sparham to be relieved of the "fruit of her shame" and had received certain drugs to procure an abortion. But these drugs were not effective and it was necessary for Miss Burnham to visit the doctor's office. The "Brockville Abortion Case" aroused a great deal of revulsion and condemnation throughout the province — there was "no crime in the Decalogue so abhorrent to a civilized and Christian community". Six years earlier a strong movement had sprung up in medical circles in Toronto to stamp out "the American crime", as abortion was known. The case against Sparham was largely based on a death-bed deposition made by the victim. She stated that she took the pills, which had been given to her by Dr. Sparham, and when the drugs proved to be ineffective, she went to his house. The doctor had her walk upstairs into the bedroom and asked her if she would like Mrs. Sparham to come up, saying it would be just as secret, and that his wife would no more tell what happened than he would. The doctor then put a handkerchief over her eyes so that she could not see what he did to her, as it "was a very serious business", for a lawyer in Montreal had been sentenced to ten years in the penitentiary for even proposing such a thing to a doctor. After covering her eyes he inserted "a long tube into me and he moved it about. I think he did that for ten minutes". "The instrument was supposed to bring on my miscarriage," she stated. However, on Sunday, coming home from church in the morning, she told the ticket agent that the operation had not the desired effect and it would be necessary to see Sparham again. She went that afternoon and the same procedure was carried out, but this time the doctor gave her some pills which he said would bring on the pains. On Tuesday she awakened in great pain and suffering terribly all day, she finally called her family doctor, Vincent Howard Moore. Moore testified that when he saw her she was suffering pains over the lower part of the abdomen and told him she had had an abortion induced. He proceeded to treat her with ergot and opium and consulted with Dr. William Weir of Merrickville for another opinion. It was necessary to get Weir because Fred Burnham, Sofia's brother, was being nursed upstairs with smallpox, and Weir, who was already in attendance of a similar case in his home town, was the only doctor who could be called upon to enter a house where there was smallpox. Miss Burnham grew worse in spite of the application of heat to her stomach with wrung-out flannel, linseed poultices, enemas of turpentine, and medications of tincture of iron, aloes, myrrh and opium.

The defense of Sparham was waged inside the courtroom and outside. A seventy-four page pamphlet was published during the trial which summarized the evidence brought forward. The basis of the defense was that death had not been due to the abortion but rather because of a smallpox pyemia contracted as a result of the presence of the disease in the house. Great pains were taken to cite many authorities: Drs. Reynolds, Thomas, J.Y. Simpson, K. Schroeder, Leishman, Ziemssen, Spencer Wells and J. Paget, all eminent overseas authorities, to show that the course of the illness was quite consistent with the smallpox theory. The pamphlet also raised the question as to whether the victim had been pregnant inasmuch as her menses had been absent for only one month and what Sparham had treated her for was amenorrhea — in the usual manner. Documents included many letters from acknowledged Canadian experts such as H. Yates of Kingston, J. Fulton and W.E. Coleman of Toronto, as well as local doctors such as A. Lander and J.D. Hall of Brockville, all of whom quarrelled with the findings brought forward by the evidence of Dr. Morden and Dr. J.E. Brouse. Brouse had carried out the postmortem and stated that there had been a wound in the womb which he felt had been caused by an instrument.

The defense then went on to point out that Dr. Sparham's treatment had been consistent with the treatment of amenorrhea and that he actually had not introduced an instrument to cause an abortion but rather to carry out an internal examination. It was obvious the patient had been suffering ill health from anxiety over missing a period, and he had treated her in the normal way with such medicaments as Sir James Clarke's pills. Certainly the evidence presented by Dr. Morden that he thought he had seen some placenta on his examination, was ridiculous as that would not be present yet after four weeks' impregnation. The final point made in the pamphlet was that the postmortem examination had been entrusted to men who "for years had been the rivals in business and professional distinction of the prisoner". No charge was made that there had been collusion concerning the postmortem examination, but it was declared that "where a few additional strokes of the scalpel were, perhaps, life or death to the prisoner", some friendliness to the prisoner might have made a considerable difference in the perception of the examiner. In support of this, the pamphlet alleged that the County Attorney had stationed himself at the door of the postmortem room and had warned off "all interlopers ... except those in whom the prisoner had no confidence."

Sparham was found guilty and convicted of murder by use of an instrument to procure abortion. His death sentence was commuted to imprisonment and he was released after serving a few years.

Malpractice problems and the need for regulation of all medical treatment continued to be paramount in the minds of physicians and legislatures in the province. Incidents such as that reported by Dr. J.M. Pemwarden of Fingal served to increase the urgency for consideration. He was called to assist a delivery in 1865, and on arriving at the house was struck by a peculiar odour coming from the patient. He found an almost imperceptible pulse with the woman nearly unconscious. On examination of the vagina, the parts were hot, tender and swollen, but with care he was able to carry out an internal examination when he found, much to his horror, that what presented to his finger was the glenoid cavity of the shoulder blade of the fetus. He confronted the midwife who had taken care of the woman, demanding to know what had been done. She answered "nothing", but when he threatened to send for a constable, she showed him what had been taken from the woman — two arms of the child, with the clavicle and scapula attached to one, and the clavicle to the other, which had been pulled out by a noose fitted above the elbow of the child and connected by a towel to the midwife's shoulders. Pemwarden was able to deliver the remainder of the decomposed fetus. He reported the patient did remarkably well until the second night after delivery, when her drunken husband returned home and told her, "he would kill her, if she did not get up and clean herself". She arose from the bed, felt faint and dropped over dead.

The desire to maintain the highest standards of medical practice and to regulate members of the profession to this end, led to the formation of The Canadian Medical Association. Although efforts had been made by local societies as early as 1826, it was not until 1867 that an effective organizational meeting could be held in Quebec City with representatives from Upper and Lower Canada, Nova Scotia and New Brunswick.

The British Medical Association, which became the main force of reform in the United Kingdom, was formed in 1856 and eventually was instrumental in urging the passage of the Medical Act of 1858, which gave self-governance to the profession and established a general council of education and registration.

The Upper Canada representatives to the C.M.A. included William Canniff, Joseph Workman and James Thornburn. However, during its early days because of the lack of cohesion, largely due to the geography, it was difficult to coerce any of its members to draft rules which would ensure uniformity of medical education and registration throughout the Dominion. More importantly, the C.M.A.'s presence led to the formation of provincial organizations such as the Ontario Medical Association, in 1880. Dr. C.W. Covernton and J.E. White of Toronto, and Dr. J.D. MacDonald, J.A. Mullin and G.L. MacKellcan of Hamilton met and after canvassing as far north as Cannington agreed to a first annual meeting of this Association in 1881. The objects of the Association were the cultivation of the science, medicine and surgery; the advancement of the character and honour of the medical profession; the elevation of the standards of medical education; the promotion of public health, and the furtherance of unity and harmony among the members, and to form a connecting link with the Canadian Medical Association.

Dr. Clarence Routley denies the O.M.A. was established with any idea of fee-generation and in justifying his statements points out that doctors were among the few outstanding men in the community and the O.M.A. could not give them greater power, — although:

> one would be unrealistic, of course, to say the founders of the association were unmindful of the possibilities which lay before them to improve the lot of the doctor and the conditions under which he might practice.

One of the Association's earliest actions was on a motion from Dr. Campbell of Seaforth and Dr. Worthington of Clinton to request the

Minister of Education to place the subject of hygiene in the school curriculum. Over the next several years the Presidents of the Association set the tone of the discussion for the current year. In 1882 C.W. Covernton uttered a caution against "being too rash to put into practice the sparkling novelties and theories" that were continually bursting forth. In 1885, in answer to a question from the Women's Christian Temperance Union, the Association asserted that alcoholic liquors were never required in health as a beverage and in medical practice only in cases of emergency. However, the president in 1887, Dr. J.W. Richardson, stated he gave alcoholic stimulants freely and would allow an adult a bottle or a bottle and a half of brandy a day in the treatment of septic tumors.

Alcohol — whisky and beer — had preoccupied physicians, and would continue to do so, since the first settlements. In keeping with the times, hard drinkers achieved a certain notoriety and standing in the community. The Lizars reported in the *Days of the Canada Company* that "whiskey and wet feet distroyed more promising young men than ague and fever". Certainly the frontier made it easy to drink — a barrel of whiskey cost 25 cents.

> *The custom of serving it to outdoor gatherings in a pail with floating teacup was one come down from the fifth century ... the home brewed ale, strong, brown, with a good cream, lay about in kegs, to be drunk at dinner soberly or tossed of at a gulp in the hay fields: again an old custom, for ancient drinking cups had round bottoms, a most convenient shape, as it necessitated emptying at a single drauft.*

Dr. Dunlop, who represented Huron in Parliament, in 1841 fought in the House for a tax on whiskey rather than a tax on stills, which was proposed by the opposition. There was considerable argument that inferior grain was used in distilleries, but he gravely informed all that the whiskey was sound in his area. (In later years the main preoccupation of the Food and Drug Adulteration branches of government was concerned with the quality of whiskey.)

In the neighbouring Talbot settlement, Colonel Talbot was equally direct in his praise of poteen.

> *Damn your calomel, pills, opium and blisters, he exclaimed to Dr. Goodhue ... there is my morning doctor — pointing to a cold bath in the corner of the room — and there is my afternoon physician — indicating a bottle of his favorite old Canadian whiskey.*

But such statements did not sit well with many physicians. Dr. Peter Schofield in June 1828, delivered a temperance address to the inhabitants of Bastard. It led to the formation of the first temperance society:

Various are the ways by which drinking people are brought to their deaths. Some die lingering; some commit suicide; some are executed; some die by violence; some are drowned, some frozen or burned up. It is well authenticated that many habitual drinkers of harden spirits are brought to their end by what is called "spontaneous combustion". By spontaneous combustion I mean when a person takes on fire, as by an electric shock and burns up without any external application. One happened under my own observation. It was a case of a young man about 25 years old; he had been a habitual drinker for many years. I saw him about 9 o'clock in the evening on which it happened; he was then, as usual, not drunk but full of liqueur. About 11 o'clock the same evening I was called to see him. I found him fairly roasted from the crown of his head to the soles of his feet. He was discovered in a blacksmith's shop. The owner of the shop discovered a bright light as though the whole building was in general flame. On flinging open the door he discovered the man standing erect in the midst of a widely extended, silver colored blaze, bearing exactly the appearance of wick-burning candle in the midst of its own flame. There was no fire in the shop nor neither was there any possibility of fire having been communicated to him from any external force. It was purely a case of spontaneous ignition. In general sloughing soon came on and his flesh was consumed or removed in the dressing, leaving the bones and a few large blood vessels standing. The blood rallied around the heart and maintained the vital spark until the thirteenth day, when he died not only the most noisome, ill-featured and dreadful picture that ever presented to human view, but his shrieks, his cries and lamentations were enough to rend the heart of the adamant.

Drunken bouts, frequently associated with parades, were the usual thing.

Anna Jameson in describing the town of London of 1837 pointed out that the population consisted principally of artisans, blacksmiths, carpenters and builders, and all were flourishing. But, how they drank!

*There is, I fear, a good deal of drunkeness and profligacy
for though the people work they had neither education
nor amusements. Besides the seven taverns, there is a
number of little grocery stores which are, in fact, drinking
houses. And though a law exists which forbids the sale of
spiritous liquor in small quantities by any but licensed
public houses, they easily continue to elude the law: as
thus — a customer enters the shop and asks for 2 or 3 penny
worth of nuts or cakes and receives a few nuts in a large
glass of whiskey. The whiskey you observe is given not
sold and no one can swear to the contrary.*

This condition had not changed, even by 1873 when there were 138
licences issued to taverns and hotels and for sale of liquor in general
stores.

The potent, cheap, badly made whiskey created problems
everywhere. However, temperance societies were springing up
which helped to diminish some of these problems. High licensing
fees for taverns reduced the number of outlets in some localities. In
the village of Ennismore it was a six-hundred-dollar licensing fee
that closed down the sales outlet for strong drink.

James Bovell felt strongly that there was a need for treatment
of alcoholism and published *A Plea for Inebriate Asylums* in 1862,
in which he presented a reasoned argument for the establishment of
an asylum for alcoholics. By showing a table of licences issued in
Toronto for 1860 — 108 shop licences, 47 butchers' licences, 4 livery
licences and 302 tavern licences — he was able to demonstrate the
facilities in that city for drunkenness. His presentation even
included a drawing of the proposed institution. The asylum was not
built in Toronto but in Hamilton. However, when the inebriate
patients failed to show up, the building was eventually used as a
sanatorium.

That doctors differ in their opinions was accepted as the
normal course of events by the Association, but that patients and
doctors should differ was usually acknowledged as being inevitable.
With this in mind, a Medical Defence Union was recommended
which would be available to "consider appeals from members of this
Association who may consider themselves persecuted by unfounded
and malicious accusations . . . will give professional advice to any
members . . . who may be defendants in cases of surgical malpractice
. . .".

Chapter XI
Victoria Prospers and Passes

... the sick, as a class, are entitled to quite as much consideration as the insane or the deaf and dumb, and it is very plain that if it be worthwhile to educate people at enormous public cost, it is worthwhile to take care of them when they are educated and are struck down with sickness.

The Toronto General Hospital
Board of Trustees' Minute Book
June 8, 1868

During the consideration of the Bills introduced by Mr. Aikins into Parliament, to incorporate, (as was alleged), the Medical Profession, an anonymous letter was widely circulated in the Legislature, intended to prejudice its members in favour of the measure, by specially damaging the character of Victoria College; while Queen's College is also treated with its share of opprobrium.

The anonymous writer of this letter states "that the students of medicine of Victoria College, may with ease, safety and despatch obtain the degree of M.D. at a private examination from Victoria College or from Dr. Rolph, and thereupon, the provincial licence". This allegation is in all respects most wilfully injurious and untrue ...

The date of this broadside was April 1859. It followed closely the submission by Mr. James C. Aikins for leave to bring in a bill to incorporate the medical profession in Upper Canada under the name of "College of Physicians and Surgeons in Canada West" (J.C. Aikins was a brother of W.T. Aikins). The words and sentiment are familiar. It shows warfare was continuing as usual in the medical schools in Toronto. But the Bill was eventually countered by submissions from Queen's and Victoria, who were concerned they would lose autonomy of their new medical schools, and voted it down.

Feelings ran high in 1856 when Rolph was forced to rise to the occasion and to conduct by himself the Victoria medical course at the new location. The site had been the result of a decision by the Toronto School of Medicine to purchase property in Yorkville, which was at least two miles from Toronto General Hospital. Even Philadelphia, the most prestigious medical centre, was asked for an opinion when Aikins queried his old instructors, Professors Dunglison (1798-1869), Meigs (1792-1869) and Pancoast (1805-1882). They felt it was an unwise and unfortunate site.

By 1859 Rolph's staff included Drs. John Reid, C.B. Berryman and E.A. Ogden. The annual announcement pointed out that:

> ... the medical department was lately, also styled 'The Toronto School of Medicine' which founded by the Hon. Dr. Rolph in 1843, incorporated in 1851, and constituted the medical department of the University of Victoria College in 1854. But this style was dropped in 1856 and the name now appertains to the Richmond Street School. This department, however, is still commonly known as Rolph's School, by which name the 'Toronto School of Medicine' was also generally known, so long as Dr. Rolph was connected with it. The department continues to enjoy a prosperity which has been increasing every year; and this practical guarantee of public confidence is a matter which claims and receives a grateful acknowledgement ...

It is difficult to say how many students were registered in the Victoria Medical Department at that time as figures are confusing and there were letters to Aikins from his friends pointing out on several occasions that false entries were being made by Rolph.

In that year, Rolph struck out at Aikins and Wright in an attempt to have them removed from the Upper Canada Medical Board because of alleged abnormalities in the examination of a student, John Lennon. The attempt was not successful. In spite of the calendar statements by Victoria that candidates in medicine were required to serve four years, criticism was reported of Rolph's examination technique in *The Medical Chronicle*, February 1858. According to this, Hodder made statements to the Board that Victoria had graduated young men who had been little more than two years on course and that from what had been stated at that Board on a former occasion, it appeared to him that Rolph was an examiner who let students off easily with the examination being anything but fair and open; "... In short, it was a complete hole-and-corner affair". To this, Dr. Richardson (a former pupil of Rolph) agreed. The charges were made even more pointed since

Rolph was sitting as Chairman of the Board at the time. Dr. Wright joined in the discussion and stated that he had personal knowledge of a Dr. Poole who had received his licence to practise before he had passed sufficient time in study.

Aside from the matter of inter-school enmity, there was a real concern that doctors were being graduated who were not competent. As for Poole, he went on to a successful career in Peterborough. To remedy this kind of situation it was urged that there be one examining board for all medical schools, a suggestion which was rejected by Rolph.

By January 1860, Victoria College claimed to have fifty students. At that time, the total number of medical students at school in Canada appears to have been three hundred and eighty-five. However, a correction appeared in the *British-American Journal* the following month which stated that there were sixty-four students at Victoria College. (This inability to get stable figures marked several of the reports in the journal.) In January 1861, eighty students were registered at Victoria College and in 1862 it was stated there were ninety-five students.

There had been some changes in the Victoria faculty. William Canniff had joined in '58. In addition to teaching pathology he started to collect and preserve early historical documents of Upper Canada and, to assist him in these activities, he petitioned the government for a grant. The following year he published *Preface of History of the Settlement of Upper Canada (Ontario)* in Toronto.

Canniff also attended at the dispensary. It had been his understanding from a faculty meeting that students who came to the dispensary for medical experience would be credited for a portion of the year's hospital attendance and they would receive a "ticket". The student was required to present certain tickets to qualify for graduation. During the spring of 1862, however, Rolph surprised one or two students with the statement that dispensary tickets would not be accepted as equivalents to regular lecture tickets. Canniff and Berryman wanted to know why there had been a change in the rules, but Geikie, Reid and Mr. Sangster (chemistry) supported Rolph in stating that the tickets would not be accepted. The argument became heated with Canniff pointing out that decisions were being made which had not gone through the proper channels at the faculty meetings. Canniff wrote:

... the next time I met Dr. Rolph he would not recognize me nor has he ever since ... from time to time subsequently it came to me that Dr. Rolph had said that my note was written to insult him ... I called upon Mrs. Rolph and told her distinctly that I did not intend to insult Dr. Rolph ...

Canniff had other causes for dissatisfaction as in the previous summer his income had been reduced to £200, on a recommendation by Dr. Geikie to Dr. Rolph at a faculty meeting. On June 2, Canniff wrote to the Board of Trustees of Victoria, reviewing the dispensary ticket affair and pointing out his regret that ill-feeling had arisen between himself and the Dean. Rolph felt deeply insulted and fired off a letter of resignation to the President of the University of Victoria College. Apparently, this resignation was withdrawn, but the deep feelings continued and finally came to a head in 1863. Canniff who had marked some examination papers, returned them to the Faculty Council, as he was sick on that day. The minutes of the Council show:

> ... March 27th, 1863: Dr. Canniff having announced to the faculty his wish to absent himself from the important duties of the Summer Session; and having communicated to the faculty (by letter) at the present meeting that he considered himself relieved of any further responsibility respecting the matters before the faculty, and therefore that he has no vote or remarks concerning the several candidates: and having thus refused any participation in these arduous and responsible duties belonging to the College and required of him by the College, this faculty regarding such abandonment of such duties as a discourteous way of renouncing his connection with the faculty, have determined to forward Dr. Canniff's letter resigning his position as professor of surgery to the president for his actions thereon ...

Canniff remonstrated that he had not resigned, but the faculty confirmed his resignation on April 6 and he returned to Belleville, where he resumed his practice.

The medical calendar of 1860-61 urged students to attend the classes in Arts at Victoria College, Cobourg, where they would acquire a knowledge of natural philosophy, chemistry and physiology. This would account for one year of the four required for the whole course.

The calendar pointed out that there was a large collection of microscopic specimens and that physiology was being taught with the aid of a microscope. There were 110 students in 1863, 102 in 1864 and 127 in 1865.

The matriculation examination, which was to demonstrate satisfactory evidence of the students' classical and general attainment, could include several works in the classics including the *London Pharmacopoeia*. On graduation, the student was required to compose a thesis upon a medical subject approved by the faculty. Twelve months' attendance at some general hospital or its equivalent was also required.

The graduate of the school would have had no practical use for any of the microscopic applications to medicine. These were used merely to teach principles. Dr. Reid in his lecture on physiology described cells:

> *The primitive cell is rounded or globe or may be club-shaped ... This cell helps in the passage of mucus in the human body; the sac surrounding the cell belongs to a protein compound, which can be shown by the action of acitic acid.*

Rolph, in his lecture, added that some people thought the cell had the power of osmosis. Rolph's lectures were commonly full of eloquence and ranged over many areas. In his opening lecture, which was a popular event attended by many of the townspeople, he inspired the students to seek for knowledge — and at the same time seemed to incorporate many of the ideas which had inspired him in the days of '37.

On the practical side, Rolph dealt with different types of treatment of inflammation, which included removing the cause (e.g. to cover an inflamed eye); sedatives (such as cold water packs or ice); stimulant gargles for the throat; astringents (such as opium or lead); purging and bleeding;

> *Bleeding is the next remedy, general bleeding is taking blood from all the body, local bleeding is taking blood from the part. You may bleed to produce sedation, that is to lessen the flow of blood from the heart ... if you have congestion of the brain and have not time to administer drugs you should necessarily bleed.*

However, whenever the body was under the influence of poison, as with muscles ... "you should never use the lancet ...".

Canniff always advised bleeding, but advocated it be done with wet cupping or using leeches. His lecture on the treatment of inflammation, given in the same terms as Rolph's, repeats the same information, with occasional additions. Berryman lectured that insanity could be divided into two classes, physical and moral. In medical jurisprudence he stressed the necessity for the medical man to note the time and date when he first sees a patient who has been "injured in unlawful violence" so that the testimony in court will be clear. However, he warned "you may go to the furthest part of Canada to be a witness and cannot collect a cent."

In 1866, a Montreal branch of Victoria College was announced. By arrangements with L'École de Médecine et de Chirurgie de Montreal, Victoria recognized it as a branch of the Faculty of Medicine, and was prepared to grant degrees on satisfactory completion of the curriculum. In the first year, 65 students were registered in Montreal, and 158 in the Toronto branch. The Montreal school had a separate faculty, with Dean E.H. Trudel. Instruction was given in French, and the calendar was printed in French for the Montreal branch; however, the main calendar produced in Ontario was printed in English. This Montreal school had been organized in 1843, incorporated in 1845 and conferred its first degrees in 1845. The admission requirements were set in conformity with the Province's licensing regulations.

In a reversal of the philosophy that medical undergraduates should not be subsidized by the taxpayer, each of the Ontario Medical Schools received grants from the Government on a yearly basis beginning in 1857, which amounted to $1,000 by 1860. (Canadian currency changed to dollars in 1858). None of those, including Rolph, who had campaigned for medical schools to be self-supporting, objected.

The Toronto General Hospital was the chief area for teaching the budding doctor, providing clinical teaching by "walking the rounds" — where the professor and an entourage of students went from bedside to bedside — and a lecture room.

The strength of medical teaching in the second half of the nineteenth century stems from the replacement of the apprenticeship system, where a student was bound to one physician for a number of years, by the lecture and clinical system where a number of instructors were teachers to a group of students. The professors of Victoria College gave their lectures to anyone who was in the room. However, Wright and Aikins of the Toronto School of Medicine insisted that each student attending their lectures must have purchased a ticket. This seemed unfair to the Victoria men and in a letter to *The Leader*, January 7, 1867, W.C. Lundy charged in speaking of the Toronto School of Medicine:

> ... *These gentlemen seem most unwilling to abide the issue of fair and honest competition between Victoria College and their own school, and not having succeeded in grafting their institution as an epiphyte upon the Toronto University, have now turned their attention to the General Hospital with a similar view and made it the theatre of most bitter contention* ...

The situation was made more difficult by the financial position of the hospital. During the first part of 1867, the Board of Trustees reports documented growing concern with shortage of funds as unpaid debts and arrears of interests amounted to more than $7,000 and the usual allotment from the Dominion Parliament had not been received because of the change in funding which went with the Act of Confederation. These shortages resulted in the closing of the hospital on August 1st, 1867. It remained closed until August 7, 1868. The closure shocked the community and stimulated wide-ranging discussions of the hospital's role in the community, with a resultant growing realization of the hospital's importance. A new Board of Trustees appointed in June of 1868 reported:

> *it is a reproach that in such an establishment ample accommodation in which all classes are interested, cannot be maintained in such a country for want of a few thousand dollars ... The sick, as a class, are entitled to quite as much consideration as the insane or the deaf and dumb, and it is plain that if it be worthwhile to educate people at enormous public cost, it is worthwhile to take care of them when they are educated and are struck down by sickness ... The basis of such a system must be public support, continuing, regular, always ready for the emergency and bearing equally upon all — not private alms, inconstant or irregular* ...

Having established a basis for funding the hospital, the role of the institution was further clarified with regard to the schools of medicine:

> *The necessity of providing for the care of patients of course stands first, it is hardly of less importance that there should be a hospital in association with the medical schools, so that students could obtain that knowledge of*

100

*their profession which can alone be had by the practical
contact with disease and accidents to the various members
of the body. Without this practice, the country will be
flooded with young men only half-taught in their
profession, men who will not be half the service that they
would be if they could but avail themselves of hospital
instruction and treatment.*

With the re-opening of the hospital, there were reappoint-
ments of the members of medical staff which included Beaumont,
Bovell, Rolph, Aikins, Berryman, Rowell, Richardson, Thorburn,
Geikie, Canniff and Cassidy. However, this had not solved the
lecture problem. *The Daily Leader* pointed out:

> *... The existence of two medical schools in the city gives
> rise to a good deal of difficulty in the management of the
> hospital. They (the Toronto General Hospital) have
> therefore decided not to permit the delivery of clinical
> lectures in the hospital. We believe this was the only wise
> and sensible course open to them ... The schools wrangle,
> carrying their eternal bickerings within the walls of the
> hospital ...*

This wrangling continued and it was necessary on September
1st, 1870 to recommend that lecturers should confine themselves to
lecturing upon patients who were their own patients, or upon
colleagues in the same school.

As mentioned above, Canniff had returned to Victoria. While
in Belleville he had achieved many distinctions, including the vice-
presidency of the Ontario division of the newly-formed Canadian
Medical Association. He appears in the 1868-69 calendar as
Professor of Surgery and Surgical Pathology.

Meanwhile, John Rolph was failing — and President Nelles
of Victoria wanted to appoint Canniff as sub-Dean! *The Globe* of
August 26, 1870 reported:

> *... The advanced age and feeble health of the Hon. John
> Rolph have of late rendered it impossible for him to
> discharge as fully as heretofore the duties of his office ...
> After full consideration, the Board deemed it expedient to
> leave Dr. Rolph still in the position of Dean, but
> appointed Dr. Canniff as sub-Dean to assist him in his
> duties and to act as Dean in his absence.*

Rolph reacted with the conditioned reflex of many years of
medical in-fighting. He collected the resignations of his son, Dr.

John Widmer Rolph, and his old friend and student, Dr. Geikie and a third staff member (subsequently withdrawn) and presented them together with his resignation to Principal Nelles. In addition, he charged the Board of Trustees of Victoria College with being sectarian in their choice of Canniff, a Wesleyan.

Nelles responded by accepting the Dean's resignation, pointing out:

> ... the Board took this step simply from regard to the interests of the school and not from any unfriendliness to Dr. Rolph ... The venerable Dean has, I think, on this, as on many former occasions, more reason for gratitude than complaint ... [with regard to the resignation of Geikie, he added] ... I am sorry to say, he is not disposed to remain with his old colleagues, and that I am equally sorry to say, some of his old colleagues are just as little disposed to remain with him ...

Canniff was appointed Dean of the Medical Faculty following Rolph's resignation, and was Professor of Principles and Practice of Surgery. During the 1870-71 session, 73 students were registered in Toronto, and 94 in Montreal.

Rolph died in the fall of 1870 after a series of strokes ending almost half a century of dedication to medical education. Physician, teacher, lawyer, Reform leader and patriot rebel — Rolph was always a contentious figure. The funereal eulogies did not speak of those who would have described him as cunning, devious and self-seeking. But hundreds of loyal students and thousands of grateful patients spoke to the fullness of his life.

In the 1871-72 year, E.B. Shuttleworth was appointed Professor of Pharmacy, the first in Canada. As a pharmacist in Toronto, he had been instrumental in the founding of the Canadian Pharmaceutical Society in 1867 and its successor, the Ontario College of Pharmacy in 1869, of which he became Dean.

There was a new spirit in the faculty and during the fall of 1871, a subscription fund was started to erect a building nearer to the Toronto General Hospital, and away from the Yorkville area. Student registration dropped to 25 that year and this low registration continued in the 1872-73 session. In that session, Shuttleworth was described as Manager, Toronto Chemical Works, editor of the *Canadian Pharmaceutical Journal* and Dean of the Ontario College of Pharmacy. S.R. Richardson was appointed Professor of Diseases of the Mind.

Canniff was worried about the school, and wrote to Nelles in January 1873:

> ... *I also wanted to speak to you confidentially in reference to the medical department. There appears to be a want of sympathy in Cobourg. I know your feelings are invariably warm ... but I have understood that strong influences are at work prejudicial to us ...*

In July, the new medical college building of Victoria was opened at Don and Pine Streets after super-human effort on the part of Canniff. The *Toronto Leader* reported in July 12, 1873, that:

> ... *the Faculty had promised, they would devote the entire proceeds of the institution for the next ten years to the removal of the financial obligations and forego all remunerations rather than see the institution go down.*

These financial problems continued to plague Canniff in addition to the low registration, and in a letter to the Board of Trustees, May 25, 1873, he stated:

> ... *I wish to call to mind the important fact that in consequence to legislation some four years ago, the degree of M.D. no longer possesses the value it previously did ... [He referred to the Act Respecting the Medical Profession of Ontario in which homeopaths and eclectics received the same recognition as medical doctors] because of the reduced number of students in attendance. Had the same money value continued to belong to the diploma, it would have mattered much less what changes took place in the staff or whether the college building was situated conveniently or inconveniently so far as the number of students was concerned.*
>
> *I pointed out that at the time of Dr. Rolph's withdrawal from the College, a rival university set on foot a movement to establish a medical department and by intriguing with both the professors of our College and the students, sought to erect that department upon the ruins of the medical department of Victoria College.*
>
> *At the present moment, we have a most pleasant building and staff, but have laboured faithfully the last year, and some three years seeing the income from the students appropriated to pay for university property, are cognizant of the fact that while they are paying for a College building, the teachers at Trinity Medical College are supplied with a building and are allowed so much for*

each lecture delivered irrespective of the number of students in attendance ...

To provide financial security and rebuild his staff who were deserting to Trinity, Canniff proposed the formation of a joint stock company to be known as The Victoria Medical School Ltd. Apparently, Nelles agreed with this step, as is seen in a communication from the assistant secretary of the Province of Ontario to him, October 8, 1874, notifying him that letters patent would be issued by the Government.

Nelles was justifiably worried whether the Board of Victoria would favour the proposition. The Board refused and in a letter, of October 26, to Nelles, Canniff stated:

... I have made up my mind that I cannot consistently with my self-respect continue to struggle against so many difficulties ...

Canniff then went back to his previous statements that there was want of sympathy and support on the part of the Cobourg group for Toronto, which was shown in the repeated snubbings he had received from members of the Board. He finished the letter by saying:

... I feel the time has now arrived when I need not hesitate to wash my hands of the whole matter ... I have expended my energy and become gray in endeavouring to build up a department of the University ...

Nelles responded on October 26, pointing out:

... If we were desirous of getting rid of the medical school, we would at once avail ourselves of the opportunity offered by your letter of the 26th ... Permit me to speak to you as a friend and as a lover of our common church interests and to advise you on every ground to do nothing rashly ... You are mistaken in your apprehension ...

A further communication to the Board from the Victoria Medical Faculty on November 6, 1874, signed by Charles Archibald, Secretary, stated:

... The medical department at Toronto during the past twenty years has presented to the Board for degree of M.D. more than five hundred students ... but owing to serious causes beyond the control of the faculty, among others, the recent legislation* whereby the degree of M.D. is no longer a licence to practise medicine ... and the general falling-

---

*The Medical Act amendment, which appointed the College of Physicians and Surgeons as the licencing body.

off of medical students at all colleges . . . it can no longer
carry on the work of the department and respectfully ask
the Board to receive their resignations . . .

This was signed by Canniff, Barrick, Archibald, Agnew, Richardson, Hillary, Parsons, Kirkland, and Carlyle and lectures were withdrawn on November 20, with students being advised via notices in the newspaper that:

. . . An alliance having been made between the Toronto
School of Medicine and the Medical Faculty of the
University of Victoria College, the lectures of the united
schools will be delivered at the rooms of the Toronto
School of Medicine, Queen's Park, November 24, 1874.

Wright, of the Toronto School of Medicine, asked Canniff to deliver four clinical lectures per month at the Toronto General Hospital, but Canniff declined. Victoria retained the right to examine students and there continued to be graduates. In addition, the Montreal branch continued to send candidates for examination at the Toronto school.

Between 1878 and 1880 there was pressure on the Montreal branch to be taken over by Laval which felt strongly that the two French-speaking schools in Montreal should be united, and offered affiliation to the École. This move was resisted by the Dean, Dr. D'Orsonnens. Further pressure was applied, and at one time, the school was debarred by the Church from attendance at the Hotel Dieu, and its members and students were excommunicated on the ground of disobedience to authority and association with a Prostestant university.

On a direct appeal to the Pope, this decision was reversed, and the school continued its teaching programme. A new constitution was given to the Laval branch in Montreal, which made it possible for the École to affiliate with it at a later date.

Victoria conferred degrees in medicine until 1887 including one to Harriet Stowe Gullen, the daughter of one of the earliest qualified female physicians in Ontario.

Canniff continued his professional life but was no longer connected with a teaching establishment. Rather he looked at the political establishment and in a highly critical manner published an article: *Canadianism: Some Reasons Why A New Canadian Political Party Should Be Established.* He pointed out that Dominion politics were based on Ontario partyism and he urged that there was a need for a party that would encompass and appeal to all areas of Canada. This sentiment was in keeping with the embryonic "Canada First Party". He followed his article in 1875, with *The Canadian Nationality, Its Growth and Development* which asserted that sectionalism limited the development of a national sentiment. On being appointed Medical Health Officer of the City of Toronto in 1873, he established a good basis for inspection of meats and other food supplies. Also, he developed an interest in medical politics and was elected President of the Canadian Medical Association in 1880.

He lived until 1910, having finished his monumental study *The Medical Profession in Upper Canada 1783-1850* in 1894. However, in spite of his brilliance as a physician and surgeon, an author and a discerning commentator on the Canadian political scene, he was unable to preserve the medical department of Victoria College.

The Founding Fathers

Dr. John Rolph, who was described as a "Father of medical education in Ontario". He was also described as a "whirl of versatility", having qualified as both a lawyer and physician, he turned his attention to divinity and applied for orders. But he abandoned the idea when he thought he would have to undergo some probation. Rolph, although a member of the Church of England, was unremitting in his struggle against Bishop Strachan and the Family Compact.

Portrait by Nelson Cook, 1837. (Courtesy tesy, Academy of Medicine Toronto)

Dr. John Rolph in later years.

The Rt. Rev. John Strachan, First President of King's College, Founder of Trinity College. Strachan was the power behind most thrones in Toronto during the 1830's and 40's. His perseverance over 20 years resulted finally in the opening of a medical school.
Photographed in 1867. (Courtesy, Metropolitan Toronto Library)

Dr. Christopher Widmer, chief physician and surgeon of the Toronto General Hospital and later Chancellor of the University of Toronto. This portrait hanging in the Toronto General Hospital shows him wearing his decoration from the Peninsular Campaign.

Early Physicians

Dr. William Dunlop, in a rare moment of repose. "Tiger" was a roistering sort of a man, who typified the rough and ready frontier life.

Dr. William Rees who practised in Toronto in the 1830's. In addition to originating the Toronto Club, he also tried to found a house for the reception of destitute female emigrants. He was instrumental in establishing the first Provincial Asylum and was the first Superintendent.

Dr. James Sampson, President of the Medical Faculty of Queen's College, Chairman Board of Governors The Kingston General Hospital.

Dr. John Gilchrist, who practiced in Peterborough.

Dr. William Charles Gwynne.

This certificate, which was in the front of all of Samuel Thomson's books, was to be framed, suitably, in the office of the "doctor" as a proof that he was entitled to practise Botanical Medicine. The book cost was twenty dollars for the first copy and ten dollars for the second, if this certificate could be produced.

The First Medical School

First Medical School of Upper Canada, Medical Department King's College approximately 1844. This building held the anatomical department. The anatomical class numbered about 18 students. Following this the anatomical department occupied the basement of Upper Canada College boarding house, and then moved to Moss Hall.
(Courtesy, Canniff, W., The Medical Profession in Upper Canada)

This drawing shows the red brick building that stood on the north side of Richmond Street, 100 feet from the west line of Knox church property, between 1845-1855. It was originally a dwelling, but was converted to a dissecting room for the Toronto School of Medicine.
(Courtesy, B. Gloster, 1904, Metropolitan Toronto Library (B10-11A))

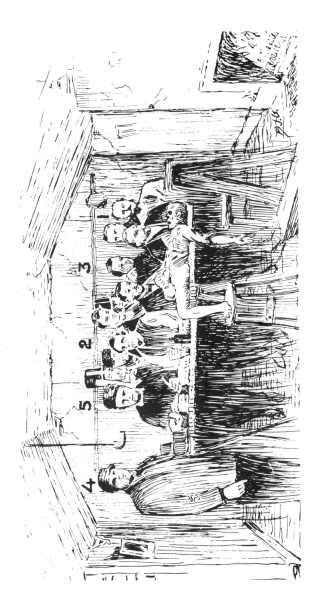

The dissecting room on Richmond Street was shown in a picture made in about 1855. The men at the table are: 1) Dr. John King, 2) Dr. George DeGrassi, 3) Tom Hays, lecturer at the Toronto School, 4) Old Ned, the janitor and custodian of the dissecting room, 5) W.W. Billy, Frances, a student who afterwards practised on Manitoulin Island. Cadavers were difficult to acquire.

Drawing by B. Gloster

113

The Toronto School of Medicine

Front view of Rolph's original school which later became McBurnie's
meat market on Lot Street, Toronto.
(Courtesy, Academy of Medicine, Toronto)

Rear view of Rolph's school, showing the stable. Photo taken about
1930.
(Courtesy, Academy of Medicine, Toronto)

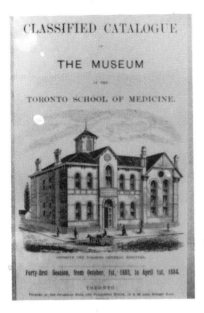

Toronto School of Medicine, 1883-84. The new museum is on the right-hand side of the picture. Corner Gerrard & Sackville Streets.

The building of the Toronto School of Medicine, in the 1930's, when it was a factory.

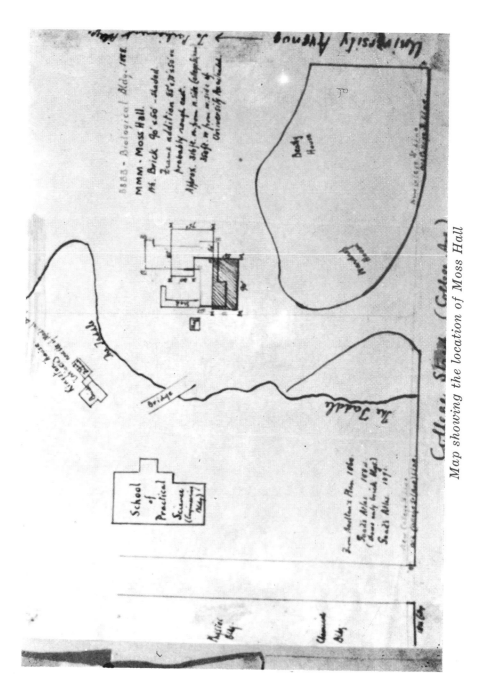

Map showing the location of Moss Hall

The St. Thomas School

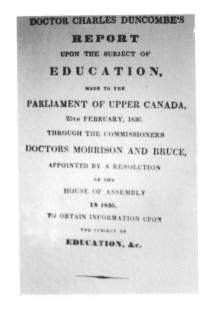

Port Talbot,

rom *Colonial Advocate, Aug. 19, 1824.*

MEDICAL SCHOOL
AT
St. Thomas,

IN THE TALBOT SETTLEMENT, AND UNDER THE
IMMEDIATE PATRONAGE OF

THE HON. COLONEL TALBOT.

NOTICE is hereby given that a Medical School is
opened at St. Thomas, in the Talbot Settlement,
under the direction of CHARLES DUNCOMB, Esquire,
Licentiate, and the immediate patronage of *The
Honourable Colonel Talbot*, where the Education of
young men for the profession of MEDICINE AND
SURGERY will be carefully superintended, and every
opportunity afforded them to become intimately
acquainted with the structure and physiology of the
human body.

Every student before admission is expected to have
a complete knowledge of the LATIN language, or to
give satisfactory assurances of immediately acquiring it; for which purpose A COMPETENT TEACHER
will be resident in the village.

CHARLES DUNCOMB

will give a course of LECTURES on the THEORY AND
PRACTICE of MEDICINE.

JOHN ROLPH

is expected to give the first course of LECTURES AND
DEMONSTRATIONS, during the ensuing season, on
the ANATOMY AND PHYSIOLOGY OF THE HUMAN
BODY.

St. Thomas, August 5, 1824.

The medical school at St. Thomas was never more than a series of lectures given by Duncombe and Rolph. However, it can claim fame to being "a first".

The 1836 Report by Duncombe, Morrison and Bruce which set guidelines for the development of education (and penitentiaries) for the next 50 years.

Dr Charles Duncombe
M. P. P. for Oxford, 1830 7.

Dr. Charles Duncombe. Duncombe, was one of the most progressive thinkers of the 1820's and 30's. When he fled the country with a price on his head, he did not return as did many others of the 1837 rebels.

PROCLAMATION.

REWARD.

By Command of His Excellency the Lieutenant Governor.

A REWARD is hereby offered, of

Five Hundred Pounds,

To any one who will apprehend and deliver up to Justice

CHARLES DUNCOMBE;

And a Reward of *Two Hundred and Fifty Pounds* to any one who will apprehend and deliver up to Justice, ELIAKIM MALCOLM; or FINLAY MALCOLM; or ROBERT ALWAY; and a Reward of *One Hundred Pounds*, to any one who will apprehend and deliver up to Justice, —— ANDERSON, (said to be a Captain in the Rebel Forces); or JOSHUA DOAN.

All the above persons are known to have been traitorously in arms against their Sovereign; and to entitle the party apprehending either of them to the Reward, he must be delivered to the Civil Power, At Hamilton, Niagara, London, or Toronto.

GOD SAVE THE QUEEN.

16th December, 1837.

R. STANTON, Printer to the QUEEN'S Most Excellent Majesty.

Early Ontario Hospitals

The Victory Medal for volunteers, which was melted down to provide funds for building the first General Hospital at York, after there was disagreement as to who should be decorated.

Two pen and ink drawings of the first civilian hospital built in Toronto in 1820. This building was used until 1854, serving as a meeting place for parliament from 1824-1829. It was at the north-west corner of King Street West and John Street.

(Courtesy, Metropolitan Toronto Library (B1-36B and B1-36C))

The first hospital at York (*Four Centuries of Medical History of Canada* by Heagerty).

The Kingston Hospital, built in 1835, to which numerous additions were made throughout the years.

The Toronto Lying-In Hospital, which was used from 1848 to the late 1850's. It was at the corner of Richmond Street East and Victoria Street.
(Courtesy, Metropolitan Toronto Library (B11-249))

Niagara had a military hospital, which was built early in the 19th century, and was still standing in 1864.
(Courtesy, Metropolitan Toronto Library (C1-57D))

An artist's conception of the building for an Inebriate Asylum proposed by Dr. Bovell for Toronto. It was never built.

The Toronto General Hospital opened in 1856, which was on the north side of Gerrard Street East between Sackville and Sumach.
(Courtesy, Metropolitan Toronto Library (X63-10))

The Lunatic Asylum, Queen Street West. This was the first mental hospital, which still stands and is in use today.
(Courtesy, Metropolitan Toronto Library (JRR-541))

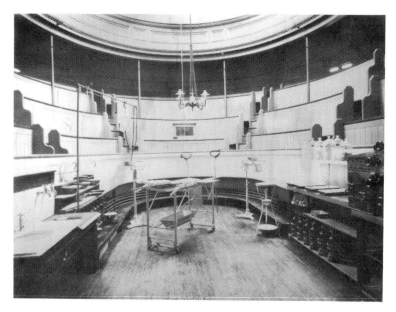

The operating room, Toronto General Hospital, 1890. Students watched from the balcony. The jars of bichloride mercury may be seen at the lower right.

Operating room, Toronto General Hospital, in action. Dr. W.O. Stewart stands in front of the patient and W.A. Shannon, D.A. Dobie, E. Clouse, W.D. Scott and George Acheson, left to right. The ether is being poured over a mask and Dr. Clouse holds a suction apparatus. No gloves or gowns are used.

Ward at the Hospital for Sick Children, about 1900, when children began to be cared for in special areas, rather than with adults.

The Physician seen by others

Upper Canada Medical Board examines a candidate in 1855. From left to right candidate Gamble; Drs. Herrich, Bovell, Workman, King and Widmer. Aaron Walter Gamble qualified and practised in Lambton.
(Courtesy, Academy of Medicine, Toronto)

Two early Hamilton physicians caricatured at the funeral of Sir Allan Napier MacNab, 1862. Left to Right: Mrs. Henry Boulton, MacNab's second wife; Mrs. David MacNab, widow of Sir Allan's brother; Most Reverend John Farrel, First Bishop of Hamilton (R.C.); Andrew Stuart, brother of MacNab's second wife, an Anglican; The Devil; Reverend John Gamble Geddes, rector of Christ's Church Cathedral; Dr. Craigie; Dr. Hamilton.
(Courtesy, Special Collections, Hamilton Public Library)

Victoria College

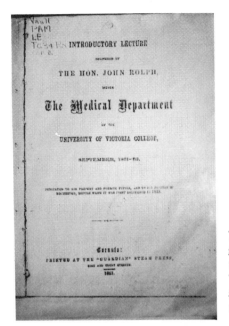

The frontispiece of the famous inaugural lecture given by Dr. Rolph at the beginning of each academic year. This lecture attracted many people and was one of the social events of the city.

Dr. William Canniff, Dean of Victoria and doyen of Canadian Medical Historians. Canniff, in addition to being a sought-after physician was active politically and a strong supporter of the United Empire Loyalists.

Victoria School of Medicine

Victoria University School of Medicine — second site on Bismarck Street (photo taken in the 1930's).

Aikins of the Toronto School of Medicine

Dr. W. T. Aikins, Dean of Toronto School of Medicine and University of Toronto Medical Faculty.

The Toronto General Hospital when it was located on Gerrard Street East in Toronto. The letter informs Dr. Aikins that he has been removed from the staff of the hospital.

PETITION

Of Drs. Aikins and Wright, setting forth certain grievances, and praying that the Royal prerogative may be so exercised as will ensure their restoration to the Toronto General Hospital.

(Mr Hartmon.)

Ordered, by the LEGISLATIVE ASSEMBLY, *to be printed, 3rd April,* 1856.

Printed, 9th April, 1856.

A petition from Drs. Aikins and Wright, asking that their privileges be restored at The Toronto General Hospital.

mirable lectures on fractures from the chair of surgery in the University of Toronto, that I, with many others of his old pupils, have never ceased to regret that its designer failed to find time in his busy life to place a description of the splint on record. And now that our much-respected professor has laid aside as well his industrious scalpel as his always reluctant pen, and has retired from active duty to crown " a youth of labour with an age of ease," I gladly take upon myself the task which his diffidence, not less than the arduous duties of his calling, prevented him from performing in his earlier years.

...rous proportions that the are free from the shoulder, otherwis ... ain- fully upon the bony prominence Then it is a distinctive fea ... ..e distance from the shoulder arch to ... ..lbow should be such that when the arch ... ...tion by strapping, considerable extension may be made on the muscles of the arm by drawing the forearm down to the horizontal limb of the splint below the elbow.

The splint may be padded to any desired extent by wrapping it with a roller of sheet cotton. (For the sake of sim-

Fig. 1

Fig. 2

The material of the " Aikins's splint," as it is usually designated, is the ordinary flexible band or hoop iron, such as may be procured at any ironmonger's or blacksmith's shop. For infants and very young children a band 1 inch wide is amply strong; for adults a width of from 1½ to 2 inches will usually be found to be of sufficient strength. The thickness and strength of the material are usually in proportion to the width. As a rule, the material can be worked by hand, bending it over the edge of a table, or around a pillar or bedpost,

plicity it is represented in the photographs without any pad-ding.)

In applying the splint the patient should, if possible, be in a sitting posture, with the spine quite erect. If confined to bed he should be turned somewhat towards the sound side, or a firm pillow should be placed under the spine and sound shoulder. The splint is now placed in position, with the arch over the shoulder, and secured very firmly (but quite free) by one or two strips of rubber adhesive strapping about an inch and a half broad, and long enough to reach well down upon

Dr. William Aikins, hoop-splint.

Lecture Tickets

Lecture "tickets". These showed the student was registered for courses and were counter-signed on completion. Without a signed ticket, the student could not graduate.

Trinity

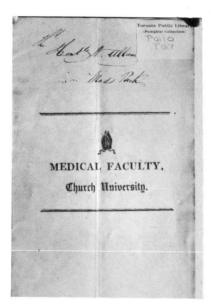

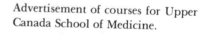

The first calendar of the Medical Faculty of Trinity Medical School.

Advertisement of courses for Upper Canada School of Medicine.

Dr. Hodder, first Dean of Trinity.

Dr. Bovell about 1865.

Trinity College Medical Faculty.

SESSION—1856-7.

THE LECTURES IN THIS DEPARTMENT WILL COM-
MENCE ON

WEDNESDAY, 15th OCTOBER, 1856,

No religious test required of students attending the Lectures.

Gentlemen not being members of the Church of England, may obtain their degree of M.D., at the University
of Toronto, on complying with the requirements of that
Institution.

N. BETHUNE,
Dean, Richmond street.

Toronto, June 19, 1856.   1932-3m Th

Advertisement of Trinity College Medical Faculties,
session 1856-57, with the contentious wording.

Dr. Geikie whose career spanned the early proprietary
schools to the amalgamation of all schools in Toronto.
He fought to keep medical education a private matter,
outside of government assistance.

Site of the old Trinity College and School on Spadina Avenue, north of Queen Street. (Photo taken in the 1930's.) Note title of movie on marquee.

(Courtesy, Academy of Medicine)

Trinity Medical College on Spruce Street. It is now a condominium.
(Courtesy, Ontario Archives, Toronto)

The London School

The medical school at London at the corner of York and Waterloo Street.

Ontario Medical College for Women

Emily Howard Jennings Stowe.

Dr. Michael Barrett, the first Dean of the Ontario Medical College for Women.

Dr. Letitia K. Meade, age 14, she was preparing to enter Medical School.

Ontario Medical College for Women.

The funeral of the casualties killed at Ridgeway during the Fenian Invasion, including William Tempest.
(Courtesy, Metropolitan Toronto Library (JRR-783))

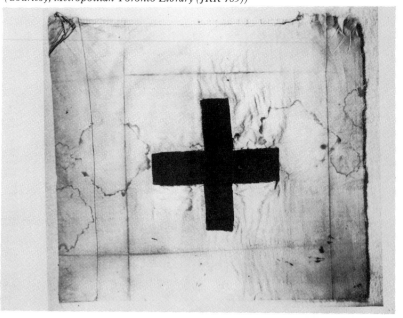

The Red Cross Flag, which was used by Dr. J. Sterling Ryerson at the engagements at Fish Creek and Batoche, 1855. This flag was improvised and is said to have been the first Red Cross flag used in Canada.
(Courtesy, Metropolitan Toronto Library (JRR-196))

Dr. Milton Ross, with some of his many decorations. In addition to his medical and anti-vaccination interests, he met and cared for Garibaldi while he was in New York recovering from a gun shot wound to the heel.

Dr. Oronhyatekha, Supreme Chief Ranger of the Independant Order of Forresters.
(Men of Canada, Volume II, by Rev. William Cochrane, 1893.)

Dr. Abraham Groves, who practiced in the countryside and performed operations on the kitchen table. He believed that washing out the peritoneal cavity with hot water was protection against infection, and proved it to be so on numerous occasions!

Charles Greenwood Moore, Dean of Medicine, 1881-85, University of Western Ontario.

A group of medical students with C.A. Hodgetts, the first on the right of the back row. This type of picture, complete with skeleton or various anatomical segments, was one of the common "class photos" of the 80's and 90's.

A map showing where Dr. Hodgetts found diphtheria in the Nipissing area.

(Courtesy, Provincial Board of Health 1888)

Dr. William Osler, about the time of graduation from McGill in 1872. Osler was actually enrolled in the Toronto School of Medicine, but left because he was uncertain that he would be able to complete his training program in view of all the quarrelling which was going on and the uncertainty of The Toronto General Hospital remaining open.

Dr. Herbert Bruce, Special Inspector General, whose report recommended that the Canadian Medical Services should be reorganized from "top to bottom".

Dr. Theophilus Mack. He established the St. Catharines Marine and General Hospital and a training school for nurses, which was the first in Ontario.

Professor Ramsey Wright, University of Toronto

Dr. Daniel Clarke.

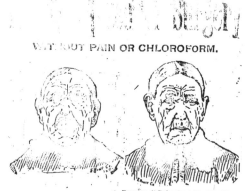

W... ...OUT PAIN OR CHLOROFORM.

HIT HIM AGAIN.

March 1888

DR. McCULLY:

TORONTO, 41 Defoe street, March 5, 1892.

DEAR SIR,—For about 23 years I have had a cancerous growth from my upper jaw filling the whole of the front of my face and making me almost unable to speak. I went over to the Hospital here a short time ago and asked them if they could take it out, they told me they could and they would have to give me chloroform and cut out the lump and also a piece of the jaw. I am an old woman, over 70 years old, and I felt I would die if they started to practice their ways on me, so I went to Dr. McCully, he gave me no chloroform, he did not lay me up one day, he did not cut a hole in my jaw, but he did take out the big lump of disease, and thank God I was not butchered and am now well again and owe my life to his skill.

MRS. SARAH RACHFORD.

This cancerous growth was in years gone by removed in Guy's Hospital, London, England, and at the Old Mill they proposed to give this poor old woman chloroform; in her feeble state, 70 years old, such a course meant death, but to make assurance doubly sure it was proposed to resect the upper jaw, cut away a large portion of the bone and destroy the last hope of recovery.

THIS CASE WAS PHOTOGRAPHED BY SIMPSON, 357 YONGE ST.

Our readers will pardon us this once for referring to the Evening Telegram. Dr. McCully no longer advertises in that paper. That paper once took great delight in publishing our characteristic ads. referring to the doings of the Old Mill. Is the editor now on his knees before the school men of this city? Evidently new faith, new love and now light have dawned on his mental horizon at the 11th hour; whether from position given, or to placate in anticipation of position dexterously being played for, will not be long in realization.

However, we have been informed by that paper that such criticism "IS ONLY DISCREDITING A PUBLIC INSTITUTION THAT IS A PUBLIC BENEFACTION." Dear Telegram, go and try to eat the butter served up to the Hospital patients within the months of January and February and we are certain if a dozen governorships of such place came begging to your door for admittance your stomach would revolt. Once again. Recently in that institution a lady of this city was confined under the following circumstances (her husband is a well-known business man on Adelaide street and gave us the information last week). The lady was told by a professor in Trinity College that she had a uterine tumor, and an operation was a necessity. Thereupon another professor of Trinity College was called in and confirmed the diagnosis of fool No. I. The unfortunate lady was then trotted off to the Old Mill to be done up. Fortuitous circumstances prevented immediate vivisection, and the night before the operation took place she was delivered of a child. I am permitted to use these facts. This institution is "A PUBLIC BENEFACTION."—Proprietor Telegram.

I HAVE TWO OTHER RECENT SIMILAR CASES of which they got in their work and found themselves wrong. One is a living witness and I have his testimony, the other died at the Mill.

INVESTIGATE! INVESTIGATE! INVESTIGATE!
REFORM! REFORM! REFORM!
I AM READY!

Remember we are Surgeons—Not Butchers. Remember that while radical in exposure of Surgical Atrocities we are conservative in dealing with human life. We Cure.

Catarrh, Consumption, Asthma, Bronchitis.

Remember we cure these diseases, remove polypus, open up closed or partially closed nostrils, heal up deep-seated and foul ulcers in the head, cure catarrh of the stomach, followed by belching, sore stomach, costive bowels, disordered kidneys, sluggish liver, palpitation of the heart, weak heart, cold purple hands and feet, pains in the back and shoulders, pains in the chest, hacking up mucus in lumps, strings and frothy mouthfuls and general debility.

Diseases of Women,

such as sterility, painful menstruation, falling of the womb, version, soreness in back and sides, aching of head and legs and thighs, whites.

Cancers and Tumors

removed without chloroform, safe and certain.

Skin Diseases,

including eczema, libra, psoriasis, syphilitic eruptions, syphilitic swellings of the glands, scrofula of the glands and skin and lupus.

Piles and Varicocele.

We cure every time, no, knife, no mutilation of parts, no ligatures, no needles, no blood poisoning.

The Follies of Youth

Young man, why go to Druggists, Quacks, and Irresponsible Medical Companies? You are a prey to these vagabonds. The reason is not far to look for. The Medical Council have for years been engaged in the delectable task of dog eat dog. They were called into existence to protect you from these Rampant, Soulless Vampires; they live now but to degrade the profession and harass and tax honest men to create an irresponsible monopoly. Dr. McCully cures the results of early indiscretion. Next week we will give the public another eye-opener of the grist ground out in the old mill. Watch for it; it's a daisy.

Office hours, 9.30 a. m. to 8 p. m. Office Suite—26 Yonge street Market, corner Yonge and Gerrard. Consultation free.

Write or call on

DR. McCULLY.

Check, brass and impudence of assertion in the Canada Lancet are its major stock-in-trade. By these does this redoubtable medical blusterer vegetate, while it in the meantime degrades its columns by advertising more than questionable compounds for the filthy lucre, upon which it has evidently staked its existence. Railing accusations against religious journals line its pages, while all the time its monthly diet is from wretched carcases infinitely more putrescent of falsehood than any tid-bits that appear in their columns. The one great difference being that it advertises a falsehood knowingly; they without any professional knowledge to discern between falsehood and truth. Behind these railing accusations and this cloud of mud filled with medical, Bankable Microbes, sits the doughty editor representing with all the devilish ingenuity of an expert that these remedies can and do cure or benefit opposite conditions of disease of the body, opposite states of condition both in form and character, produced by opposite forces and producing opposite causes. The indications that are attached to these compounds are sickening and disgusting flap-doodle; but all are tolerated by the medical fraternity effects, and that toleration is but another indication of the profound depths of ignorance in which the average medical man flounders from day to day under the present regime in this province. No advertiser will continue to advertise any article he cannot sell; as these so called remedies are not advertised to meet the eyes of "the regular herd," it follows that medical men tossed about from the Scilla to the Charybdis of empiricism in their professional ignorance, are glad to seize upon anything to give patients whose diseases are baffling them from day to day, Celerina, "Nerve-tonic—stimulant and Anlispas modic," says the Canadian Lancet, composition, common garden celery, cocoa, kola, viburnum. There are seven kinds of viburnum, but which one this ad. saith not, and it makes no difference, because not one out of the seven is worth its room in the drug store. The one medicine in this compound is the cocoa, and this is a stimulant, first in small doses, and a sedative in its secondary action, leaving behind like all other stimulant narcotics or sedatives no perceptible change of condition of improvement, while in many instances they are positively hurtful and dangerous. Now this inert medical compound cures, or it is "indicated in nervous headache, neuralgia, paralysis, (opposite conditions,) hysteria, opium habit, drunkenness, dysmenorrhœa, prostatitis, dyspepsia and all languid and debilitated conditions of the system; also "impotency, spermatorrhœa, loss of nerve power and peculiar to preachers, lawyers and business men." (HERE IS A NEW LIGHT SURE). Happy remedy: in one man it cures and soothes a painful nerve, in another it rouses by its stimulating forces a dead nerve into action! It stirs up the virile forces in impotency, and in

Dr. McCully claimed in his advertisements that his medications were far better than those approved by the establishment doctors.

140

INCOMES AND PERSONALTY

The Assessments of Some of our Leading Citizens.

THE DOCTORS AND CLERGYMEN.

The Singular Poverty of the Medical Profession —A Fearful Warning to Medical Students —Keep Out of Such a Poor Business.

We continue our extracts from the assessments to income and personal taxes, taking the doctors and the clergymen as the classes to be exhibited. The assessments of other classes will be given to-morrow :—

DOCTORS.

Norman Bethune, income, $1,000.
James H. Burns, income, $2,000.
Chas. W. Chaffer, income, $800.
Jerrold Ball, income, $1,000.
Thomas Pyne, income, $800.
J. H. Richardson, income, $2,000.
Hugh Spiers, income, $800.
Wm. Oldright, income, $2,000.
R. H. Robinson, income, $1,000.
James Carlyle, income, $350.
John E. White, income, $1,000.
W. S. Clark, income $1,000.
W. H. Howitt, income, $1,000.
J. A. McDonell and S. E. McCully, income, $1,010.
James Ross, income, $2,400.
John S. King, income, $1,500.
J. H. Cameron, income, $1,200.
H. H. Wright, income, $2,000.
James F. W. Ross, income, $2,500.
James Baldwin, income, $1,000.
G. A. Clarke, income, $900.
C. M. Foster, income, $450.
A. J. Johnston, income, $2,500.
B. Spencer, income, $900.
T. McCausland, income, $1,000.
Thos. Armstrong, income, $1,500.
James P. Danter. income, $800.
W. B. Nichol, income, $1,000.
James A. Temple, income, $2,000.
Geo. Wright, income, $1,000.

Rev. E. A. Stafford, income, $2,500.
Rev. H. G. Baldwin, income, $1,600.
Rev. John D. Cayley, income, $1,400.
Rev. Thos. Griffiths, income, $800.
Rev. Robt. Wallace, income, $1,500.
Rev. T. W. Jeffrey, income, $2,000.
Rev. A. F. McGregor, income, $800.
Rev. J. F. Sweeny, income, $900.
Rev. Ira Smith, income, $1,000.
Rev. Robt. J. Moore, income, $600.
Rev. A. Gilray, income, $1,500.
Rev. S. A. Dyke, income, $1,000.
Rev. R. A. Bikley, income, $1,000.
Rev. John Mutch, income, $1,000.
Rev. Joshua P. Lewis, income, $1,600.
Rev. Hiliary Bygrave, income, $1,500.
Rev. John Langtry, income, $1,400.
Rev. John E. Starr, income, $1,200.
Rev. Geo. I. Taylor, income, $800.
Rev. Wm. Frizzell, income, $1,000.
Rev. Jno. M. Cameron, income, $1,800.
Rev. R. W. E. Greene, income, $1,400.
Rev. B. D. Thomas, income, $3,000.
Rev. S. J. Shorey, income, $1,800.
Rev. John Burton, income, $2,000.
Rev. Dr. Wild, income, $3,000.
Rev. H. M. Parsons, income, $4,000.
Rev. John Pickering, income, $800.
Rev. G. M. Milligan, income, $3,000.
Rev. Arthur Baldwin, income, $2,500; income from stock, $300; total, $2,800.
Rev. R. N. Burns, income, $900.
Rev. Septimus Jones, income, $2,000.
Rev. Elmore Harris, income, $2,000.
Rev. John Salmon, income, $800.
Rev. Thos. Jolliffe, income, $800.
Rev. E. G. Daniel, income, $800.
Rev. Manly Benson, income, $1,500.
Rev. Dr. Sutherland, income, $2,000.
Rev. John Shaw, income, $1,200.
Rev. John Pearson, rector Holy Trinity, income, $1,600.
Rev. Dr. Scadding, income, $1,863.
Rev. Joshua Denovan, income, $1,800.
Rev. John Potts, income, $2,000.

The doctor's income has always been a matter of public interest. This story appeared in the Globe, July 1886, pointing out the singular poverty of the medical profession.

Number of Cases Investigated, Prosecuted, Etc.

Name and Address.	Amount of Fine.	Amount Paid.
R. S. T. Gilmour, Wiarton........	$25 00	$25 00
James Beaton, Kincardine	25 00	25 00
Dr. G. E Fell, Ridgeway.........	35 00	35 00
J. S. Powley, Toronto............	25 00	25 00
William Gilbert, Huntsville........	27 00	27 00
J. W. Black, Toronto............	25 00	25 00
A. P. Sterrit, Toronto............	35 00	35 00
Ruth Beasley, Toronto............	25 00	25 00
Dr. N. Washington, Crysler.......	50 00	50 00
W. R. McNab, Tara..............	25 00	25 00
T. A. Pine, Northbrook...........	25 00	25 00
F. H. McCarthy, Ottawa..........	40 00	40 00
Dr. A. Oumet, Ottawa............	25 00	25 00
Mrs. R. Thompson, Ottawa.......	25 00	25 00
Mrs. R. Lange, Ottawa...........	25 00	25 00
T. A. Pine, Flinton.............	25 00	25 00
A. Robertson, Maberley..........	25 00	25 00
A. Finley, Mountain Grove........	25 00	5 00
Professor Glen, Wasego..........	25 00	Not paid
T. H. Blow, Wiarton.............	25 00	25 00
Professor Millar, Walkerton.......	25 00	25 00
Dr. N. Washington, Crysler.......	50 00	Not paid
R. S. Sneadley, Toronto..........	25 00	25 00
H. R. Buckley, Toronto..........	25 00	25 00
Mrs. A. McKelvie, Ottawa........	25 00	Not paid
Professor Crane, Dunville........	25 00	Not paid
M. A. Graham, Toronto..........	25 00	Not paid
T. Pine, Northbrook............	25 00	25 00
W. F. Coulson, Toronto..........	75 00	75 00
D. McCarthy, Paris.............	76 02	76 02
Loftus Med. Co., Stratford.......	50 00	Not paid
Chas. Wright, Tor. Junction......	25 00	25 00
D. McCarthy, Paris.............	75 00	Not paid
Professor Gardeau, Thessalon......	25 00	Not paid

Total... $1,113 02

Kickapoo Indians, Stevensville, case dismissed ; J. McKelvey, St. Catharines, no case ; Henry Musson, Allenburgh, no case ; Sent man to Cornwall to prosecute Washington, found he had skipped ; A. McLeod, Owen Sound, no case ; A. N. Cadieux, Toronto, case dismissed ; Mrs. Beauvine, Crysler, no case ; Mary A. Lebreik, Toronto, no case ; Mrs. A. McKelvie, Ottawa, gone to jail ; S. Townsend, Ottawa, withdrawn ; Prof. Gustin, Orangeville, skipped, warrant for his arrest ; J. Bealing, North Bend, withdrawn ; Mrs. John Kane, Ottawa, no case ; Mrs. E. Thompson, Ottawa, no case ; Mrs. Ann Kelly, Ottawa, no case ; Mrs. W. Ackland, Ottawa, no case ; Mrs. Sharron, Clarkstown, no case ; Mrs. Beeton, Baytown, no case ; Dr. Jebb, Orangeville, left the day I arrived there ; Mrs. Mitchell, Delaware, no case ; J. W. Black, Orangeville, case dismissed ; Dr. High, Doon, information laid, he did not appear, warrant issued for his arrest ; Matilda Spring, Dorchester, no case ; Mr. Doreland, Hawkesbury, left the place, no case ; Joseph Zehr, Topping, could not be found, was travelling with his father ; Professor Shrieves, Moraviantown, no case ; J. H. Chatton, Fenelon Falls, no case ; Opticians, Ottawa, does not come under the Medical Act ; Mrs. J. E. Fox, Whitby, agent for Viavi, case dismissed ; Philo Crane, Dunville, went to jail ; Kickapoo Indians, Tilbury, the information laid, the professor skipped, there is a warrant out for his arrest ; James Upham, Gardo, case dismissed ; Professor Gardeau, Georgina, fined $25.00 but skipped ; Kickapoo Indians, Chelsea, case dismissed with costs ; Professor Bell, Evanstown, no case ; Professor Chamberlain,

A list of cases investigated and prosecuted by the College of Physicians and Surgeons, 1896-97.

Chapter XII
New Country — Old Medicine

. . . a simple plug to a patented thrashing machine . . .

Dominion Medical Journal, 1867

At the time of Confederation, a new political start was made in the country, but medicine continued as before. Although the Canadian Medical Association had its inaugural meeting, it was not to have any effect on the practice of medicine for many years. In some circles the stuffing of the minds of medical students with the new "scientific" knowledge was questioned. The 1834 publication of the Bridgewater Treatise on *Chemistry, Meteorology and The Function of Digestion,* which was concerned with gross chemical and physiological organization, remained the major philosophical basis for diagnosis — in spite of the fact it did little to differentiate several causes of diseases having similar manifestation. The microscope was being used to look at urinary deposits following the publication by Golding Bird in 1844 of his paper on Urinary Deposits. This work along with *Organic Chemistry In Its Application To Agriculture and Physiology* by J. von Liebig (1842) represented the scientific approach to medicine. However, there was little in any of them which looked at therapeutic indications.

Objections in the minds of the practitioners in Ontario to the new emphasis which was seen in school curricula on scientific courses was based on the concern that this would mean there would be less time for observation and first-hand collection of information from the sick patient such as would be gained by an apprenticeship. After all, most doctors would be working in the patient's house with little scientific equipment to assist them in diagnosis or treatment. This was the case with Dr. William Comfort of Pelham who, although he was close to both the Welland and St. Catharines Hospitals, did most of his work in the home. Following graduation in 1855 he practised as a student under Dr. John Frazer and eventually settled in the Ridgeville area. To keep up his medical knowledge over the next forty-five years he relied on medical journals and books. After his death, in 1899, it was found that his library contained:

> Bartlett, Elisha: "The History, Diagnosis, and Treatment of the Fevers of the United States," 1856.
>
> Bedford, Gunning S.: "Clinical Lectures on the Diseases of Women and Children," 1855.
>
> Bennett, Jas. Henry: "A Practical Treatise on Inflammation of the Uterus, its cervix and Appendages and on its Connection with Uterine Disease", to which was added the same author's "Review of the Present State of Uterine Pathology," 1860.
>
> Druitt, Robert: "The Principles and Practice of Modern Surgery," 1853.
>
> Esquirol, E.: "Mental Maladies. A Treatise on Insanity." Trans. E.K. Hunt, 1845.
>
> Flint, Austin: "A Practical Treatise on the Diagnosis, Pathology and Treatment of Diseases of the Heart," 1859.
>
> Goodwin, Chas. H.: "The Hospital Treatment of Diseases of the Heart and Lungs," 1883.
>
> Headland, Frederick Wm.: "On the Actions of Medicines in the System," 1870.
>
> Hirst, Barton Cooke: "A System of Obstetrics," 1864.
>
> MacKenzie, Wm.: "A Practical Treatise on the Diseases of the Eye", with: Jones, Thomas Wharton: "An Anatomical Introduction explanatory of the horizontal Section of the Human Eyeball," 1855.
>
> Murry, Wm.: "A Treatise on Emotional Disorders of the Sympathetic System of the Nerves," 1867.
>
> Neligan, J. Moore: "A Practical Treatise on Diseases of the Skin," 1860.
>
> Smith, Edward: "Consumption — its early and remediable Stages," 1865.
>
> Toynbee, Joseph: "The Diseases of the Ear — their Nature, Diagnoses and Treatment," 1860.

Twenty-five years after Comfort had begun to practise, he subscribed to "Wood's Library of Standard Medical Authors" which sent monthly reprints automatically and unselectively. These included recent and older works. Many of the books used during the height of his active practice were published about the time he started practice, so in effect his knowledge had remained at the undergraduate level. He also subscribed to medical journals and most likely read on a variety of subjects.

For example in 1864, Dr. Rosebrugh published an article on a new ophthalmoscope for photographing the posterior internal surface of the living eye. This was a small photographic camera to which were adapted two brass viewing tubes. Although this development would have been of interest to Comfort, it is doubtful whether it had a practical application.

In the year of Confederation he would have read in *The Dominion Medical Journal* of a lecture by David L. Philip, coroner for the county of Uxbridge, on the problems of retroversion of the impregnated uterus. In the same issue William Canniff wrote on Carbolic Acids as a Remedial Agent in treatments of wounds. This article followed closely on the publication by James Lister in the *British Medical Journal* of the use of carbolic in the prevention of infection.

Drawing from another medical article, New York, the *Journal* in 1868 published an article on the Microscope as an Aid in the Diagnosis and Treatment of Sterility by Dr. J. Marion Sims. It described a detailed method of examining spermatozoa, post-coitional, to determine the cause of barrenness. However, it is unlikely that Comfort possessed a microscope as even by Confederation there were only a small number in Canada.

The problems associated with conception and contraception were frequently brought to the family physician and much ingenuity was being used in the production of different apparati to prevent conception. The *Journal* carried a copy of an address by Dr. W.D. Buck of New Hampshire in which he decried that 23 different kinds of pessaries were available, ranging from "a simple plug to a patented thrashing machine ... all of which made a Chinese toy-shop out of the vagina."

The same issue of the *Dominion Medical Journal* carried an article by Dr. Walter Lambert of Amherstburg on the Use of Phosphorus in Locomotor Ataxia. His case, a 22 year-old girl, took ferruginous preparation for treatment of anemia and scanty menstruation. For the chlorosis, Lambert sometimes gave Misturia

Ferri Comp. Recently, from exposure to wet and cold, her menses had ceased and all the symptoms of progressive locomotor ataxia had appeared. Lambert visited her in the farmhouse and saw that the patient staggered and swayed her body from side to side, unable to keep her equilibrium. She would suddenly jolt to recover herself and then would plunge forward, seemingly in a great hurry to reach the point to which she decided to go. She was unable to feed herself, from lack of co-ordinate action of the muscles, and in fact, unless she was watching her hands continually, she was liable to drop objects. Her speech was also affected and she could not articulate some words perfectly.

As soon as he recognized the disease as "Locomotor Ataxia", Lambert gave Potass. Bromid. and "submitted the patient to the action of magneto-electricity, once every 24 hours". He also gave pills of Aloes and Iron. Fortunately, he remarked, he received the September number of the *New York Medical Journal* which told that Dr. Desjardin Baumatz had given phosphorus in the same disorder with excellent results. Consequently Lambert's patient received Acidi Phosphorici Dilut and in a short time began to improve. Within two weeks she was able to sit up and had sufficient control over her upper extremities to be able to knit and within one month was able to walk about the house tolerably well. Lambert followed the case over the next two months, at which time she was able to take long walks, do housework and was beginning to put on weight.

In 1869 the *Dominion Medical Journal* carried an account of a medical meeting in Toronto where Dr. Reeve reported his success in treating cases of typhoid fever by keeping the temperature of the body down to 102 degrees by means of baths. This followed on a report from Germany of Dr. Ernest Brand's (1827-1897) treatment of various fevers, which consisted of cold water packs and sometimes injections of cold water into the veins.

His paper *Die Hydrotherapie des Typhus* was published in 1861, and remained a guideline for treatment of typhoid into the 20th century. Simon Baruch, of Columbia University, New York, reported a reduction in mortality from 24.66 percent to 2.7 percent using the Brand baths in the Bellevue Hospital, New York City.

The following year Dr. W.W. Ogden, an eminent member of the Toronto teachers' group, delivered a paper on Rheumatism and Rheumatic Gout with specific treatment by Kino-Colocynthine. He began his paper by pointing out that there most likely was a zymotic element (a general term for infections caused by a process analogous to fermentation) as a pre-disposing cause of typhus, typhoid, scarlatina, measles and smallpox. However, this element was not a factor in the constitutional diseases such as rheumatism, rheumatic-gout and gout, (constitutional included irritative or inflammatory disorders of various tissues). Rather the cause of these was a "specific poison generated in the system as a result of mal-assimilation or faulty metamorphic action of lactic and uric acid". To prove this he pointed out that lactase and urates had been invariably discovered when sought after in the urine of persons labouring under these diseases, and to treat this problem he recommended the discovery of Dr. Laville of the Paris Faculty, which consisted of yellow bark and red bark, equal parts, powdered and mixed and digested with alcohol. Then the residue was pressed with very dilute sulfar trioxide to make a preparation of cinchona. Following further chemical processes the result was mixed with Spanish wine, alcohol and water. The action of this medication was to eliminate through the skin and kidneys urate of ammonia and soda, since those salts caused gout and in the presence of lactic acid were thought to be the specific cause of rheumatism. Dr. Ogden then gave several specific cases where he had caused a significant improvement.

In 1872 the *Canada Lancet* published an article on syphilis which pointed out that:

> As long as the patient is suffering under the syphilitic diathesis arising from an indurated chancre, he cannot have another indurated chancre. So if you want to know if the system of a man is altogether free from syphilis, you can do so by innoculating him with an indurated chancre; if it takes, he was free; if not, he was susceptible. That is a great point to be reached in the science of medicine.

In another portion of the journal in that year William Kerr of Galt wrote of a new remedy for dysentery. He reported that a fellow physician in Berlin, Ontario, who had been seized with epidemic dysentery, was treated with the usual remedy — Opium, with increasing doses up to 24 grains daily with Mercury, Acetate of Lead, and Ipecacuanha. Kerr devised a more effective medication consisting of a combination of Opium, Henbane, Hemlock, Strammonium and Digitalis. The remainder of the article pointed out the man had "successes which attended this medication".

The majority of the articles in the journals came from the larger teaching centres. Occasionally someone like David L. Philip of Plattsville was published, but in general the medical school teachers were the major contributors. In 1881, towards the end of Comfort's active practice, J.H. Burns of Toronto read a paper at the Toronto Medical Society in which he reported on several remedies from current periodical literature. These included Grindelia Robusta, or wild sunflower, which was used for asthma and bronchitis. Yerba Santa, which was imported from the United States, was recognized as "consumptive's weed" as it contained a resin in its leaves which limited bronchial secretions and which Burns had used as a fluid extract as prepared by Mr. Shuttleworth. Eucalyptus, coca, kava-kava were all potent medications. Coca was used as a nervous stimulant and kava-kava was used as a remedy in gonorrhea and gleet. It was described as a sialagogue (i.e. producing saliva) which improved the appetite, was a special stimulant on the central nervous system (called kavic stimulation), and was not a sudorific. It increased secretion of water in the urine, did not produce priapism and was "endowed with remarkable blennostatic properties". Burns reported that his experience in the use of kava for gonorrhea was not favourable. He also described other products including the bark of the ironwood tree and the bark of the coto tree which were used to reduce fevers and chaulmoogra oil which was used in scrofula, skin diseases, rheumatism and leprosy.

One of the last medications he described was nitroglycerine, which according to the *British Medical Journal* of 1880 was in general use in the London hospitals and was considered a valuable agent in treatment of angina pectoris.

In that year Comfort reduced his practice and developed a much larger interest in raising the standard of farming in the Niagara peninsula. One of his later activities was planting maple trees one of which, "the Comfort Maple" still stands today.

Chapter XIII
Bloody Flux, Pus and Miasma

"... The medical practice of today has no more foundation in science, philosophy or common sense than it did one hundred and fifty years ago."

Dr. Alexander Ross, 1897

The government "has enticed sick emigrants into the country in order to decimate the ranks of the French Canadians," was the charge made by Louis Papineau, patriot rebel leader of Lower Canada. One could not say that in Upper Canada. Cholera had arrived without the assistance (or negligence) of the government. In York, with a population of 5,500, there were almost 600 deaths, and in Peterborough, Hamilton, Kingston, Ottawa, Osnabruck, Ennismore, Pickering and all the other small towns there was a similar grim toll.

It was in 1832 that the first major epidemic struck the young colony. Measles had almost reached epidemic proportions in York with the death of many youngsters in 1829, but had vanished quickly. Malaria or ague had been and would continue to be endemic from the miasma in York, along Lake Erie and Niagara until the 1870's. While there had been cases of smallpox in previous years, they had never reached epidemic proportions and control had been maintained by variolation — passing the disease from one poxed person to another by direct contact.

But cholera! Here was an epidemic with victims dropping dead in their tracks within six hours of being infected. It had started in India, and worked its way through the Near East to Poland and then to England. Immigrants arriving in Canada with the first overseas ships brought it to Quebec and then it leap-frogged down the St. Lawrence system to Cornwall, Brockville, Kingston, Cobourg, York and Hamilton. A crowd watching a circus in London spread it into the backwoods. A church congregation in Hamilton inhaled it with the good word. A drunk carried it into the jail in York. An AWOL soldier brought it home to the garrison in

Kingston, and a voyageur carried it into Lac Coulonge, north of Ottawa.

The citizens had never seen anything like it before. It would not be until 1855 that the work of Dr. James Snow (1813-1858) in London, England would convince the world that the horror was spread by contaminated drinking water. Cholera was considered a moral disease — the consequence of intemperance — or of being drunk or of eating oysters — the wages of sin. After all, these ne'er-do-wells who lived in one room in Stuart's Lane at the York market lived like pigs. (And they all drew water from the same well.) However, when a few clergymen and respectable ladies contracted the disease, these ideas changed. Miasma was a prime suspect as the cause. Animalcules which could be dispersed by cannon fire, were likely to be the reason for the spread of cholera. So cannonades were used for a time, without effect. But, Dr. Elam Stimson of London, put cholera's cause down to atmospheric impurity and stated in *The Cholera Beacon* "... is easily cured if taken in time...". Many of his patients, including his wife and son, died.

Each of these theories resulted in new ornamentations of a prevention programme — burning pitch, smoking tobacco, carrying coffins underhand or holding days of prayer. None of these worked, of course, and the disease continued its relentless spread. Porters at the steamship docks at the lake ports normally hustled immigrants' baggage to the nearest hostelry. But by the end of June, no porters dared go to the docks. The steamships *Great Britain* and *William IV* brought a new crop of cholera patients each time they crossed the ocean. The only greeting they received on their arrival in Ontario was a wagon to cart moribund patients to the cholera sheds. Even the carters succumbed early in the epidemic.

What few hospitals existed were rapidly overcrowded and it was necessary to throw up temporary cholera sheds. An abandoned house was taken over in Burlington, a schoolhouse at Port Stanley; a warehouse in Kingston served as shelter for dead and dying. No patient wanted to be condemned to go to the hospital — that was a one-way ticket to the grave. Members of well-to-do families were usually nursed at home — thus managing to spread the disease within the family circle.

The disease itself was terrifying — a healthy adult could be reduced to a blue emaciated corpse within 24 hours. Bodies were buried at night in pitch-lined coffins beneath six inches of lime. Most of the victims in York were buried in Potters' Field, which was situated at the corner of Yonge and Bloor Streets. Each lake port in Ontario still has an identifiable cholera cemetery.

When it was realized that "cholera was with us", Governor General Colborne appointed Medical Boards throughout the province. In York, Baldwin and fourteen other doctors were selected to mobilize all resources. Two doctors, James Cathcart and James Muttlebury, were dead within three weeks. The Board met each evening and prepared a summary of the cases; a woman dead of cholera was found on the street; Hewitt, a bricklayer at the new market house, "was taken with it and died in about two hours"; Edward, Mary, Delia and James Cox of Newgate Street all dead. Pipeneau, a Canadian Indian, died in the park. Colborne had made £500 available for cholera care in Canada West, but when the Medical Board of York approached him for more money, he informed them there was no more. The Board responded with a request for 50 barrels of lime to disinfect ditches and privies, and pointed out that a better method of transporting infected patients was urgently needed. In addition, the Board complained it was unable to enforce its regulations. A pub owner at the northeast corner of Jarvis and King Streets had refused to clean up the filth in the area. He contracted cholera and was buried the next day, an incident which heightened the Board's feeling of helplessness in controlling the disease. Because Colborne dragged his feet in answering their requests, and demanded instead more paper work, the Board resigned. A new Board was appointed the next day, with W.L. Mackenzie as Chairman, but it did little more than tabulate statistics until the disease died out with the cold weather.

During those months of the epidemic it was not unusual to see Rolph and Strachan working shoulder-to-shoulder caring for the sick in the sheds. It must have been embarrassing though to read the charge that a too-eager undertaker had been a little previous and buried a young girl who continued to move. It was ominous to read a newspaper editorial censuring another journal for creating alarm by printing news of the dread cholera, which would prevent the summer influx of pleasure seekers from the U.S., who spent large sums of money in our cities.

Wave after wave of sick immigrants were deposited on the wharves of each of the lake ports, much to the dismay of the local inhabitants. No ship was allowed into the Kingston harbour until an inspection was made — so skippers attempted to land in the darkness. Hamilton greeted the immigrant with a notice — "Bread,

Quick-lime and Transportation out"! At Cobourg, where the local newspaper, *The Star,* had reported the imminent threat to the community, immigrants were held in quarantine for three days at "hospital point".

Cholera returned to Ontario in 1834, 1837, 1847, 1849 and 1854. Although there was a pandemic over the world in 1863, it missed Canada. A conference in March 1866, at Ottawa, issued a memorandum that the problem of cholera could be handled by separation, hygienic precautions and sound advice. Unfortunately, this did not save the lives of 145 people in Toronto nor had it helped a similar number throughout the province when cholera re-appeared mysteriously in 1854.

Baffling too was the variety of therapies used in the early days. Doctors in London used calomel, half a pint of hot ginger tea laced with brandy, capsic and bleeding — "draw blood until it flows a fullstream". By the last pandemic, in 1866, Bovell was using intravenous milk, and Sampson of Kingston was transfusing saline. Their patients appeared to rally for a short time but all eventually died.

Bovell reasoned that F. Magendie (1783-1855) had described the effects of transfusing milk and water into animals with safety, in 1821. A recent paper by a French microscopist, A. Donne, had demonstrated that transfused milk was taken up by the blood — and it was a complete natural food. In addition, A.H. Hassall (1817-1894) had published *The Microscopic Anatomy of the Body in Health & Disease — 1849,* which suggested that it was advisable, in the restoration to health, to "inject into the system a supply of similar material to fill up the place of that drained away." (An article in the *British-American Medical and Physical Journal* suggested death resulted from loss of fluids, so it prescribed fluid injection by catheter into the bladder.) Bovell performed his injections in 1854 (several months before Dr. W.B. Herapath in England published the "first" account of a similar treatment) and reported his results to the Canadian Institute in January 1855. Although he had considered the treatment for some time, he had hesitated to carry it out without consultation with his colleagues. Hodder agreed it should be done, and performed the venipuncture. Widmer agreed, but at the same time:

> ... requested us to be very cautious, as to what we did, least in case of immediate death, the public mind should become excited ...

Four cases were injected by Hodder and two by the medical student, John McKenzie. In each case the intravenous injection was delayed until there was no doubt that the patient was dying:

> ... *An ordinary glazed earthenware bowl was placed in warm water ... a cow which was grazing close at hand, was brought up to the shed, keeping the teat close against the side of the vessel to prevent frothing ... a brass, anatomical injecting 4cc syringe was now filled with the fresh living milk ... in a few minutes the pulse was distinctly felt ... almost simultaneously the eyes responded ...*

Hodder reported the procedure in *The Practitioner* in 1873:

> ... *Dr. Bovell and myself then applied to the Corporation (of Toronto) for a good cow and a few articles indispensable for the comfort and well-being of the patient: these were refused and we therefore sent in our resignation ...*

Sampson was following the lead of Dr. Latta of Leith, who used seawater. This method had been communicated by the central Board of Health, London, in *Lancet* of 1832. At that time it was proposed that a new method of treating the blue cholera epidemic, by the injection of highly oxygenated salts into the venous system, should be tried. A Dr. W.B. O'Shaughnessy had analysed the blood of cholera patients, which showed him that there had been a loss of a large proportion of its water and neutral saline ingredients. Dr. Latta was stimulated to try the treatment. He gave it to an aged female and noted after a half hour, when six pints had been injected, that she was improving. Attempts to use the procedure continued as late as 1873, as reported in *The Gazette, Hospital Paris*, but were abandoned because of difficulties, uncertainty of the treatment, and poor results.

The 1854 epidemic, twenty years after the first major epidemics, saw considerable improvement in the standards of hygiene. Butcher supplies were cleaner, and water had been drained from stagnant cellars. Clothing and bedding of the dead were destroyed by fire, or "baked" at high temperature in an oven followed by washing them thoroughly in chloride of lime. Acid vinegar was used to cleanse the rooms of cholera patients. There was more emphasis on proper ventilation. This approach to disease control, although it still admitted ignorance of the true cause, produced practical results.

Sensible and practical remarks were also made by Dr. John Corson of the Brampton Board of Health during the 1866 epidemic.

He had had considerable experience with cholera, having been in English hospitals in 1847, in Brooklyn, New York, in 1849, and in New York City itself in 1854 during a severe epidemic. He stressed proper ventilation of cellars and pointed out that in England soakings of privies and sewers into wells was thought to be a cause of cholera. He was concerned that the Brampton topography, with the overflow of the river into the wells every year, was a cause for contamination of wells. He advised that a flannel apron or belt should be worn over the bowels, that hard drinkers should reform, and that fresh milk was beneficial. In the treatment of a cholera patient, he used an immense mustard plaster covering the whole stomach and bowels, which he advised should be applied from 20 minutes to one hour. He pointed out that many Irishmen considered their stomach to extend from the chin to their heels, and therefore should be given the benefit of an extensive mustard plaster.

Kingston, in 1847, was the major receiving area for immigrants infected with typhus — a fatal fever passed on by body lice. *The Kingston Herald* reported 7,140 cases by September, most of them carried off ships by new arrivals from Ireland — escaping from the potato famine to die in the new world. There were 5,293 reported deaths among those crossing the Atlantic. The Quarantine Hospital at Grosse Isle was a primitive collection of huts, with straw-covered floors — a large amount of straw was not necessary as it was re-used with each new entry. Kingston hurriedly erected sheds, which rapidly became overfilled and had to be torn down as a public nuisance and danger. Entire families and the survivors of others huddled in City Park begging for food, while the immigrant dead were buried in a huge trench.

To cope with the disease in Toronto, where there were 3,876 cases, the government obliged doctors to attend the hospitals and see approximately 200 patients a day. To visit a sick patient twice a day, in a ten-hour day, the doctor could give a minute and a half to each. Such a work-load with primitive facilities lead to the deaths of Dr. G. Grassett, the Medical Superintendent of the Emigrant Hospital, and of Dr. J. Hamilton, within a few weeks.

It was difficult to differentiate any fevers; typhoid was confused with typhus and proper identification could not be made in the 1847 epidemic. Early 19th century French observers had pointed out the difference in postmortem appearances of both diseases, and in 1839 Dr. J.L. Schonlein (1793-1864) also differentiated the two diseases. The clinical appearance had been shown clearly by Dr. W. Gerhard (1809-72), when he examined an outbreak of "jail fever" in Philadelphia, which he showed was the same as "ship fever" and was highly contagious. Following this, Dr. W. Jenner, in 1849 to 1853, by a clinical examination of patients in a London, England, hospital, showed that typhoid fever was rarely passed from one individual to another. To the practising physician in Ontario it made little difference since their treatment was the same for all fevers.

Various theories were held in mid-century as to the mode of transmission of typhoid, such as "... contagion requires a ripening stage in the earth and the spread of the epidemic depends in the falling of the ground water ...". But more importantly, the concept of disease as a moral problem was superseded by social factors as the cause:

> *Had the sanitary measures which are now in fashion, imperfect as they are, been in existence in 1832; could Hercules have purified that Augean stable, muddy York, — closed the buildings, ventilated the dwellings, and applied all our modern disinfectionals of 1861, — the pestilence would have been stripped of much of its horrors ...*

wrote Rev. C. Dade, M.A., in the *Canadian Journal of Industry Science and Art* in 1862.

His optimism in that year was slightly desperate. Epidemics continued to decimate the country. In 1868:

> *... In almost every other house in Mitchell and in some instances whole families are prostrated. Measles seem to be the prevailing disease, and is more confined to children.*

or

> *scarlet fever is very prevalent in St. Mary's near London.*

In 1874, Hamilton reported 83 cases of typhoid, with 12 deaths recorded. The *Registration Report* for the province, 1871-1882, showed of the ten most common death causes, typhoid as always being present. But by 1880 Dr. T.A.E. Klebs (1834-1913) identified short rod bacilli in typhoid patients which was quickly followed by the work of Drs. R. Koch (1843-1910) and C.J. Eberth (1835-1926) who showed these bacteria were the causal agents. Dr. William Budd (1811-1880) published a book in 1873 which re-established his earlier work that typhoid was transmitted by excretions from the human body which got into the sewage and then into drinking water.

With the identification of typhoid as a bacterial disease from polluted drinking water, it was possible to recommend real steps for its prevention and in 1887, a severe epidemic of typhoid in Ottawa made urgent the need for proper bacterial analysis of water. That city had always had chronic typhoid problems, with a death rate of about 37 per 100,000 people, over a period of many years, a very high toll. The Ottawa Water Works in 1881, after a chemical analysis of the water, suggested a filter should be used to remove debris. Water for the city was pumped from the river using three pumps in a section of the river which was "protected" from the sewage by a breakwater. Even though sewage began to pile up in the Ottawa River, a report in 1884 gave an "A" rating to the water. Rating of water was done by the currently accepted technique — the Wegner standard — which examined for solids, chlorine, free ammonia and poisonous metals, but it was not until 1888 that Massachusetts began to examine water for bacteria. Dr. Ramsay Wright maintained bacteria could be present even though the chemical analysis was clear. In 1887, there were 1,500 cases out of 45,000 people. There was, of course, a major inquiry with accusations made against the company, and during the political recrimination period it was revealed that the medical officers presumed typhoid bacteria could not live in water and therefore it was not necessary to alter the water supply in order to protect the public.

In Toronto, drinking water was drawn from the lake by a combination of wooden and steel conduits. The wooden conduit under the bay began sucking polluted water in the 1890s with a doubling of the rate of typhoid mortality (see Table B). Following this, a steel conduit was put in place but this leaked in 1893 and in 1910, with an accompanying rise in the mortality rate. The sanitary engineers did not have to inspect the pipes — all they had to do was count the cases! About 1910, the German idea of chlorination using slow sand filtration was introduced but there was considerable opposition to this from outlying communities in later years who argued: "You're not going to use that chlorine that killed our boys during the war". Similar gradual upgrading of water supplies took place in other parts of the province. In Windsor, Dr. John Coventry was able to insist on proper water supplies. He was the mayor.

As early as 1835 the Upper Canada Medical Board recognized the importance of proper drainage and garbage disposal for the health of the city of Toronto. It empowered the Mayor, W.L. Mackenzie, to spend up to £10 in order to import drinking water from the Humber. However, many bloody fluxes occurred before Dr.

Canniff was appointed Medical Health Officer in 1873. His annual reports from that time on show water quality, food inspection and environmental hazards to health were given a higher priority, with reduction of morbidity.

While it was understood that water could be contaminated and pass on disease, it was difficult for the ordinary person to realize that milk could carry the seed of the wasting sickness — tuberculosis. From the *Registrar's Report* from 1871 to 1882, tuberculosis was always the highest cause of death. Of 9,182 deaths in the province in 1871, tuberculosis claimed 1,042 and in '82, 2,464 out of 21,800 died of the disease. Even many years after Pasteur had made his momentous discoveries, the wards of the children's section of the hospital were full of young, their diseased bones oozing tuberculous pus. In 1901, mortality from all forms of tuberculosis was 180 per 100,000.

Although milk bottles instead of the public ladle were first used about 1900 as a public health measure, opposition by some large dairies to bottling continued until well after World War I. Those same dairies joined with doctors in opposing pasteurization of milk. The milk producers feared a monopoly would develop and the doctors feared deficiency diseases in children (a legitimate fear as the techniques were primitive). Dr. J.A. Amyot of the Ontario Health Department spoke out against his colleagues early in the century arguing for pasteurization of milk. He was joined by the Canadian Medical Association and the Toronto Academy of Medicine; finally Dr. Charles Hastings, Medical Officer of Health of Toronto, was instrumental in the passage of a by-law which required milk to be "certified" to be from tuberculous-free cattle and with a low bacteria count. Further pressure from the medical profession resulted in a by-law that the total supply of milk be pasteurized in 1915. This preventive programme and the establishment of centres, such as the Muskoka Cottage Sanatorium, by Dr. Jabez Elliott, started the process which reduced TB and resulted in the "miracle of the empty beds" — thousands of beds which were no longer needed for the treatment of tuberculosis by the end of the first half of the twentieth century.

Children were the main beneficiaries of milk pasteurization. They were also the target of smallpox. While public reaction against pasteurization was high, it was violent against smallpox. A massive wave of pox wiped out Indians in Western Canada in 1837 but an epidemic in Toronto in 1870 did little to stir Ontario families to demand Jenner's vaccination. They already knew the side effects of that. Besides, you could still get smallpox after vaccination! Laws enforcing vaccination were passed in Britain and the U.S. in the 1850s but they were not enforced until the 70s because of anti-vaccination movements. By 1885, Dr. Alex Stewart of Palmerston had established the Ontario vaccine farm to produce good quality vaccine. Calves were inoculated with the virus, and five days later, the lymph was taken from the calf and vaccinated into the arm on the spot as the lymph did not keep. In 1899, a preservative, glycerine, made it possible to store the lymph.

A leader in the resistance to the preventive measure was Alexander Ross, a Toronto doctor, the founder and president of the Anti-Compulsory Vaccination League. Abolitionist, confidante of President Lincoln and spy for the Union Army, he held strong political opinions — and vehement medical views. Almost, it seems, to balance his forcefulness, he spent ten years writing a beautiful quiet book on the flowers and birds of Canada. He himself was a rara avis. He ate only natural foods, grains, fruits, vegetables and water. In 1893 he wrote his *Memoirs of a Reformer,* in which he recounted his work as an extreme abolitionist, who assisted in setting up the underground railroad in Philadelphia. His youth had been shaped by meeting such politicoes as Horace Greeley, William Cullen Bryant and the Italian revolutionary, Guiseppe Garibaldi. Ross's sympathies were clearly with the North, with the result that he was asked by President Lincoln to report on activities of the Confederates in Canada.

Following the American Civil War, Ross offered his services as an army surgeon to President Juarez of Mexico to aid in his struggle against the French. He founded several societies including "The Society for the Diffusion of Physiological Knowledge" after he was convinced by a study that masturbation was the cause of one-third of all insanity. Like his friend John Brown, the abolitionist of Fort Sumter, he raged through the land rallying the churches and the clergymen to publicize *Self and Sex* books, which graphically showed the results of self-abuse.

In fact, Ross's estimation of the correlation between the "solitary vice" and insanity was low compared to that held by other medical practitioners — and society. Although masturbation was considered a moral offence in the eighteenth century, it was transformed into a disease with physical and psychological effects by the writings of Dr. S.A. Tissot (1728-1779) of Switzerland. His books stated that masturbation results in loss of vital fluid leading to

158

insanity, blindness, headaches, leuccorhea, weakness etc. The waste of 1 cc of seminal fluid, according to Tissot, was as bad as losing 40 ounces of blood. This loss, he claimed, was adjusted during normal intercourse by a magnetic-electric power that passed from the female to the male. Tissot's translations led to a report in 1854 by S.G. Howes in New York which linked insanity and "onanism":

> ... *There are those enumerated in this report who not long ago were considered young gentlemen and ladies who are now raving idiots ... idiots of the lowest kind, lost to all moral sense, to all shame ...*

The concept of masturbational diseases provided the physician with an acceptable reason for the cause of sickness (particularly in the young) and for the inability to work a cure. But many tried to treat the seed-spilling disease, such as F. Tumblety M.D., whose book was to be *A Guide to the Afflicted, containing at a glance the most common certain diseases which arise from abuse of the genital organs*. Dr. Tumblety practised in Toronto. Stating he had seen 60,000 patients, he asked, in the hard-selling preface: "Are the many wretches who will not seek medical aid to perish without one friendly hand outstretched to save them?"

But vaccination? That was an outrage of human rights, stormed Ross. "... They have been taught to believe in its efficacy. They have vaccinated because it was the custom and they were paid for it ...". Vaccination, according to Ross, also propagated the disease — and others such as leprosy or tuberculosis. Armed with this knowledge, Ross urged the citizens of Montreal to resist vaccination in the face of a smallpox epidemic in 1885. A series of citizens' riots forced the government to call out the troops to maintain the peace. Ross knew how to popularize his thoughts with the people of the country, and it is no wonder the rumour went around that compulsory vaccination was an English plot to suppress the fertility of the Montreal French. Three thousand, one hundred and sixty-three died of the epidemic.

Resistance to compulsory immunization was not unique to Canada. The theory that vaccination resulted in immunization was not accepted universally by parents — or doctors. Sir John Reynolds' (1828-1896) *System of Medicine,* the standard textbook of the mid-century, gave two theories of the action of vaccines, neither offering a satisfactory rationale. Compulsory vaccination, as enacted under the Vaccination Acts of 1861, 1867 and 1871 in Great Britain, could be justified and accepted by the population only if complete immunity could be provided, and in the absence of this guarantee, there was a turning to "natural" measures rather than scientific ones. Objections grew and were championed by anti-compulsionists, who argued there was an abrogation of basic political freedoms, thus linking the argument with other civil rights and progressive traditions. Ross easily fitted into these groups.

On the subject of medical reform, Ross thought that medicine was a colossal system of humbug and self-deception, creating an unreasoning faith in toxic and poisonous drugs, which was a heritage from a barbaric and ignorant age. He felt that ... "the medical practice of today has no more foundation in science, philosophy or common sense than it had one hundred and fifty years ago. It is based on conjecture and improved by sad blunders, often hidden by death ... The medical practice of the future will be preventive, hygienic." He contended that health should conform to the laws of nature, and disease was a remedial action of the body; the doctor should aid in eliminating sickness by the use of food, water, rest, hope, peace, temperature, exercise and other natural agencies. The right use of these agents would balance the system and rid it of poisons, thereby repairing and rebuilding itself. Nature was the best physician and people should be taught to live better, purer and more natural lives.

Possibly nature was benevolent, but the Registrar of Ontario each year continued to report deaths from scarlatina, dysentery, pneumonia and diphtheria.

Aylmer experienced a smallpox panic in 1872. The local physician, Dr. Ezra Foote, attended a sickman. He was not certain of the nature of the man's ailment but strongly suspected it to be smallpox. The good doctor resigned the care of his patient as he himself developed a rash, and sent for the pioneer physician of the area, Dr. H.T. Ault of Montreal. Ault arrived by train from Montreal to St. Thomas, and hired a horse and team to drive to Aylmer. Unfortunately, the hotel at which he was put up burned to the ground and the horse and team were lost. As a result, in addition to having to pay for the visiting specialist's attendance, it was necessary to reimburse him for the horse and wagon. The patient died. Foote recovered.

It was several decades before antitoxins for diphtheria, preventive measures against scarlet fever, measles or poliomyelitis were announced. Many of these developments resulted from advances in public health teaching which led to the establishment of

160

an Antitoxin Laboratory in the department of hygiene at the University of Toronto.

Instruction in hygiene was first included in the curriculum of Trinity University in 1871, a step forward initiated by Dr. James Fulton and continued by Dr. C.W. Covernton. Covernton became one of the first internationalists, attending many congresses overseas. Because of his enthusiasm for the importance of public and personal health, he was able to convince the council of the College of Physicians and Surgeons to include the subject of Sanitary Science in an examination for medical licensure. His son, Theodore Selby, as Chief of the Staff of Medical Inspectors for the Ontario Government, was influential in preventing the spread of smallpox in Eastern Ontario during the 1885 epidemic in Montreal.

Efforts such as these were matched by Professor William Oldright, who occupied the chair of hygiene in the Toronto School of Medicine. He was influential in establishing the Museum of Hygiene in the University of Toronto in 1896 which gave great attention to models, drawings and slides illustrating ventilation, heating, plumbing, drainage, sewage disposal and other aspects of sanitary sciences. One telling exhibit illustrated defects of plumbing and water pipes which led to unsanitary conditions and the spread of typhoid.

This enthusiasm, combined with the newer bacteriological knowledge, led to establishing a diploma in Public Health in the Faculty of Medicine by 1904 which stressed sanitary models for the countryside.

In 1883, after discussion with the Honourable Mr. Mowat, Premier of the Province, Dr. Canniff was able to persuade the federal government to establish a Department of Health and Mortuary Statistics under the Department of Agriculture. This department provided vital information to epidemiologists, but caused considerable friction between the provinces and the federal government, because of jurisdictional rivalry. Canniff also brought forward many recommendations, including that the inspection of saleable meats should be carried out more rigidly with penalties attached for bad produce. During his enthusiastic pursuit of public health, an editorial appeared in a Toronto newspaper which condemned him as being inefficient. He was charged by one of the city aldermen as being "so drunk that he could not stand" during an inspection to obtain water samples in Parkdale. There followed an extended argument in City Council as to whether his services should be terminated or not. Canniff wrote a letter of resignation pointing out, "I find that in consequence of brain disease, I do not think, in the interest of the city, I can any longer continue to fill the post". Fortunately, his "brain disease" did not prevent him from continuing his prolific writing career.

He, like many of his professional colleagues, was categorized in the Registrar's Report of 1882:

It is pleasant to record that old age was the principal cause of death in many workers ...

Chapter XIV
A Doomed Phoenix

... for competition is obviously no longer fair, when one medical college possessing no special claim or merit, is subsidized by the state ...

W.B. Geikie
December 27, 1889

Whether the death of the first Trinity Medical College came as a surprise to the Corporation of Trinity is not known, but the precipitate action of the medical staff suggests that the doctors had a hand in its demise. Even though the medical staff transferred quickly to other schools, there was still an interest in medical education at Trinity. The Thirty-nine Articles remained the offending mote and a movement was started by Vice Chancellor Spragge to remove it. That this was defeated in 1853 was not surprising as John Strachan, although aging, was still carrying the crosier, but one month after his death in 1866, a corporation committee was set up to discuss with Hodder and others, the resurrection of the medical department. The result was that Trinity medical students were exempted from making any religious declaration by 1871.

One of the master builders of the second Trinity Medical School was John Rolph — incarnate in his pupil Walter Bayne Geikie. Ironically, after years of confrontation between Rolph and Strachan, Geikie, who had stayed with Rolph until 1870 and had joined the old man in resigning from Victoria, united the aspirations of both the former rivals in the new school.

The reborn Trinity rapidly shook off the ashes of the establishment school of the 50's. Its enrolment grew rapidly and it offered new courses, including Sanitary Science and Microscopic Anatomy. This led to a new awareness and when young William Osler, peering down a microscope saw "little specks in the muscles", his training in natural history wouldn't allow him to pass them by as normal finding, as had Professor Richardson. Osler noted in his journal — "numerous trichinae seen in the muscles of the janitor of the hospital" and identified the common health problem of worms in pork. But this was only the beginning of scientific medicine. Cells and bacteria were being observed under high power magnification. Specific applications of the laryngoscope, ophthalmoscope and sphygmograph and various forms of electrical apparatus added to the student's knowledge — and the school's debt. Scientific medicine had to be served and courses in Chemistry with elaborate laboratory fittings and instruction in practical experiments all became part of undergraduate life.

Balancing the budget became as important as the teaching of medicine. Student fees provided only a limited amount of new scientific equipment and Hodder reported: "We managed to survive and my income as surgeon to the Burnside Lying-In Hospital provided well and the students managed to carry off most of the prizes." But Aikins, at the Toronto School of Medicine, wasn't happy about that. He was all for prize competitions as long as the Toronto School of Medicine won. So when Trinity boys picked up all the gold and silver at the University of Toronto, he managed to get the government of Ontario to change the terms of affiliation of all medical teaching bodies with the University of Toronto. The change meant that no medical body which formed part of any other university empowered to grant degrees in medicine could continue to be affiliated with the provincial University, and so was not eligible for prize money.

Naturally such a thrust by Aikins demanded a riposte from Trinity. The medical faculty arranged to have a bill introduced in the legislature, which would make Trinity Medical School an entire teaching body independent from any University. Therefore, graduates would be eligible for the prizes.

The speed of this action caught Aikins as well as the Corporation of Trinity unprepared. At first feathers were ruffled, but realizing the urgency and desperation of the situation, the Corporation accepted the action the medical school had taken — and in the spirit of bifideism, Trinity University recognized the school was separate but still regarded Trinity Medical School as its medical faculty.

But the dollar drain continued. When the University of Toronto raised the standard of its examination in medicine in 1882, Trinity in particular found itself unable to provide students with proper laboratory facilities to meet the higher level of knowledge required. Geikie, now Dean, while agreeing that more science was needed, insisted that Trinity students should be pounding away at practical courses in medicine which would send out graduates well informed in all subjects certain to be useful to them at the bedside in future life. His arguments were not unnoticed.

University of Toronto Vice Chancellor, Sir William Mulock, acknowledged the high theoretical attainments of Canadian medical students, but said, "... however I regret their deficiency in practical training and hope that more attention will be paid to practical training and practical examination ...". He went on to muse that "... there is advisability of amalgamating the two medical schools here in Toronto and combining their resources to have more practical courses ...". The Honourable G.W. Ross, Minister of Education, put forward feelers along the same line and suggested the Government might fund such a project.

Geikie gave a Rolphian response. Immediate rejection. In addition he pointed out that if every Toronto medical school had affiliation with the provincial university and if a single teaching faculty was established as the University of Toronto Faculty, it would cripple all other medical schools in the province. He also reiterated that the existing medical schools had improved their capability by out-of-pocket expenses for the last few years and furthermore, this record of successful work was acknowledged by the university, "... and all of this without a farthing cost to the country ...". It was obvious that Geikie, like Rolph, had been deeply affected by government opting out of payment for medical education in 1853. Not only did he approve of that action but he was convinced that medical schools were not costing the country one dollar and did not see why they should be changed in order that the government could put money back into the classroom. He held these beliefs firmly — and published them widely. Of all the physician polemicists, Geikie spread the most paper. Letters to the editor, memorials to the government, open letters to the citizens, journal articles, all flowed in a steady stream from his nibs. He flogged private enterprise and medical education with the same fervor and skill as a medicine man on the tail-gate of a buck-board.

But he was in a tough league. As early as 1874, the University was suggesting that the government should be paying more money into medical education through one provincial medical school. William Mulock had already shown he was more interested in practical courses, and Geikie felt that to improve the product turned out by Trinity he could hold off the pressures to be felt from the university, by stressing less "frogology" (a derisive term for zoology and comparative anatomy) and more bed-side medicine.

To this end Trinity underwent another expansion in 1879 providing more facilities for the undergraduates. Somehow the additional buildings and furnishings were paid from the student fees and the enrollment continued to grow.

The University of Toronto was still the authority which issued graduation certificates. The standards of its examinations in medicine were raised to keep up with those in the U.S. and Britain. The new licensing examination of the College of Physicians and Surgeons demanded proper laboratory facilities in such subjects as physics, chemistry, biology and physiology, all of which were now mandatory. Ross once again came to Geikie and Trinity to discuss an amalgamation, but once again was refused. The year 1887 began with discussions with other colleges on the "Federation Act" — a confederation of the colleges in Toronto carrying on works embraced in the Arts curriculum, with representation from federated colleges and the University of Toronto organization. It was to include the Toronto School of Medicine. Geikie and Trinity Medical School stated their opposition to creating a new teaching medical power. "... it will lead to constant intriguing and planning and everlasting hot water — besides destroying our affiliation", threatened the Dean. "Everlasting hot water" proved to be an understatement.

The familiar arguments were repeated. Geikie pointed out that "... a little school held by Rolph in a Queen Street stable" was enough to bring down a university medical school funded from university funds and the public purse. He further twisted the knife by emphasizing the current (chronic) weakened state of the University of Toronto income.

Was there a need for more doctors in the province, Geikie demanded? Was there a shortage of good recruits? The answer was an emphatic "no". Was it seemly or just for the legislature to destroy at one blow the affiliation which other teaching institutions held with the University of Toronto? The answer, again, was "no". Was it fair, that the existing medical schools, after many years of low-pay drudgery had to transfer to the university just when their position was improving in attendance and equipment? To each question, Geikie and Trinity gave a resounding "no".

Geikie's arguments were not persuasive. Ross wrote to Premier Mowat that he felt the Act should be passed establishing a new teaching faculty within the university. He even added that Geikie should not be afraid of the competition with the prestige which Trinity enjoyed! But Ross knew why Geikie was so perturbed and to forestall any criticism that government was footing the bill for one medical school he wrote, "I think we must take special care to prevent the new Medical Faculty being a charge upon university funds. Neither directly or indirectly should we be responsible for the salary of a single professor, or contingencies of any sort."

Geikie had no choice but to accept that the University of Toronto was once again involved in medical education, however, he chose to interpret the facts in a way which would result in some good to Trinity. He proposed that moneys sent to the University of Toronto should be matched by moneys to other medical schools. The bill for physiological and chemical apparatus was mounting yearly. If the Government of Ontario was prepared to aid all institutes of higher medical education, then it seemed reasonable that Trinity Medical College, "the medical institution to which the largest number of Ontario young men come for their education for a medical profession", should have a fair share of any new money.

This had a very practical application in the proposal for the building of a Park Hospital on the grounds of the University. In 1890, the Hon. John Macdonald offered to the University an added clinical facility from the legacy of his deceased daughter. This was contributed in hopes that it would continue the advancement of medical science at the University. The money was to be put up by Macdonald and a University Hospital was to be built on land occupied by Wycliffe College and two adjoining lots on College Street. The benefaction was hailed by many, but Geikie and others were concerned that this was a University Hospital and would not necessarily add to Trinity's facilities. Geikie's concern was echoed in part by the Arts Faculties of the University who felt that this addition to medical teaching might be a serious drain to the University. This threat by medicine to the other faculties resulted in the decision to refuse the offer, although the land and money were available.

Geikie's problem of meeting expenses was becoming more acute. Improvements and additions to the medical college were vital and there was a need for added teaching in the sciences. The Toronto School of Medicine had benefitted from the affiliation by chairs of chemistry, physiology, biology and natural history, on which it drew for courses without increasing cost, but Trinity had to pay on a cash basis for these subjects. He asked for and received $1,500 in 1890 to keep up with the University of Toronto.

Geikie was now in an untenable position. On the one hand his open palm was ready to receive any equalization money which might be spent by the government in funding the newly affiliated school, but on the other hand he continued to fulminate against spending public funds for medical education. William Mulock did not agree. While he wished the Trinity Medical Faculty every success, he stated "I have no sympathy with those who contend that no public aid should be given towards the advancement of medical science". To put his beliefs into action, he instructed that the new university biological building should include provisions for dissection rooms for the Faculty of Medicine. Possibly, in anticipation of the expected demand by Geikie for equal funds, he ordered the architect to conceal the purpose of the rooms until after the building was completed. This surprise ticked away in the attic of the building while Geikie showered Mowat with letters. He had already written on November 28, 1888, that it was highly desirable that all medical colleges should be placed on precisely the same level. On December 27, 1889, he pointed out there was general dissatisfaction throughout the province by the medical fraternity because there had been no loud outcry in favour of affiliaton. Further they were saying:

> ... for competition is obviously no longer fair, when one medical college possessing no special claims or merit, is subsidized by the state, by being provided out of the public funds with costly buildings and equipment ...

Geikie then tried to de-fuse the government spending by diffusing it, and urged that, if funds were available for education, then general education such as the public schools up to the university level should receive the benefit of this, thereby permitting each student to serve his country in a better manner. At the same time, a campaign was being mounted from another direction. An editorial in *The Canada Lancet* was derisive of the so-called modern medicine which did not arrange that the trainee should see smallpox or scarlet fever, or tie a ligature. The editorial questioned the need to thrust into the medical course every newly-discovered science or to use every new piece of scientific apparatus. Why, the editorial demanded, when there was a wide need for practical courses, were the medical courses being turned into a science course, especially in a young country which required practical medicine? The journal continued in this vein by printing a letter to the editor from a Dr. W. T. Harris on January 24, 1890, in which he stated that the public had not been asked whether the government should get back into the area of funding medical education. In addition, he pointed out the medical profession had not asked for it and actually the interest of medical education did not call for it.

But rather than back away from Geikie, the university, under Sir Daniel Wilson, continued on the course laid out by Mulock. Wilson, in opening the new biological buildings in 1890, trumpeted that the university had spend $130,000 to equip magnificent buildings which would provide for better medical education for medical students. Geikie protested this to Mowat. However, it was another year before he realized the import of the building. In November 1891, the University Finance Committee's Report showed that in the Number 2 Biological building, completed a few months previously, the initial intention had been to use it primarily for medical teaching purposes. While Geikie could abide that the first building was for the Arts students and it was possible for the medical students to have leftover time, it was just too much that Building Number 2 with its secret construction of medical facilities, including a dissection room, should also be for meds. In addition, it was obvious from the budget that certain professors were to be paid from university funds. He went to the public with an open letter. Wilson wasted no time to reply — after all, he had been professor of law in 1853 when Rolph caused the disintegration of the University. He stated that he had always been strongly impressed with the beneficial influence which a medical faculty exerted in stimulating all departments of science, and had learned of the abolition of the '53 medical faculty with surprise and regret. He continued that with the affiliation with the medical faculty in 1877, a "counter-revolution" had taken effect with many advantages to all parts of the university.

He then proceeded to deal with Geikie by denying that there had been any impropriety or false pretenses in using government funds for the building of the biological building or its extension. After the fire in University College in 1889, it had been necessary to find a new place for the biological museum and this fitted well with medical education needs.

He countered the specific charge which Geikie had made that fees paid by medical students were retained by the medical faculties, while professors were being paid from general university funds. Geikie had denounced this as "an abuse worthy of Ottawa". Wilson pointed out that the fees generated were used to buy equipment and other instruments for scientific research, and he announced that the services of the professor were voluntary without remuneration.

Wilson charged that the necessity for scientific equipment was something Geikie could not comprehend and it showed how little concept the Dean of Trinity College had of the requirements of a well-equipped medical school. To substantiate this, Wilson pointed out that he had received numerous letters from past students who had gone to other schools in Europe and had been struck by the inadequate and petty provisions for scientific medicine which were available in Toronto.

But the most telling argument was against Geikie's repeated statements with regard to "our self-supporting medical colleges". Wilson wrote:

> ... it is inevitable when any great public improvement on existing systems is inaugurated, that the old Ephesian cry of 'our craft is in danger' should be anew heard ...

And to top his critique, Wilson questioned the altruism of Geikie who, while protesting against the application by the state of public funds for medical education, was more than willing to accept money for Trinity Medical College. This personal attack upon himself gave Geikie the platform he needed. In an open letter to Mowat, now Attorney General of Ontario, which was widely distributed as a broadside, the Dean of Trinity Medical College was properly outraged. He pointed out the many errors, misrepresentations and misconstructions in Wilson's letter but he allowed that they were "perhaps not altogether wilfully". Wilson's slur on Rolph, who had now been buried more than 20 years properly eulogized by the great of the country, was characterized as a matter of bad taste which would have been much better omitted. The President's garbling of Geikie's words was something which was unacceptable and "had Sir Daniel been a younger man, I would with utmost indignation have thrown back these words upon him". But, after repeating all the arguments with some embellishments, Geikie was able to say in the true Christian spirit that he hoped Sir Daniel Wilson would, "if spared, as I trust he may be, soon reach the four-score limit of human life and adopt the very opposite course".

Geikie ended his charges with the hope that a settlement of the question would soon be reached by the government. This hope was answered by the Legislative Assembly which in April of 1893 appointed a special committee of the Senate of the University of Toronto to inquire into the erection of the Biological Buildings and other matters which had been raised by the fighting Dean.

The office of the Provincial Secretary published the Return of the Special Committee on February 19, 1894. It was an extensive report. Correspondence between Geikie and the government was reviewed back to 1887 and testimony was taken from a large number of witnesses. It was established that there was clear incontrovertible evidence that the university was paying the salaries of professors who taught physiology, general chemistry and biology to the medical students, in spite of the Premier's earlier statements. But that was only one of the points issuing from Geikie's charges. His major claim had been that the Biological Building comprised in essence a medical school building including dissection rooms and a vat for preserving anatomical material. He asked if the government knew of the purposes of these rooms before the completion of the buildings. Further, did the Senate or the Board of the University of Toronto approve of the plans?

Letters from the Honourable G.W. Ross, Premier, showed that he had been informed by J.E.B. Smith, the Bursar of the University, in October of 1889, that plans for the proposed addition to the Biological Laboratory had been approved by the Board. But the letter pointed out that Ross had not seen the proposed plans. Furthermore, it appeared from the correspondence that the Bursar had not communicated with the Senate nor had he recalled sending the plans to the government.

Additional correspondence showed that Dr. Henry H. Wright, who had been entrusted by the Vice-Chancellor, William Mulock, to sketch out plans for additions to the biological buildings, was asked to keep secret the additions to the building. In particular, the designed purpose of several rooms, which had been pencilled onto the plans, was erased before being presented to the Minister of Education. Wright, in testimony, stated that he was unable to comment on the eventual use of the building as he was in Germany during this particular time. Mulock admitted quite freely that he had directed that no names appear upon the plan which would reveal the true purpose of the biology building, partly because of the possibility of loud objections which could be made by residents in the neighbourhood over such a use. He admitted the anticipation that Geikie would be "busying himself", as he had done previously in his continued opposition to the efforts of the university to advance the cause of medical science. However, without wishing to avoid any responsibility, Mulock pointed out that he himself was not responsible, since he had been absent from Toronto for many years.

As far as the Senate of the University was concerned, the Vice-Chancellor admitted that nothing had been communicated as far as he knew. He also confessed that he "did not wish that it should be withheld from any one authority, but simply from the troublesome public". Nor had there ever been a personal explanation to the Minister about the plans, either preliminary or final.

Further testimony was heard by the committee, with President William Loudon of the University asking many of the questions. Dr. Wright was recalled and asked if he was aware of the fact that Ross had denied, in the House, that public monies were being spent for medical education, and in view of that, was there any reason that Ross did not know of the dissection room feature? Wright could not answer. William Christie, a member of the Board of Trustees of the University, was called. The question was put: "Had Sir Daniel Wilson requested the Minister to explain capital arrangements for the biological building?" Christie was unable to answer; he had not been present during the last portion of 1889, and he could not remember, the questions were beyond his knowledge or ability and with regard to the plans for the biology building he only knew it was not his business.

Mr. Dick, the architect, was recalled; Dr. Adam Wright was recalled; Dr. Alexander Primrose was questioned; but from none did Loudon get complete answers.

One thing did emerge during an exchange between Mulock and the committee. He admitted that he felt someone was instigating the Government against the University and that inciter was Geikie!

But Loudon would not accept this statement and proceeded to draw evidence from Dr. A.B. MacAllum, Professor of Physiology, that he himself, Loudon, had been the person who had alerted the Government to the presence of this dissecting room. He had done this because he had been astounded to learn that the Government did not know there was a dissection room in the new building. This revelation led to a motion that the Minister of Education, Ross, be brought before the committee to explain his relation to the building scheme in its various stages. The motion was lost and was replaced by one to appoint a committee to draft a report.

A further motion that Edward Blake, Chancellor of the University, be invited to attend before the committee for purposes of being examined was also lost. Finally a motion was passed: "That in the opinion of this committee it is not expedient for them to inquire in any way into the discharge of their duties by the members of the executive government of this province". Among those who voted for the motion was Dr. W.T. Aikins, the previous dean of Rolph's school.

The counter-revolution was complete. Entrepreneurial medical teaching was dead and the government of Ontario had knowingly resumed the cost of medical education. This role had been achieved over the objections of many of the doctors in the province.

Chapter XV

From Alms to Grants

*... it being a subject of general notoriety that there exists
in the minds of the poor classes in all countries, that
prejudice against such institutions, that it is the opinion
of this meeting that this prejudice, partly natural, arises
principally from an illgrounded apprehension that medical men requite themselves for unpaid services by the
extensive field of experimental practice thus open to them
...*

The Toronto General Hospital, Dr. C. Clarke

With the French Revolution and a shattering of traditional
authority there developed a new clinical approach to the teaching of
medicine, where more emphasis was placed on the hospital as the
place for students to become doctors. The great hospital schools,
such as Mr. Guys', St. Bartholomew's and others in England,
demonstrated the necessity of a clinical base. But Upper Canada, an
outpost, found it difficult to support a hospital in the early 1790's
apart from a small missionary station at Sault Ste. Marie.

There is also record of a military hospital in Kingston before
1788, where Dr. Robert Kerr was stationed, which became the centre
for treatment of immigrants and transients. When military rule
ended in 1788, care of the sick became the responsibility of the town,
and a hospital was set up in a part of a building which was used as a
storehouse for gifts from the government to the Indians. After the
War of 1812, with an increase of population of disbanded militia
men and their families and a new flood of immigrants to build the
Rideau Canal, there was demand for a larger hospital.

The Yanks had been beaten back and celebration was in
order. The town of York had shown it could defend itself — at the
cost of blowing up its own fort, including the two huts which had
been the hospital. What more fitting way was there to recognize the
glorious exploits of the brave soldiers and citizens than give them
medals to commemorate the victory of 1815. The Loyal and Patriotic
Society of Upper Canada collected money, struck the medals and

prepared to reward the heroes.

But there was a problem. Who should get the gongs? Should it be John Strachan who had been in the fort or, should it be Widmer, the garrison surgeon? No one could decide, and feelings were beginning to rise when there was a proposal by one of the citizens: Why not build a brick hospital instead, to provide relief and comfort to the poor of the province? The idea was accepted enthusiastically, the medals were melted down and £4,000 was made available to build Upper Canada's first civilian hospital at York.

As this grant was the entire amount available, hopes were dashed of giving any funds to Kingston, which had already collected some private money to build its hospital.

Construction of the facilities at York began quickly but instead of opening as a hospital, the new building was preempted for the meetings of Parliament after a fire had destroyed the original Legislature building. Finally in 1829, just in time for a severe measles epidemic, the hospital opened and admitted the indigent sick (the well-to-do were cared for at home). The prime purpose of the hospital was to nurse the sick and it was not until much later that the second and third purposes of hospitals — teaching and research — were acknowledged as part of the function of the Toronto General. There has never been a formal announcement of a fourth purpose — to be a battlefield for medical factions — although some feel that is their chief reason for existence.

Obviously it wasn't possible to melt down medals every time it became necessary to start a hospital. The government in the 1820's began to vote money for their establishment, and in 1832 Kingston was given the go-ahead to erect the Kingston General for the reception of the destitute sick, followed in the 1850's by other hospitals in Hamilton, London and Bytown. These early hospitals were founded by religious orders or benevolent individuals, for there had to be some place for the poor who had no home, where the doctors and nurses could care for them. Growth was slow — about one hospital was built every six years — but about 1855 the hospital industry began to hit its stride and an average of two hospitals were built in Ontario every year.

In the early 1840's patients in the charity institutions were considered excellent subjects for the purpose of teaching medicine, so the Toronto General Board of Trustees offered their patients' unprotesting bodies to King's College for just that purpose. The arrangements continued with successive schools, with varying degrees of co-operation and confrontation.

In other centres, probably because they were not teaching centres, hospital affairs went more smoothly. Dr. Theophilus Mack, in 1865, founded the St. Catharines Marine and General Hospital with only four beds. The charter states:

The intention is that all persons engaged in navigation of the Lakes shall be admitted upon payment of a sum barely remunerative.

This was no mean feat in view of the considerable resistance by the townspeople who argued against the establishment of a hospital which attracted transients and destitutes. The first superintendent was Dr. Augustus Jakes, who later became senior surgeon of The Northwest Mounted Police.

Mack had also set up a spa to cure the wealthy, at Springbank in London. This development was in keeping with a great interest in the use of water, especially plain cold water, as a panacea for chronic sufferers. The spa movement, which developed about the same time as Homeopathy and Thomsonianism, resulted from the activities of Vincenz Priessnitz (1799-1851) of Silesia. After observing the effect of water on the treatment of disease in cattle, he urged that cold water would be effective in curing diseases in humans. He sometimes combined this with sweat baths, and was able to give relief with rheumatism and gout. His book, *A Cold Water Cure, Its Principles, Theories and Practices,* published in 1832, led to the development of Hydropathic establishments in England, particularly at Derby. The rationale of treatment was to make "better blood", by restoring the reduced nervous fluids or electricity which came from the inability of the gastric juices to dissolve food. Rheumatism was relieved by relubricating, with blood serum, the dried-out muscles and nerve sheaths. The first spa in Ontario was the Caledonia Springs, situated five miles south from the Ottawa River and nine miles from L'Orignal. Business commenced in 1836, and by 1849 there were a 150-person hotel, a bath house, a circular railroad for the amusement of the invalids, a resident physician and three taverns. There were four springs in the place called Saline, Sulphur, Gas and one later discovered, called the Intermittent. Analysis of the waters of the different springs showed a mixture of chloride of sodium, magnesium, potassium, carbolic acid and iodine of sodium. The proprietors of the springs pointed out their extraordinary virtues in the treatment of liver infections, dyspepsia, and "complaints engendered by the injudicious or indiscriminate use of mercury". Other springs were located at the Kingston Mineral Wells Company and at Ancaster, Ontario.

The hydropathy movement fell out of favour by the 1850's after a series of articles published in *The British Lancet* and *Medical News* reported several deaths from the effects of cold water treatment, and termed hydropathy a humbug.

The usual pattern of establishing a hospital was that a group of volunteers (usually women) banded together, managed to get their hands on a small property, blackmailed the local doctors by social pressure, wheedled council into setting up the founding funds, and then managed to get a grant from the government.

The Female Benevolent Society Hospital at Kingston was an excellent example of this. They provided subscription funds for the first hospital and hoped for aid from the Loyal and Patriotic Society of Upper Canada. It wasn't given. After that the society provided hospital care yearly from November to May in one of the old blockhouses at Fort Kingston, where they persuaded half-pay naval and military surgeons to give free medical care to the poor. In 1833 the Kingston General Hospital opened its doors, and nine years later, as in Toronto, patients were displaced by the Government who used the building as a legislature. The hospital re-opened in 1844, was enlarged in 1864 and was up-graded to 400 modern beds in 1917. On such slender bases magnificent modern edifices, such as "The Hospital for Sick Children" in Toronto and "The General" at Belleville and Hamilton, were founded.

Of course, these "magnificent" edifices had primitive origins. The Hamilton City Hospital began as a rented house on Catherine Street in 1848 to accommodate three typhus patients. This was replaced by a two-storey frame building in 1850, where doctors such as Gerald O'Reilly and W.C. Billings practised. They were joined in 1873, shortly before the opening of the new building, by William Osler, who was spending a locum at the General. He remarked later that the hospital was full of three things — patients, streptococci and cockroaches.

By the year 1882 there were twelve hospitals in the province which received aid from the government under the Charity Aid Act.

In spite of government aid, most hospitals led a hand-to-mouth existence. A Toronto plebiscite in 1867 decided that the city should grant $10,000 to aid the General Hospital, but in spite of an affirmative vote by a small turnout of voters, sufficient money was not available to keep the hospital solvent, and on October 15, 1867, the hospital, "once so noted for its hospitality and valuable charitable institutions", closed its doors.

During the closure the Trustees met several times to try to re-open the hospital, but faced with deficits, foot-dragging on the part of the city council and buck-passing from the Legislature of Ontario, the building remained closed. All this led the Trustees to suggest that there was something radically wrong in the current system of hospital management. They maintained that the sick, as a class, were entitled to quite as much consideration as the insane or the deaf or dumb (already fully funded by the province). Furthermore, it was worthwhile to take care of the sick, especially if they were educated, and there was a duty to the community to control dangerous infectious diseases. Consequently, they argued, treatment should in most cases be at public expense, and they called for continuing regular public support and not private alms for hospital operation.

Other community members were also aware of the necessity to re-open the hospital. The Roman Catholic Bishop Lynch who toured the hospital said his order could take over the building and operate it as a good works. To soothe outraged Orange protests, he promised there would be no "converting" in the hospital. Bishop Darling, of the Church of England, responded it was quite possible his church could assume the operation. Such rivalry between Roman Catholics and Protestants was not uncommon in hospital operation. In Chatham there were two sectarian hospitals by 1890 — St. Joseph's and The Chatham General — and the same duplication occurred at Ottawa and other centres. Whether the aim of the church was to prolong life or to be in at the death of a patient is not clear, but their service contribution was enormous.

This service contribution saw both children and adults housed in the same hospital wards, and it was not until 1875 that a children's hospital opened in Ontario at 31 Avenue Street in Toronto. Its origins were humble — a donation of some English coins and a $20.00 contribution from Fergus, Ontario — but the hospital expanded rapidly, requiring successive moves to larger quarters. For many years it was supervised and managed by a committee of sixteen women. The original committee pointed out to a furnace contractor that the hospital received money "only as the Lord sends it", but, as he seldom sent a surplus, the contractor "... might either work, trusting God for the money as we do, or not at all

...". The furnace was installed eventually, and the Hospital for Sick Children grew to world fame.

But the major push to build more hospitals depended in part on the availability of nurses. Mack's Hospital in St. Catharines graduated its first class of nurses in 1879. One of them helped in the founding of the Nicholl's Hospital in Peterborough. The nursing school at the Toronto General began in 1881 and provided staff for areas such as Belleville, a centre for the Grand Trunk Railroad, with numerous vagrants and beggars. The local women who proposed a Belleville hospital were attacked in the newspapers and by the man in the street, who accused them of bringing all the poor of the country into the city for care. The resolute ladies stuck to their guns, pried a piece of land from the city, and eventually the hospital was opened in 1885.

Being able to make a poultice was the chief qualification of a nurse in the early days. While Florence Nightingale's notes on nursing were written for those who would nurse in the home, Mack insisted on training professional nurses to work in the hospital. He taught that, in pneumonia when the breathing rate was 40 and the temperature 104, the patient was to be raised to a seated position so that the nurse could apply the poultice. The weaker the patient the more poultices and if he survived five or six days he would be sponged with soap and water and a blister applied. All these activities were part of developing nursing expertise as the Sarah Gamp model of a nurse, depicted by Dickens in *Martin Chuzzlewit*, was replaced by the new breed.

Surgeons were drawing more courage as they saw their patients living longer with the new antiseptic procedures. In every ward of the hospital large bottles of 5 percent solution of carbolic acid were used by the surgeon or obstetrician to wash his hands as he entered and left the wards. Patients were thoroughly washed around the operative area — catgut sutures were used and antiseptic dressings, using pine sawdust mixed with mercury and glycerin, were becoming common.

Chloroform and ether anaesthetics were used more freely, although there were occasional accidents. A young girl aspirated and choked. Others failed to regain consciousness; and The Toronto General recorded a death from chloroform in 1863 (Bovell administered the anaesthetic). But with better anaesthesia, and an increase in the sophistication of operating rooms and operating techniques, confidence returned and there was an increasing demand for surgical beds. Those same techniques were carried into the countryside. Dr. Abraham Groves, using a kitchen table in a farmhouse at Fergus in 1883, performed the first appendectomy in North America. The patient survived without infection, and Groves wrote enthusiastic accounts of his sterile technique — boil the instruments and flush out the abdomen with gallons of boiled water.

When Groves graduated in 1871, Lister had already published several papers on the importance of the use of carbolic acid to prevent infections — but Lawson Tait (1845-1899) of Birmingham, England, had argued that washing with soap and water was more effective, and in 1880 published a case describing a successful appendectomy using that technique.

With the development of a large modern hospital, in association with a medical school, it slowly became apparent to one man that there was a connection between cadaveric dissection and maternal death. Ignaz Philipp Semmelweis (1818-1865), in Vienna, compared the mortality rates of two wards, one of which was directly adjacent to the dissection room, from which students and doctors emerged to examine expectant mothers, and deduced that somehow disease was transmitted to the women. To prevent this he ordered the precaution of personal cleanliness of all physicians on his ward, and particularly the washing of hands with a nail brush and calcium chloride before examinations. The mortality figures dropped, but fierce opposition from orthodox obstetricians rose, and eventually Semmelweis was driven from the Allgemeines Krankenhaus back to his native Budapest. In 1861 he published *The Cause, Concept and Prophylaxis of Peripheral Fever*, but he became depressed over his failure to persuade his colleagues and died in an insane asylum. Students registering at the Toronto Lying-In Hospital in 1869, were given a ticket which carried a notice on the reverse side. The notice read:

> *The Lying-In Hospital of Munich, despite its excellent ventilation and many admirable arrangements has been very unfortunate for the prevalence of peripheral fever, which broke out among the inmates in December, 1856, a few months after the hospital first opened ... An investigation showed that both these patients had been examined by one of the Assistants, who had just come from making a postmortem inspection of an infant, having previously washed his hands in a solution of chloride before leaving the dead-house ... Here, then, was*

*clear proof that cadaveric infection was one specific cause
of the outbreak ... All of these facts proved the correctness
of the theory of Semmelweis of Vienna, that peripheral
fever may be originated, and propagated by inoculation of
the maternal passages with putrid animal fluids. Nay,
further, that it may be induced by the mere presence of
cadaveric odours imported into the atmosphere of the
Lying-In chamber on the clothes of the accoucheur; ...
The moral of the whole story is just the truism that no
accoucheur is justifiable in going to a case of labour, who
has recently been engaged in dissection of dead bodies, or
attending cases of erysipelas, or of surgical or typhoid
fever.*

Perhaps Princess Louisa stimulated local pride to build
hospitals in 1879, when she visited the St. Catharines graduation
class, because after that visit there was a boom in hospital
construction in Ontario. Most small communities appointed
hospital boards (usually including a bank president) and opened a
hospital (usually with an entrance foyer looking like a bank).
Marine or railway hospitals opened in places such as Collingwood,
Owen Sound, Cornwall, Goderich and Port Arthur.

The growing number of hospitals resulted in competition
and rivalry. The Toronto Orthopaedic Hospital in 1902 specialized
in bone problems and boasted that in general hospitals frequent
deaths were inevitable, but there had been no deaths in the
Orthopaedic during its third year of operation. Part of the success
may have been due to the fact that patients were treated in open-air
tents on the hospital grounds and thus avoided cross-infection. The
Toronto Western Hospital also used tents for its summer operations.

While tents were common at the beginning of the twentieth
century, buildings were necessary in the middle of the nineteenth
century for the hospitalization of mental patients. And usually those
buildings were jails.

Originally, the only care for the mentally ill had been to let
them wander at large or put them in jail. It wasn't until 1830 that the
Ontario Legislature authorized payments to maintain lunatics in
county jails. The first "real" asylum, an abandoned jail building,
opened in 1841 on King St. in Toronto. With the cleaning of the
building by the new administration and the washing of the inmates,
it became apparent that many who had been confined as confirmed
lunatics were suffering from physical problems only and recovered

181

with proper treatment.

Non-restraint of mental patients had been advocated by P. Pinel (1745-1826) in France in 1801, and by Benjamin Rush (1745-1813) in the U.S. in 1812. Dr. William Rees was the first Ontario superintendent to strike the chains from his patients, and let them go to the Toronto Bay to fish — an early form of occupational therapy. He was one of a series of five superintendents of the Provincial Asylum at Toronto who were appointed and dismissed in rapid succession. Appointees to senior positions were the direct responsibility of the Board of Trustees, a political body, which used favouritism and patronage to reward the faithful, with the inevitable result that Rees charged that there was anarchy and neglect of the patients. During his term he received a severe head blow from one of the inmates, which may have affected his mental abilities, and he was retired. By the appointment of the fifth superintendent, the asylum occupied the east wing of the old parliament buildings on Front Street. There were some who thought that it was difficult to tell the inmates of the former institutions from the latter.

To ease the administrative problems, in 1853 Rolph used his influence to appoint Joseph Workman as superintendent at the new quarters at 999 Queen Street. He did his best to clean up the stench surrounding the institution when it was discovered that the builders of the new provincial lunatic asylum had failed to connect the drains to the sewers and that the chief mental institution of the province was standing shakily on three years of accumulated human excrement. With the evacuation of the cellars, it was noted that the chronic dysentery disorders, which had perplexed many of the medical staff, diminished.

Workman was a pioneer in out-patient care. He urged there should be better provision for their care, including half-way houses for mentally ill patients. He was a founding member of the Unitarian Church and a keen observer of politics, maintaining a detailed diary of public events. On July 1, 1867, he duly celebrated Confederation with the entry, "May our new stage of political existence realize all benefits promised by the promoters of the measure. My fear, however, overweighs my hope".

In describing a meeting of the Canadian Medical Association in 1879 he said:

The discussions were spiritless and rapid. Those who

spoke merely showed they could not be silent but had they
held their tongue, they might have passed for wiser men.
The meetings were full, but a few more such will bring the
Association to a natural death.

The use of mechanical restraints continued to be the "most useful and least disagreeable, the cheapest and least injurious" for particular cases, according to Richard Bucke, the newly-appointed superintendent at the mental hospital in Hamilton in 1876. However, unlike his colleagues, he reduced his annual treatment budget by two-thirds by refusing to give alcohol to his patients. But over the next few years he observed his patients carefully and reversed his position on mechanical restraint so that by 1884 he was able to say that no restraints were used in the hospital. He encouraged useful occupations for patients and initiated the "open door" policy at the London Asylum in 1882. "Restraint", he said, "makes restraint necessary". He was a curious mixture of the physiological and psychological as may be seen in his interpretation of the relationship of man and the universe in his book, *Cosmic Consciousness*.

Workman's appointment had been a political one. Politics also influenced the appointment of his assistant, Dr. Charles Clarke, who was the son of the Speaker of the Liberal Party and later a Clerk of the House. Clarke began his career at the Hamilton Asylum and was transferred to Rockwood at Kingston, where chaining and seclusion were the standard daily treatment. In company with Dr. Metcalf (who was killed by a patient), he tried to change the asylum from a prison into a hospital. Cages were dismantled, brutal attendants dismissed and well-trained nurses were put in charge of sick patients. In order to occupy patients who were no longer restrained, he set up a brush manufacturing operation in the hospital, which was highly successful until complaints from labour, the brush manufacturers and politicians forced it to close down.

A similar disappointment faced him as superintendent at the Toronto Asylum, when he authored a report recommending the establishment of a psychiatric institute in the city, and public apathy and delaying tactics on the part of his colleagues allowed the government to withdraw its support. He did, however, convince the Toronto General to open an out-patient clinic with Ernest Jones, Freud's disciple, as its medical director.

Even though his political pedigree was first-class, Clarke

fought furiously with the political machine, and he constantly railed against "the malign influence of politics over psychiatry". He remained in psychiatry because of his love of the profession and his hatred of politics, and wrote, "I felt that much could be accomplished if the politicians could be fought off with any degree of success".

But politicians were necessary to the hospital system. The Charity Act passed in 1874 provided that every institution in schedule A would receive 20 cents for each day of actual treatment and stay of every patient. This aid was limited in 1879 by not permitting the patient to receive the aid for longer than 270 days, and a further amendment in 1895 limited payment to 120 days.

Limitation of hospital days meant that many chronic disorders had to be funded in other ways, which particularly affected tubercular patients, the most chronic disorder. In 1871 more than 1,000 out of 9,100 recorded deaths were because of phthisis. By 1882 there were 2,464 from the same cause out of 21,800. At the turn of the century it was noted that:

> *Every time the clock struck the hour during the night, two*
> *Canadians died of the same disease (tuberculosis).*

While Britain had set up the Hospital for Consumption in 1841 (this was gradually expanded with the eventual opening of the Brampton Hospital Sanatorium in 1904), Ontario did not establish segregation beds until 1890, when six beds were set aside in the old Toronto General Hospital on Gerrard Street.

Following that start, the Muskoka Cottage Sanatarium was built by the National Sanatarium Association of which Sir William Gage was Treasurer. Initially it provided for 25 patients, but was expanded within a short time. There were some problems because a flat charge of $6.00 per week was made to each patient, most of whom were indigent, and although attempts were made to maintain free beds, it was not until the opening of the Muskoka Free Hospital for Consumptives at Gravenhurst that patients could receive treatment without charge. The "sanatarium movement" gathered strength as the excellent results of treatment seen at the Muskoka Cottage by Dr. J.H. Elliott were publicized. In the first year of operation he reported that of 83 patients, 12 were discharged apparently cured; 23 with disease arrested and 23 with marked improvement. This represented an enormous improvement over previous treatment results.

By 1904 The Toronto Hospital for Tuberculosis at Weston was opened, the first to set aside a ward for children with pulmonary tuberculosis. It was followed in 1906 by the Mountain Sanatorium in Hamilton and later by the Niagara Peninsula Sanatarium and the Royal Ottawa Sanatarium. Much of the impetus for the Sanatarium movement, which resulted in the decreased morbidity, came from Dr. Peter Bryce, who in 1882, as Secretary of the Board of Health of Ontario, made sure that the notification of communicable disease and the vital statistics of the effect of tuberculosis were properly publicized.

By 1912 the responsibility of the municipality to indigent patients in public hospitals was set forth under the Hospitals and Charitable Institution Act with a grant of $1.00 per diem. The old days of funding of hospitals by benevolence were gradually being replaced by government formula, and to ensure that hospitals received their fair share, the Ontario Hospital Association was organized in 1902, and began to achieve some success in increasing the amount of government grants to hospitals. Clearly it was impossible to maintain a balanced budget with the meagre income from the few paying patients, especially with the increasing costs of equipment and staff wages. The efforts of the hospital industry to maintain a benign influence were to continue.

Chapter XVI
The Distaff Doctors

. . . no one knows or can know what a furnace we are
passing through these days at the College. We suffer
torment, we shrink inwardly, we are hurt cruelly . . .

Dr. Elizabeth Shortt, *The Queen's Review, March 1899*

Unlike the urgency felt at the beginning of the 19th century to
educate physicians in Ontario, by the time of Confederation there
seemed to be no pressing need to educate female physicians.
Although, in other parts of the world, Elizabeth Blackwell managed
to graduate from the Geneva Medical College in 1849, and Sophia
Jex-Blake was vociferously attempting to enter the venerable halls at
Edinburgh, the issue of women in medicine did not appear in
Ontario until Emily Howard Jennings Stowe applied for admission
to the Victoria College Medical course in 1863. She was refused — no
females were accepted in any Canadian medical school. Bitter but
undaunted, she enrolled in the New York College and Hospital for
Women, graduated in 1867 and returned to her native province. She
hung out her shingle on Church Street in Toronto, and soon had a
large number of patients — albeit she did not have a licence to
practise in Ontario. In 1869, the Ontario Medical Act empowered
the College of Physicians & Surgeons to be the sole licensing board,
and Dr. Stowe applied for registration. She was refused on the
grounds that she was unqualified since she was a foreign graduate
who had not taken the required series of lectures in an Ontario
medical school. Once again the Toronto School of Medicine
received an application from Emily (by then Dr.) Stowe. Once again
she was refused, but Dr. Stowe persisted, vehemently, and finally in
1870, along with Jennie Gowanlock Trout, she was permitted to
attend lectures. Mrs. Trout, a school teacher, had been urged into
medicine by her neighbour, Dr. Stowe.

To accommodate their sensitivities as females, the directors
of the school pointed out it would be necessary for them to sit in special seats and observe through a loophole, before entering the room,

to see if the seats were clear of embarrassing material.

Jennie Trout left the school after one year and enrolled at the Women's Medical College of Pennsylvania, from which she graduated in 1875. She returned to Toronto, sat her examination and qualified to become the first woman licensed to practise medicine in Canada. Emily Stowe, still bristling from the refusal of the schools to accept female students, refused to be examined by the males of the College of Physicians and Surgeons until 1880.

There were three further applications by women for entrance into medicine in Toronto in 1879, but no school there was accepting females. However, one of the matriculant examiners, Dr. A.P. Knight of Queen's University, mentioned that Queen's had opened university courses to women and it was possible that the medical faculty would consider their application. They contacted Dr. M. Lavell, Dean of The Royal Medical College of Kingston, who agreed to issue a circular with an announcement that a special summer course of lectures in medicine would be offered for women exclusively. The lectures which began in 1880, were to be of normal content — the same material that was given to the male students, leading to the degree of M.D.

Four candidates appeared at the opening of the course including the daughter of Dr. Emily Stowe, Augusta, and Elizabeth Smith (later Shortt). Dr. Shortt wrote in her diary:

> ... the days were crammed with work, as we were zealous students and had literally no counter-attractions. We were up at 6:00, down to the Royal, practical work for 1½ hours, and back to anatomy at 10:00. Then physiology, histology and therapeutics, dinner and back at 2:00 for materia medica. Then up to Queen's University for chemistry, 3:30 to 4:30, and again for time in the early evening to the Royal for practical work, and back to study until a late bedtime ...

In spite of the success of the first session, the second term did not begin until April of 1881. It was still necessary to have separate dissection rooms for the ladies, and there was a classroom adjacent to the general classroom where the female students could hear the lecture which was being given to the male students. This followed the pattern set up by the University of Edinburgh, which insisted upon separate facilities for the female in the medical subjects, but some of the non-medical subjects taken at Queen's were in co-educational rooms.

Initially all went well, but by the year 1882 the seniors in the classes were composed of a "not desirable element", according to Shortt, and the previously cordial lecturer in physiology, because of some quarrel with senior members, began to voice his objections to women studying medicine. The situation worsened and Shortt wrote on November 22,

> ... no one knows or can know what a furnace we are passing through these days at College. We suffer torment, we shrink inwardly, we are hurt cruelly ... it is that encouraged current through the class of whispers, in the window, of derisive treading, the turning of what was never meant as unseemly into horrible meaning and the thousand and one ways they can be devised by evil minds to bring responsive smiles from their own kind. Day by day it seems harder to bear for we have borne so much ...

The flash point was reached in December when the physiology lecturer and the males managed to drive the women, as a group, from the classroom. The men then petitioned the university demanding that co-education cease since it was necessary to water down lectures in the presence of females. They pointed out that as they had paid full fees for their lecture, they expected to receive full lectures. To add urgency to their petition they sent a telegram to Dr. Geikie at Trinity in Toronto, asking if he would accept students on transfer.

Dean Lavell immediately realized the implications to the College and to the Town of Kingston. Any mass transfer of students would threaten the main source of income for teachers and also affect revenue to the Town of Kingston. He managed to smooth over the situation and came to an agreement by which the women could continue to hear the lectures in separate rooms on the basis that no more females would be accepted into the course.

But times were changing. Lavell, Knight and Principal Grant of Queen's held a meeting early in the summer with the townspeople of Kingston and a resolution was passed that "Kingston offered special advantages for the successful working of the Women's School of Medicine and that in the opinion of this meeting, it is right and fitting to establish such a College in Kingston". The townspeople enthusiastically gathered $1,500, including $200 from Dr. Trout in Toronto, to begin funding for the school. About the same time a meeting of the Women's Suffrage Committee was held in Toronto. This group was dedicated to opening up educational prospects for females and invited Dr.

Michael Barrett, Professor of Physiology of The Toronto School of Medicine to the meeting. A resolution was passed urging the establishment of a medical school for women in Toronto. But, Barrett, who had previously espoused the cause of medical women, felt he could not accept one of the conditions put forward by Dr. Jennie Trout that the "chairs" should be open to women when and if fully qualified and competent, and that the governing Board of Directors should include women. He based his objection on consultations with his prospective faculty and their refusal to work under a board composed partly of women, and their unwillingness to admit women to fill any of the chairs, although they could be demonstrators. Knight in Kingston heard of these meetings and, concluding that Toronto would not be establishing a college for women, he proceeded to encourage a Kingston College. However, Barrett after further discussion, changed his mind and announced that he would be willing to go ahead with the establishment of a Toronto School.

Thus, in 1883, there were two colleges for women in Ontario — one in Kingston and one in Toronto. The Kingston Faculty included Lavell, Dr. M. Sullivan, Dr. A.S. Oliver, Dr. Thomas N. Finwick and Dr. J.J. Saunders. Later Miss Beattie and Dr. Stowe were appointed demonstrators. In Toronto, the Faculty of The Women's Medical College included Barrett, and Drs. Nevitt and Wishart. Dr. Emily was appointed demonstrator in anatomy. The Women's School opened in premises at 291 Sumach Street and continued in those quarters until 1890 when it moved to 1 Sackville Street. At that time Dr. R.B. Nevitt was Dean and *The Canadian Practitioner* reported that "prejudices against female physicians are much less pronounced at this time than they were a few years ago". The new building was well equipped with a lecture hall for 50 students, laboratories for microscopy, chemistry, and a large library and reading room. There was a large basement in the three-storey brownstone house which, in 1898, was opened as the first clinic for women in Toronto with Dr. Jennie Gray and Dr. Ida Lynd in charge. The Kingston school, after ten years of success, transferred its students to the Toronto school. By 1905 there was a medical staff of 32 with ten female instructors. During their existence, Toronto qualified 109 female physicians and Kingston 26. Many outstanding physicians, including Dr. Helen MacMurchy, C.B.E., and Dr. Rowena Hume, were graduated with others practising in Ontario, other parts of Canada and overseas including Peking, Shanghai, Ceylon, Persia, India and Africa.

The tumultuous early days of medical education in Toronto were caused partly by the times — but in greater part by the personalities of the men who led the different schools. It is not unseemly that women's education should have had a similar course. Strong-willed females were pressing for medical education. Elizabeth Shortt, who died at 90, was a founding member of The Victorian Order of Nurses, The Women's Canadian Club, The Ontario Council of Women; and she fought for many years to convince The National Dairy Council to accept oleomargarine. Emily Stowe was a dynamic person, born of a Quaker family, who was wholly committed in her youth to women's suffrage and a balancing of the role played by women. She was already a successful high school principal in Brantford before she decided to enter into medicine; and by a strange coincidence she lived in the same house as Jennie Trout — another brilliantly qualified teacher. Having forced their way into The Toronto School of Medicine and persevered in the face of the opposition, their paths separated. Trout, in writing her examinations and taking the oral, fell out with Stowe who held to her feminist principles.

Both worked hard at medicine, and also at gaining equality for women. Stowe was a founder of The Toronto Women's Literary Club in 1877 and in that highly respectable venue continued to preach suffrage. This resulted, in 1883, in a change of the name of the club to The Toronto Women's Suffrage Club and later to the Canadian Suffrage Association. The important platform offered by the Suffrage Club during the early founding days of The Women's Medical College in Toronto was not accidental — it resulted from years of preparation on Stowe's part. But Trout grew impatient with Toronto and possibly the outspokenness of Stowe and joined in founding the opposing school at Kingston. The schools opened within a day of each other, monuments to the driving force of the two Ontario doctors who somehow could not work together in a common enterprise. Actually Kingston seemed to be on a firmer footing as it had three enrolled students. The Toronto school had only one candidate, who had transferred from a special summer course at Kingston — Augusta Stowe.

The clinic established in the basement of the successful school led to the organization of "The Women's College Hospital and Dispensary Board" which eventually purchased a building and established The Women's College Hospital in 1910. In barely 30 years the distaff doctors had moved from behind the loophole to a modern teaching hospital.

Chapter XVII

The Master-Words

. . . some half witted dupe of the Clairvoio-Electro-Thero-
Cura-Pathic strip — a sort of hybrid no doubt, — a half
free-love moralist and half abortionist . . .
Practitioner, *The Canada Lancet,* 1880

The early-century shortage of locally trained physicians and the inability to regulate medical practice was solved, partially with the foundation of medical schools. But there remained a problem in the conduct of medical practice for while the Christian ethic was sufficient to guide some physicians' actions, it did not spell out all those activities which were within the revealed dogma and which were apostate.

Guidelines were sometimes arbitrary as may be seen in a meeting of the Medical Alumni Association of Victoria College in 1868, which conducted trials against members of the association on the basis that they had failed to comply with normal ethics. Dr. G.A. Carsaw, of Whitby, was charged with advertising publicly on fences and other places throughout the country, a certain medicine called "Carsaw's Victoria Wine Bitters" recommending the same to the public. A lengthy discussion took place before a "jury" of the Association and testimony was heard from the accused which stated that the article in question was not advertised or sold, or intended to be sold, as a medicinal remedy, but simply as a "bitters", having for its object the reformation of drunkards. Carsaw admitted that his bitter contained 1/13th of the whole content of pure alcohol. He was cautioned.

Dr. Joseph Fife, of Peterborough, was charged with resorting to the practice of "cancer cures". This practice was deemed by his peers to be derogatory to the medical profession.

A Dr. Abner Roseburgh, the founder of the Toronto Eye and Ear Dispensary, 12 Shuter St., Toronto, was charged with improper conduct. He admitted that posters had been erected in the town of

Cobourg, which invited special attention to the importance of his visit to that town as an oculist and aurist; however, this had been inadvertent as he had not authorized the printer to publish any such advertisements. With this he apologised to the alumni and promised that it would not happen again.

Dr. William Wade, of Cobourg, had to leave the chair of a meeting in order to face a charge that he had involved himself in partnership with an Eclectic — considered to be an irregular practitioner. This was seen to be derogatory to the medical profession and contrary to the constitution, which had been adopted by the Alumni Association. In his defence, Wade stated that he had entered into the connection "prior to any expression from the Alumni Association" and therefore had not informed the association of his status. A special motion was passed exonerating him from all blame, and Wade promised he would keep the association better informed in the future.

With the death of Thomson in 1843, the Botanical Family Physician movement lost much of its impetus and its members gradually drifted into the eclectic camp, which became one of the major alternate sources of medical care. This group was soon matched and outnumbered by the homeopaths, a sect which based its system on the theory stemming from a "discovery" made by a Saxon physician, Samuel Christian Hahnemann (1755-1843), who had become unhappy with his practice, and had turned to translating for a living. He translated *The Works of William Cullen* (1710-1790) of Edinburgh, and became interested in claims made for the use of cinchona, peruvian bark, which contained quinine, as a means of treating people. Hahnemann experimented on himself with the bark, and noted that it caused fever, which had all the hallmarks of the fever caused during illness. He found that when he discontinued the drug, his fever disappeared and he soon became well. From this he deduced that cinchona, which could cause fever, was specific for curing fever. However, this could not happen unless there were vital powers within the body, which were mobilized as a "native army", to defeat the "enemy". The vital spirit, which could be mobilized, did not require massive doses of medicine, but rather could be stimulated by infinitesimal amounts. Such doses had a high potency in the body where there was illness, because there was greater sensitivity to drugs than in health. His original theories were published in 1810, with an English translation in 1833. In this book, *The Organon of Homeopathic Medicine,* he coined the term "allopath", which meant that drugs were not prescribed on the basis of a system of contaria, nor of similia, but rather on allos, meaning by no particular theory.

The first homeopath arrived in the United States about 1828, and was followed in 1833 by Dr. Constantine Hering. He had been commissioned to write a book which refuted homeopathy, but during his investigation became a supporter of the sect. This was a common occurrence during the early days, before there were homeopathic colleges, because orthodox physicians became disenchanted with the effects of bloodletting or large doses of mineral and metallic medicine. The homeopaths used all the medicinals in the allopathic pharmacopoeia, but in only infinite-simal amounts. In addition, homeopaths urged patients to treat themselves from a domestic kit, which was sold to families after its merits had been publicized in *Domestic Physician* by Dr. Hering in 1848. Each medication was identified by a number, rather than a name. Number 8, for example was to be taken when measles prevailed in the neighbourhood. Free dispensaries were established, and it appeared homeopathic medicine seemed to do less harm then allopathic medicine, particularly in the treatment of children's diseases. Besides, the homeopaths sugar-coated their pills, an innovation which the allopaths did not adopt for several years.

The movement had a slow growth in the 1830's and initially was not considered a threat to allopathic medicine. However, in 1842, Dr. Oliver Wendell Holmes (1809-1894), the dean of American medical educators, gave an address on *Homeopathy and Its Kindred Delusions,* which ridiculed the claims of the homeopathist. This was followed in 1851 by Dr. Worthington Hooker, who wrote a prize-winning essay on *Homeopathy, So Called, Its History and Reputation.* The attacks on the philosophy of homeopathy were altruistic, but motivated somewhat by the fact that the homeopaths were making real inroads on the earning ability of the allopaths.

In Ontario the first homeopathic practitioner was Dr. Joseph J. Lancaster, who was born in Oxford county. Before studying medicine, he was suspected of being a sympathizer in the Rebellion of 1837 and spent three weeks in jail before being cleared. He qualified after studying in New York, with Dr. Henry Weeks of Norwich. He was followed by Dr. D. Campbell, who migrated to Ontario from Scotland, where he had qualified. The earlier homeopaths were all graduates of allopathic schools, who became convinced that infinitesimal doses associated with rest, diet, bathing and exercise provided a much more effective means of treatment.

Much of this persuasion came from observing the inability of allopathic medicine to be effective in major diseases, such as cholera.

However, the opposition to homeopathy mounted higher and higher. Allopathic medical licencing boards, in the United States, refused to give licenses to homeopaths. (Many states found medical licencing laws were unenforceable, and repealed them during the 1840's). Professional societies, such as the American Medical Association, expelled members who consulted with homeopaths. Homeopaths were not permitted on the staffs of hospitals and they were not accepted into the military. Although, after much dispute, they could attend the medical lectures of allopaths, no school would give them a diploma. The latter stricture resulted in the opening of the first homeopathic school in Cleveland in 1850.

The allopaths in America remained obdurate, refusing to recognize or work with homeopaths until well into the twentieth century. In England there was similar opposition. Even Queen Victoria, when she requested Sir William Jenner (1815-1898) to attend Benjamin Disraeli, was refused on the basis that ethics prohibited him from attending a patient who was under the care of a homeopath.

In 1850, Dr. Lancaster petitioned the Legislative Assembly on behalf of himself and other homeopaths to be granted leave to practise in Upper Canada. The application resulted in the passage of a bill known as "An Act Respecting Homeopathy" (8 Geo. IV., Chap. 3.) in 1859, which appointed a board of examiners qualified to give a licence as a homeopathic physician.

But, whether he was qualified by a government-appointed board or not, the allopathic physicians, while tolerating him, did not wish to consort. Dr. C.T. Campbell, a Toronto homeopath and President of the Homeopathic Board, was described in the press as being "unjustly treated and made the object of a bitter attack" by the allopathic physicians. He was involved in an inquest at the Toronto Asylum, in which one of his former maid-servants had died. The coroner insinuated that the use of galvanism in the case of this unfortunate girl "had no pure or proper motive to serve", according to *The Daily Leader*. Campbell's detractors, the allopathic physicians, had even gone so far as to publish a pamphlet on the iniquity of this treatment by a homeopath, and demanded his conviction. However, the coroner did not find sufficient grounds for a charge.

Dr. Lancaster had to defend himself against a charge of manslaughter, which was a frequent manoeuvre on the part of the allopaths, who sought to undermine public confidence in homeopathy. However, none of these charges laid in Ontario, the United States, Germany or England were ever upheld.

In addition to the problems created by non-regular physicians, even the regular physicians were beginning to adopt some strange new practices. Many of the younger graduates were more than eager to put the new-found uses of electricity to service. G.F. Crusell (1810-1858) in Germany, and Duchenne de Boulogne (1806-1875) in France had demonstrated clinical use of electro-therapy in the 1840's and an English translation of Duchenne's book appeared in 1871. Shortly after, Dr. Jennie Trout established the Therapeutic and Electrical Institute in Toronto in which special facilities for giving treatments to ladies by galvanic baths or electricity were offered. Her partner was not registered to practise medicine in the province.

Others were attracted by the drama of static electricity. The "Practitioner" in Oshawa pointed out that the public could not be too strictly protected against these would-be gifted scientists. He accused them of "plying their trade by bluster and pretense attracting the weak and credulous by their glittering pretentious signs and wonderful stock of parchments, bought by the yard from the swindling institutions operating in some cities of the United States." Apparently one of these "disease slayers" had settled in Oshawa and had advertised that the pole of his battery would "snuff out any disease in the twinkling of an eye". He rubbed some, soaked some, stewed some, and applied artificial and animal magnetism to a good many others.

"Practitioner" called upon the recently passed Ontario Medical Act to prosecute this type of practitioner. The Medical Act was the result of an Act passed by Parliament in Canada in 1865 to regulate the qualifications of practitioners in medicine and surgery in Upper Canada. After the proposals of J.C. Aikins to regulate licencing in 1859 had been turned down, the cause was picked up by Dr. T.H. Parker, which resulted in the creation of a General Council of Medical Education and Registration in Upper Canada in 1865. This body, made up of regional medical representatives, had the power to grant a licence to practise medicine, upon receiving written evidence that the applicant had graduated from one of the educational bodies, whose representatives sat on the Council. This was an improvement over the previous arrangement, where the licencing board was appointed by the government. The Homeopathic and Eclectic Acts had given those professions the right to be self-governing, and the 1865 Act now did the same thing for physicians. The Act also clarified that unregistered practitioners could not prosecute in court for unpaid accounts.

But, there was still a need to unify all of the practitioners in Ontario under one Act, because there remained discrepancies in matters of education and licensure. This led to the Ontario Medical Act of 1869, which established the College of Physicians and Surgeons of Ontario. This Act made the College the examining board for all practitioners, uniting the three separate licencing Boards. It also allowed the College to establish the curriculum for medical schools and raise standards. This reform action was not received kindly by all members of the medical profession. There had always been some feelings that the regulatory body — be it the Upper Canada Medical Board or the College of Physicians and Surgeons — was in effect a monopoly by some doctors over others, and might be used for profit. In 1836, after some years of grumbling, it came to an outburst by physicians against the Board and those who managed the General Hospital, which resulted in a public meeting with, according to *The Patriot* of January 14, a large number of angry physicians. They passed a resolution that the two or three medical practitioners were "holding their inquisition in utter darkness" when they pronounced on various applicants, and held limitless power in being able to pronounce, without appeal, on the professional merits of their own pupils. If an applicant happened to be at variance with the feelings of the Board, there was little hope that he would be accepted and given a licence. The meeting petitioned the Lieutenant-Governor to make changes in the Medical Board, and thus restore confidence in the medical men in the country. Changes of minor nature were made, but there continued to be an undercurrent of dissatisfaction.

With the announcement of the establishment of the College of Physicians and Surgeons, there was again some outcry against too much centralization of authority. This grumbled along for years and came to head in 1894, with a series of newspaper articles, which attacked the College on several grounds. The first was against the payment of a one dollar (later two dollars) registration fee, which was collected from all physicians in Ontario and which was regarded as a taxation without representation, and was looked upon as providing funds where there was no need. In evidence of this, it was asserted that the College had erected a building in Toronto, at considerable expense, when quarters could have been obtained much more economically in other areas of the province. There was also great objection to the make-up of the Council which, it was claimed, tended to leave unrepresented the physicians in the outlying areas and put most power into the hands of the medical college representatives and homeopaths. This charge was denied, with convincing statistics, by President C.T. Campbell. The compulsory registration fee was considered intolerable by some of the profession, who went to their elected members in the Provincial House, and started a movement to amend the Ontario Medical Act, in order to do away with the fee. Part of their campaign included a series of newspaper articles stating that members of the College of Physicians and Surgeons had wined and dined various members of the House in a lobbying attempt. More than $600 had been spent on champagne and lobsters to maintain the fee, which was necessary for the College's existence. Eventually some of the complaints were resolved by an amendment to the Act, which changed the basis for representation and increased the number of rural delegates, but the contentious registration fee remained.

This Act of 1869 was remarkable inasmuch as no other country had reached such accord with the homeopaths or eclectics. The situation in the United States was getting worse rather than better, and Great Britain remained adamant that it would not permit consultation with irregular practitioners. The wisdom of the Act may be seen in the gradual disappearance of the eclectic from the scene while homeopaths were slowly being absorbed into the allopathic framework. By 1925 there were only 40 homeopaths left in Canada, of whom 32 were located in Ontario.

The passage of the Act received acclaim from *The Globe* on January 15, 1869:

> *A very important step has been taken by the medical practitioners of Ontario ... It is creditable to the old school, who have hitherto given the cold shoulder to the other sects that they consent to meet them on the same Board. We are not aware that this step, or any similar one has been taken in any other country; and we congratulate all parties to the agreement on the liberality, which has been displayed ... We have always, contended that there should be nothing exclusive in medicine — that no set of men should be able to dictate the principles on which disease should be treated, and to refuse the right of practice to all who do not repeat their shibboleth.*

While there had been a great deal of discussion prior to passage of the Act, some allopathic physicians claimed they had not been consulted and would never have agreed to the inclusion of homeopaths and eclectics. However, they had to live with the fact that the clarification of the legal rights of those two groups had been made exact by one of their own members (none other than Dr. H. Yates of Kingston) in putting forth an amendment to the proposed Ontario Medical Act, which clearly specified that the eclectics and homeopaths should have representation on the new Council of The College of Physicians and Surgeons, The Act had been shepherded through the House by Dr. W. McGill of Oshawa, for Dr. T.H. Parker had died the previous year.

Many hours were spent at the first meeting of the General Council in 1869 delineating who was responsible for the lumping together of the others with the allopaths, and frequent acrimonious statements were made that "our medical diplomas would be ignored in the old country" and that McGill had not told the Ontario group of the change in content. After a long debate, the members reluctantly agreed to abide by the new Act, as it worked for the protection of the public.

The eclectic representation on the Council ceased about 1875 and further amendments to the Ontario Medical Acts made throughout the years consolidated the ability of The College of Physicians and Surgeons to enact by-laws for the regulation of all matters connected with medical education — including admission to enrollment of students of medicine and determination of the curriculum of studies.

McGill was also a key figure in another area of effective medical care — pharmacy. An attempt by physicians to regulate the practice of pharmacy by legislation in the 1840's failed, but some success resulted in the Strychnine Act of 1840. Prior to that date poisons could be easily obtained.

A similar situation held in England where at the beginning of the nineteenth century there were three separate orders of the medical profession — physicians, surgeons and apothecaries. Each was governed by its own corporate body or guild, known as the Royal College of Physicians, the Royal College of Surgeons and the Worshipful Company of Apothecaries. The industrial revolution had begun to erode the guild system, causing defensive moves by the profession to more closely control the members and prevent outsiders from entering the healing field. The apothecaries, who were in reality general practitioners working in the countryside, as opposed to the physicians who practised in the cities, had neglected the art of dispensing and were being gradually replaced by a new group — the druggists and chemists. This did not greatly concern the apothecaries, as they were increasing their numbers and therefore their political strength. However, the College of Physicians viewed the double events — a burgeoning group of druggists and a stronger group of apothecaries — with alarm. In order to stop this "decay of authority", the College tried to extend its powers of control over medical practice in 1806 by a Bill, which brought apothecaries, chemists and druggists under their control. This led to a series of negotiations between the apothecaries and the College of Physicians, which resulted in a strengthening of the old guild-like structure and at the same time seemed to control the activities of the chemists and druggists.

However, this control was not clearly defined, and druggists and chemists continued to attend the sick by prescribing over the counter. This disputed area of medical practice was not resolved until 1870, when it was decided in a court of law that if a chemist prescribed medicine and then sold it to a customer, he was infringing on the provisions of the Apothecaries Act.

This situation was reflected in Ontario, where there were no effective restrictions on who could practise as a pharmacist, druggist or apothecary until the passage of the Pharmacy Act in 1871. The legislation, introduced by William McGill, controlled the sale of poisons and regulated the professions of apothecaries, chemists and druggists in the province, enabling them to form later into a society called The Ontario College of Pharmacy. There was great debate in the House on the basis that the druggist could monopolize the drug business to the great disadvantage of those country storekeepers who were selling drugs. However, McGill, a Reformer, persevered over Edward Blake, the Liberal, and the first Pharmacy Act was passed.

Much of the impetus for the Act came from Mr. E.B. Shuttleworth, who in the early 1860's urged Toronto druggists to organize themselves into the Toronto Chemists and Druggists Association, and hold monthly meetings at the Mechanics Institutes in order to lay the groundwork for the opening of The Ontario College of Pharmacy. He had been acutely aware of the attempts of medicine to control pharmacy. To counter this several organizations of pharmacists in Ottawa, Montreal and Toronto established a professional basis, including the publication of the *Canadian Pharmaceutical Journal* beginning in 1868.

While part of the opposition to passage of the Pharmacy Act was the desire of certain members of the Government to maintain free enterprise in the sale of pharmaceuticals at grocery stores, it was acknowledged that most of these were patent medicines. Beginning in 1809, homemade proprietary medicines had become available in Upper Canada. Clavendon Younger offered an iron ointment for sale that year, and he also hawked Stoughton's Bitters and Lee's Pills, imported from London. By the 1840's advertisements for proprietaries appearing in most newspapers of the province, included among others Hamilton's Scorbutic Ointment, Mr. Bartholomew's Pink Expectorant Syrup and Hewe's Nerve and Bone Liniment. These advertisements served as the perfect sales milieu for the patent medicine manufacturer as can be seen by the January 12, 1877 issue of the *Cardwell Sentinel* of Keenansville, County Simcoe, which carried 107 ads in its weekly issue of which 28 were for patent medicines and quack institutes. Perry Davis's Pain Killer, Dr. Chase's remedies, Ayer's Cherry Pectoral, all were properly trumpeted.

Many of these medicines were not safe. Nuxated Iron which allegedly made Tye Cobb the greatest ball player in the world, contained a daily dose of 1/4 grain of iron and 1/80 of a grain of Strychnine. Mrs. Winslow's Soothing Syrup soothed through the presence of morphine. Shiloh's Cure for Consumption controlled the cough with heroin and the Compound Oxygen Association treated the opium habit by supplying morphia.

Many of the advertisements stressed the curative power of electricity. J.H. Hambly, chemist and druggist in Belleville, offered patented spectacles, which delivered a "soft continuous stream of electricity", vitalizing and giving health to the entire system. This resulted in "absolutely and certainly curing" partial paralysis of the optic nerve, weak or diseased vision, neuralgia, nervous twitches in the muscles of the face, noises in the head, or losses of mental energy. Electric belts were advertised for men suffering from sexual debility, impotency, drains, losses, atrophy, etc. The electricity was passed from a series of batteries in the belt to a pendulum which was suspended over the weak area. Dr. D. Sanden, of 140 Yonge Street in Toronto, advertised that his electric belt was better as it was applied "all night while you sleep". If the belt was not suitable, then electric oil could be used for the cure of deafness, headaches, ague, rheumatism, and all sorts of pain. This was supplied by Lyman and Brothers of Toronto. Of course, the weakness might not be due to anything other than the fact that "thousands of overworked business men, weary brain-workers, industrious mechanics and tired women" in all parts of the country were working too hard! Indeed, it was noted in one advertisement by a London physician that "a new and distinct form of nervous disease is produced in Canadian women by worry about servants and over-work in caring for the house". The cure for these conditions was Pain's Celery Compound.

Attempts to control patent medications began in 1875 when "an Act to impose licence duty on compounded spirits and to prevent the adulteration of food, drink and drugs" was passed. However, the Act did not cover proprietary medicines. In 1883, *The Canadian Practitioner* published several articles which viewed the problems of the charlatan and proprietary medicine. (Unlike others, this journal did not carry any proprietary advertisements). By 1892, Dr. Edward Plater of Schomberg was able to persuade the medical press to take a firmer stand, which resulted in an editorial in 1902 in *The Canadian Practitioner* urging appropriate legislation. In 1904 an amendment to the Post Office Act, introduced by Sir William Mulock, curtailed the distribution of matter containing advertisements representing "marvellous or extravagant cures". Finally, as a result of campaigns in *The Ladies Home Journal* and *Colliers* in the United States, the Federal Government introduced a report on the proprietary medicine trade which clearly showed the need for regulation. It took another ten years for the introduction of a Bill, the Proprietary and Patent Medicine Act, requiring the manufacturer to notify a government agency of the contents of the product.

But the hawkers continued. Dr. Jerrold Ball reported his advice when he was unable to relieve a patient of tapeworm: "Take a dollar and take the streetcar on College Street to Bathurst, then go south on Bathurst as far as the carline will go. When you come to the end of the carline, walk south until you come to the most disreputable looking window in the world, which advertises cures for everything. That is Doc Mulveney's shop. Go in. Don't tell him I sent you. Tell him what your trouble is." The patient came back three days later rejoicing he no longer had his tapeworm.

This was the hallmark of medical practice — a combination of science and practicality and concern. Nowhere could the concern be reflected more feelingly than in a letter sent by the residents of the Township of Nipissing when they heard that Dr. Charles A. Hodgetts was being recalled by the Ontario Government.

... we cannot allow this opportunity to pass without rendering to the Ontario Government our thanks for their

*sympathy and liberality in sending you to assist us against
the ravages of diphtheria.*

*We also extend to yourselves the thanks of all classes here:
for your successful efforts in its arrest and being confined
to its separate places: by your promptness and skill. We
will always cherish a kind remembrance of you for your
obliging and courteous manner to all whom you came
into contact with . . .*

The problem of endemic diphtheria had been present in the
district for several years in the late 1880's. In January of 1889 the
Provincial Board of Health, with Dr. Peter Bryce as Secretary, sent
Hodgetts and Dr. William R. Wade to the area. Their reports to the
Board of Health over the spring months of the year told of deaths in
many families. They travelled by rail-lines to solve a problem that
had plagued communities for years — the transportation of disease
by rail. Obviously, the life-line, which connected the settlements of
the north, became a death-line, when it transported contagious sick
passengers to the hospitals in the south. The natural isolation of
settlements was no longer a bulwark against disease.

On March 7, Dr. Hodgetts reported that he had arrived by
horse and sleigh at Rye Post in Commanda to find a three year old
child with diphtheria. Even though the father had kept his wife and
two children on an island in Lake Nipissing, thinking that thereby
they would escape the trouble, food shortage had made it necessary
to leave the island and come back to Rye and diphtheria. Most
families did not realize the degree of contagion from the disease, and
in many cases Hodgetts had to give lectures on the necessity of strict
quarantine within the family itself. But the disease continued to
appear, and in 1900 more than 100 cases were reported in Algoma.
They were treated in six especially set-up double-wall tents in
Sudbury, the victims having been transported to that centre in a
special coach by the Canadian Pacific Railway. Later, Hodgetts
became Chief Commissioner of the Canadian Red Cross and
Honourary Secretary of the St. John Ambulance Association.

While written or spoken thanks were always welcomed by the
doctor, there was still a need to generate cash fees. Early records show
the financial difficulties of doctors like Rolph, Canniff and others
who, while they had adequate funds, never became rich. The 1877
tariff fees of the Medical Association of the county of Simcoe listed
the following:

Medicine, exclusive of medicine —

day visit, within the mile $1.00 to $2.00
night visit $2.00 to $4.00
advice at the office $1.00
stethoscopic examination of the chest $1.00 to $4.00
administration of chloroform $2.00 to $4.00

Surgery —
adjusting fractures of the thigh $10.00 to $20.00
amputation of thigh $25.00 to $50.00

Venereal diseases —
cash and advice for first consultation $5.00 to $10.00

Midwifery —
ordinary cases $5.00 to $10.00
instrumental or complicated $7.00 to $30.00

Things were a little more expensive in Toronto. In 1875 an ordinary visit was $2.00 to $4.00 for the 1st Division, $1.00 to $2.00 for the 2nd Division and $1.00 for the 3rd Division. A Certificate of Lunacy or Sanity was $5.00, $3.00 and $2.00 respectively. The divisions, on which the charges were made, were based on the presumed income of the patient. The 1st Division covered income over $3,000, the 2nd Division $3,000 to $1,000, and the 3rd Division under $1,000. In 1875 fees were charged accordingly. Major operations, such as lithotomy, ovariotomy or ligation of larger arteries, were from $200 to $500 for the 1st Division. The 3rd Division was charged $30.00 to $60.00. In 1866, a tariff of fees for the city of Toronto and suburbs signed by Dr. D. Bergin, showed lower charges. Ordinary visits were $1.50 to $5.00 and major operations were shown as $100 to $1,000. At this time no divisions were shown of the fee scale.

Whether practice was well rewarded is open to question judging from an article that appeared in *The Globe* that year. A news story, headlined "The Singular Poverty of the Medical Profession", detailed the incomes and personal taxes of a large number of doctors, including most of the teaching staff of the medical schools, showing that the level was uniformly low. The average income, the writer said, was in the neighbourhood of $1,200. per annum, compared to the clergy which was well over $2,000.; and he went on to issue a "fearful warning" to medical students to keep out of such a poor business.

To generate this type of income frequently required operations such as that described by Dr. Herbert A. Bruce, when he was a student and assisting W.T. Aikins. He reports a procedure on a young woman in a private house on Gerrard St. at 8:30 a.m. one Saturday morning. The patient was placed on a table in the front room adjoining the kitchen while the surgeon's son, Wilberforce, gave an anesthetic by pouring ether on a piece of gauze stretched over a metal frame and held to cover the nose and mouth. After removing his coat, the surgeon turned up the cuffs of his shirt, washed his hands and dipped them in a solution of bichloride. He used a solution of carbolic acid to soak his instruments and then transferred them to a dish of boiled water. Bruce held the arm while Aikins made a vertical incision over the elbow joint and removed the end of the humerus and ulna after which he closed the skin and covered it with a dressing. While Aikins observed some of the Listerian methods of antisepsis, Bruce reports that when he wanted to "park his knife, he put it between his teeth"! In the early afternoon, the mother called out to say lunch was ready, so the patient was "kept under" while the three operators had a hearty meal; the operation then resumed after an hour's delay and was finished about 4:00 o'clock.

The fee for such a procedure was $40.00. The Ontario Medical Association did not concern itself particularly with fee generation except to condemn the evils of "lodge practice", where a physician contracted to care for lodge members at a set annual stipend, which John Coventry of Windsor characterized in 1897: "A vampire never bled its prey more effectively than do the lodgers their medical attendants".

In this matter the OMA did not receive the support of Doctor Oronhyatekha. Born on the Indian Reserve near Brantford, he so impressed the Prince of Wales when he toured Canada in 1860, that the young Mohawk Indian was invited to spend a year furthering his medical education at Oxford. On return to Ontario, he opened his practice at Frankford and became active with the Independent Order of Foresters, eventually devoting his full time to that organization.

The OMA also urged that the law should be amended so that medical men of each electoral district could draw up their own schedule of fees and that in all cases of malpractice, security for costs should first be furnished by the plaintiff. This had a practical value as seen in the matter of Dr. John Hyde of Stratford. He was involved in a lawsuit with a Miss Jackson, who had lacerated her hand six years previously in a thrashing machine; Hyde had ordered the hand to be amputated. After considerable delay, she launched an action against Hyde claiming negligence. The jury decided for Miss

Jackson and brought in a verdict against Hyde with damages in the amount of $250.00. *The Dominion Medical Journal* in reporting the case, wondered whether there was not some local professional animosity in the evidence presented before the jury and suggested that a physician was all too ready to testify against a rival. The matter was eventually settled on appeal with the plaintiff withdrawing the suit.

Discussions of money and liability suits took only a minor place in the annual meetings. The 1890's saw the pinnacle of the struggle between "practical" versus "scientific" education for physicians. *The Canada Lancet* stated, "the public mind must before long recognize the fact that doctors must be eminently practical ..." and went on to point out that, while the first-year medical student may be scientific with a tuning fork to determine the number of its vibrations per second, he would achieve more useful medical knowledge if he spent that time in the dissection room. The old canard, revived from the 50's, that, "I'd rather see a man with a telescope than listen with a stethoscope", went the rounds.

However, the meetings of the Ontario Medical Association were much concerned with scientific medicine. The recorded minutes of the early 1890's are full of discussions of the treatment of perityphlitis which was rest, moving the bowels, warm fomentations and operating if pus formed. By 1911, H.A. Bruce took the view that operating was a preferable course, while R.D. Rudolf leaned to the side of giving medicinal treatment a fair chance. In the interim, a discussion in 1895 had pointed out that, if the abscess ruptured and the peritoneum was invaded by pus, there was no use in operating.

The treatment of diphtheria remained a constant problem. By 1895 the calomel fumigation treatment was popular but ineffectual, and the new use of antitoxin by Dr. C. Sheard at the Isolation Hospital, Toronto, was reported to be of no value.

This antitoxin was the result of work done by Theodore Klebs (1834-1913) and Friedrich Loeffler (1852-1915). They had isolated the diphtheria bacillus, which when properly cultured by Emil Roux (1853-1933) and Emil Yerson (1863-1943), produced a toxin. The toxin, which was demonstrated in Paris in 1880, was taken to the laboratory of Emil Behring (1854-1917) in Germany, who in 1890, by innoculating guinea pigs, produced an antitoxin which protected against disease. By 1893 Behring was able to demonstrate protection against diphtheria in man with an antitoxic serum. By 1894 antitoxin, obtained by injecting a horse, was used by Dr. Charles Sherington in England. It was brought to Canada the following year. However, the antitoxin was not the ideal preventive and it was not until the 1920's that Dr. John FitzGerald, of the Connaught Laboratories, began the use of diphtheria toxoid — a toxin treated with a formalin.

A recurring topic of discussion throughout the years was the large number of specialists. Dr. Daniel Clark of Toronto, in 1884, felt that the tendency to engage in specialties was to be regretted because of the importance of general knowledge to the physician who practised outside the cities in the small communities where the majority of citizens lived. By 1897 there had been no significant change, as Dr. John Coventry of Windsor, in his presidential report, stated:

> ... each member of the family is now in the habit of having his or her own medical attendant, as an eye, heart, lung, or surgical specialist and so on ...

In the same year a committee urged that the Legislature look into the matter of the number of quack remedies which were so prevalent, and another committee, appointed to investigate the establishment of the Victorian Order of Nurses, reported that while the O.M.A. was fully cognizant of the "kindly motives" which were back of the movement:

> ... it would be neglecting a serious duty if it failed to express its unqualified disapproval of the scheme, on account of the dangers which must necessarily follow to the public should such an order be established ...

The 1901 meeting continued to propound the Association's objection to the advertisement of cancer cures, osteopathy and Christian Science. At the same time it warned manufacturing firms against many new preparations and combinations of pharmaceuticals which were appearing on the market. In that year the Honourable R. Harcourt, Minister of Education, addressed the annual meeting and received strong representation from Drs. W. Britton and R. Ferguson to lessen the burden of examinations and studies on children by making the educational system more educative with less competition. Three years later the Association spoke out strongly against the slavery that was inherent in the employment of children in factories, which should not be permitted any longer. At the same meeting, Dr. Charles J. Hastings urged that it was the duty of the State to conduct systematic medical inspection of school children and to issue pamphlets for better child care. He stressed the importance of preventive medicine which had been suggested in 1903 when the Association had approved of the principle that:

> ... we are gradually passing from "how shall we treat" to "how shall we prevent". This is the main issue for the future ...

And the future was clearly outlined by William Osler (later to be knighted) when he opened the new medical building at the University of Toronto in 1903. Osler, who had been born at Bond Head had been stimulated to microscopic studies by Dr. James Bovell when a student at Trinity College where he developed keen observation abilities and a tremendous facility at organizing those observations. Although enrolled at the Toronto School of Medicine, he left Toronto to go to McGill in 1867, because the hospital facilities there were superior and, more importantly, were not threatened with shut-downs. At that school he developed a deep interest in pathology and great skill at conducting autopsies, and on this basis of truth he achieved clinical acumen as a diagnostician. This led to appointments at the University of Pennsylvania and later in Oxford, England. He was preeminent in teaching the use of pathology in the interpretation of clinical signs and symptoms, and achieved a world-wide recognition as a writer, humorist, classicist and philosopher.

As a post-graduate student, Osler described blood platelets, outlined several blood dyscrasias and became an authority on smallpox, lobar pneumonia and malaria. His papers on malignant endocarditis, sub-acute bacterial endocarditis, including "Osler" nodes, polycythemia vera, the anemias of pregnancy and erythema exudative multiforme, became classics. In addition, his lucid and humorous style was used with great effect in describing the *History of Medicine, Evolution of Medicine* in 1921, and *The Albama Student* in 1908. His greatest impact was on the thinking of the medical profession at a time when there was a great need to re-assess century-long practices and concepts. His presence at the 1903 inauguration of the new University of Toronto Faculty building was appropriate — the most famous Canadian physician to open the newest teaching and research facility in Ontario.

Medicine was changing and Osler was one of the movers. The heroic use of medicine of the first half of the century was being slowly replaced by a more rational use of medication — or no medication. In 1835 Jacob Bigelow (1786-1879) had published *A Discourse on Self-Limited Diseases*. Dr. O.W. Holmes claimed that "this work did more than any in the English language to rescue the practice of medicine from the slavery of the drugging system". Holmes pointed out, during his attack on homeopathy, that 90 percent of illnesses "would recover sooner or later, provided nothing were done to interfere seriously with the efforts of nature". It took some time for this message to arrive in Ontario.

In 1855 a Mr. Dixon, a student of John Rolph at the Toronto School of Medicine, answered a call to treat a man with severe dysentery. After determining that he had passed bloody stools, was vomiting and had been ill for the past three days, Dixon left dysentery powders, each containing one grain of opium, with directions to take one every two hours until the patient was relieved. The next day there was no significant improvement and Dixon then, on the advice of Dr. Aikins, administered one quarter grain of morphia every half hour.

That line of treatment was considered ideal in the year it was given. By the third quarter of the nineteenth century Osler pointed out that many changes had been made. Sensible doctors had reached the conclusion that typhoid fever was not a disease to be treated with medicines, but that in a large proportion of all cases, diet, nursing and bathing met the needs. Osler acknowledged the battle against polypharmacy had not been fought to a finish, but felt the growth of the sceptical spirit fostered by Paris, Vienna and Boston, and the valuable lessons of homeopathy were two contributing factors on the side of progress.

His acute observations on man, the only animal who felt the need to take medicine, were matched by his statements that:

> ... *for the crass therapeutic credulity, so wide-spread today, and upon which our manufacturing chemists wax fat, there's no more potent antidote than the healthy scepticism bred of long study in the postmortem room* ...

To meet the problems of medicine of that day and the future he gave his most famous advice in "the Master-Word in Medicine":

> ... *it is open sesame to every portal, the great equalizer in the world, the true philosopher stone which transmutes all the base metal of humanity into gold ... and the Master-Word is work* ...

Chapter XVIII
Twentieth Century Prelude

... a standing menace to the other medical colleges of the province ...

Sir William Meredith

With the arrogance natural to the largest city and the intellectual centre of the province, Toronto tended to ignore what was happening in medical education in other centres. But in spite of this attitude, there were alternatives to going to the stormy capital, the stronghold of the Church of England and special interest groups. Certainly the Presbyterians, who founded Queen's University in 1841 to provide clergymen for the church, felt that from the beginning their school should have a medical department. With this in mind, Principal Hart Liddell consulted members of the medical profession in the United Kingdom, and after observing in 1852 that Trinity College had established its medical department under Bishop Strachan, decided to set up faculties of medicine and law as soon as possible.

Part of the new-found haste may have been prompted by a letter from Bovell of Trinity in 1854, asking if the Senate of Queen's would grant medical degrees for work done at Trinity. In this way, Bovell hoped to be able to qualify eight students of Trinity who were unwilling to subscribe to the Thirty-Nine Articles of the Church of England, but were not unhappy to live with their Presbyterian brethren. It was not Bovell's intention to have them take a medical course, but rather to be given credit for the work done at Trinity. However, Dr. John R. Dickson, a Kingston physician, had already met with the Hon. John A. Macdonald and a group of Kingston medical men, including Drs. J. Sampson, J. Stewart and Horatio Yates, with a purpose to found a medical school. The trustees of Queen's were cautious and pointed out that there were only four professors in the entire university; and here a group of doctors was proposing a new department which would contain at least six professors, albeit there were no funds for salaries.

It was noted by Dr. Sullivan, a Kingston physician, that the smallness of the city, the capability of its hospitals, and the number of qualified men who could teach were all unfavourable to the establishment of a medical school. In addition, and more to the point, there was no demand for the school, as Quebec, Montreal, and Toronto had well-equipped schools and would be able to handle all demands. However, faced with a request from the eight Trinity petitioners, and knowledgeable about the group of doctors who were willing to make up a faculty, the trustees, under the Rev. Dr. Machar, voted to recommend the installation of a medical faculty. This was a bold decision inasmuch as the entire student registration at Queen's was only 36 students, and the medical school began with 23 registrations, eight being the Trinity group.

The faculty of the new school was composed of men who had received their education mainly in Great Britain. James Sampson, surgeon, had qualified at Trinity College in Dublin, settling in Kingston after serving in the 1812 war. He was named president of the faculty, possibly because he had been three times the Mayor of Kingston. John Stewart, who taught anatomy and physiology, was described by H.P. Gundy as "obstinate, egocentric, quarrelsome and litigous: he was forever slandering or being slandered. He once fought a duel with a customs official . . .". In addition to his medical career, Stewart published a newspaper, *The Argus.*

Another faculty member was Horatio Yates, who had taken his degree at the University of Philadelphia and later trained in London. He was joined by John Lithfield who had sailed as a ship's surgeon to Australia, and it was rumoured that he had served a brief period in debtor's prison. He, like Stewart, was a newspaper writer and had practised journalism in France before becoming the medical superintendent in a lunatic asylum near Liverpool. Dr. Fife Fowler, the last member, had spent two years in Greenland before coming to Canada. Gundy remarked:

> . . . not the least remarkable thing about the establishment of a medical school at Queen's was the fact that six practitioners with such varied backgrounds, experience and ability could be found in a single provincial town in 1854.

The Board of Trustees showed a canny approach to financing, and all appointments were for one year as medical lecturers, not as full-fledged professors. All salaries were generated from student fees, and for other expenses there was a provision for a total of £250. A strict accounting of all funds was required from Dr. Stewart, who acted as secretary, and was asked repeatedly for statements, particularly after a government grant had been obtained in support of the school. Stewart felt that the money could be spent without going through the trustees. Although he felt no need to be responsible to the trustees for money affairs, when some quarrels developed within the faculty, he took the stand that he was not responsible to the members of the medical faculty either.

The second session, which began with a grant of $1,000 from the government, allowed the school to move to better quarters in "Summerhill", Archdeacon Stuart's house. Forty-seven students were registered and it was possible to buy much needed apparatus and equipment, but Sullivan, a student, reported he would be ashamed to name the common appliances which were lacking in the school.

The heterogeneous group which comprised the faculty managed to get along with each other only in fits and starts. By 1857 a severe quarrel erupted which resulted in Sampson's resignation but, after considerable persuasion by the Board of Trustees, he reconsidered and remained. The faculty-fighting in the medical area was matched by quarrels in the Faculty of Arts and the latter finally resulted in Sampson's resignation as President. He was succeeded by Dickson, which was not a happy event for Stewart who was smarting under a failure to receive an appointment as Surgeon to the penitentiary. In order to bring pressure to gain that appointment, he had revived *The Argus* and had attacked testimonials put forward by Dickson, the other contender for the post. These attacks reached the level of insults resulting in the Board of Trustees' suspension of Stewart. This brought forth a further stream of insults from Stewart in which he slandered Dr. Yates, who launched a libel suit, with the result that Stewart was sentenced to a term in the local jail. He was released when a petition signed by 2,000 citizens was circulated, to which the trustees of the University drew up a counter-petition to keep Stewart incarcerated. The latter did not receive sufficient public support.

The situation was finally resolved, much to the Board of Trustees' relief, when the entire faculty, except Fowler, refused to subscribe to the Westminster Confession of Faith and resigned. Following the resignations the members incorporated themselves as The Royal College of Physicians and Surgeons of Ontario and obtained a new charter with the aid of John A. Macdonald. This charter permitted the college to affiliate with any institution which would grant degrees and it forthwith affiliated with Queen's.

Queen's was having a difficult year. By the terms of Confederation, education had become a provincial matter and John Sandfield Macdonald, the first Premier of Ontario, announced that grants to denominational colleges would cease. A further blow was encountered when the Commercial Bank, in which a large portion of the Queen's endowment was invested, failed. In addition there was a marked decline of registrants in the college, and, combined with the withdrawal of the medical faculty, fewer than forty students were registered in 1875.

On this shaky base, it would not have been surprising to see the end of medical teaching at Queen's, but the College persisted. The small sums paid by students for instruction were never enough to ensure a regular building, and so the College moved about, first to the House of Industry and then to the Commercial Bank building. New strength was gained with the arrival of Dr. Donald McLean, a pupil of Sir James Syme (1799-1870) in 1868.

In that year Sullivan became Professor of Surgery, in which post he continued until 1904. He was an enthusiast for the use of Gray's *Textbook of Anatomy* arguing that the book was so clear that students did not need to go to an anatomical dissection. Part of this argument was on the basis that dissection was a lost art and, in order to prove his case, he sat as examiner in Toronto taking with him a prepared cadaver in a water-tight case. He recounted his experiences with the students:

> ... *most of them came for an oral, and oh, what consternation for medallist, honour men and others in proportion. Such a slaughter of innocents was never known. The leading papers had many letters complaining of my justice. How did the Kingston students pass? ... I often meet students who now tell me they were one of the victims but invariably say it was needed and it is upheld to this day thus proving the benefit it has been to the profession ...*

According to Sullivan, Kingston was the first school in the country to introduce practical examinations.

In 1877, Principal George Grant took over direction of Queen's and urged that the university should again include a medical faculty. After many years of trying to persuade them, The Royal College dissolved itself to become The Faculty of Medicine,

Queen's University, in 1882. Grant reorganized and revitalized Queen's University and his ability to lead others and to raise money for the school benefitted all the faculties, with medicine showing immediate improvement. Entrance requirements were brought up to the matriculation examination of Queen's College, and by 1882 there were 48 matriculant with 11 graduates, and the following year 105 matriculant with 11 graduates. The faculty was enlarged and in 1890 there were 12 professors, two lecturers and one demonstrator to which a full-time professor of pathology was added in 1895. New laboratory buildings were constructed in 1906 and the facilities at the Kingston General Hospital were enlarged in the early part of the 20th century with laboratory and clinical facilities.

This rather stormy history was not matched at the University of Western Ontario in London. Although there had been a summer school for medicine in Fingal in 1866, in which Dr. John Fulton gave instruction in every subject, daily, with up to 20 students, the school continued for only three summers. It was not until 1881 that there was any further opportunity for medical education in southwestern Ontario. At that time the Right Reverend Isaac Hellmuth, Bishop of the Diocese of Huron, announced the opening of Western University at London. This was a sectarian university under the guidance of the Church of England. In October 1881, the formation of a medical faculty was announced with Drs. Charles J. Moore, Richard Morris Bucke, Charles S. Moore, James Niven, John M. Fraser, Henry Arnott, Thomas J.W. Burgess, John Wishart, John A. Stephenson and William Waugh. Moore was appointed Dean. While the Faculty of Medicine was part of the university, it was independent in all matters, including finances, except granting degrees, and had no representation on the Senate of the university. Initially, it occupied a cottage on the university grounds, which was rapidly outgrown and space was taken in the Hellmuth Boys' College. Cadavers were stored in vats in the basement of the cottage and brought up to what had been the dining room and now served as the dissection room. One bedroom of the cottage was used for histology and pathology teaching, and there was a table with one available microscope. Other equipment included a skeleton owned by Dr. Waugh, and books, which were the property of faculty members.

Of the original ten faculty members, 8 had been born in Western Ontario and were educated in Toronto. All of the teachers were practising physicians and relied to a great extent on the income from their practices to support their teaching responsibilities.

During the first year, fifteen students attended the medical course and arrangements were made for clinical experience at Victoria Hospital by an agreement with City Council. The original site of the school was a good distance from the hospital, but in spite of this, W.J. Roche, a student, claimed that it was possible to make bedside examinations and have bedside clinics, which was simply not feasible save for the chosen few at Toronto.

The initial enthusiasm by the teachers at Western seemed to slacken, with the result that in the session of 1885 and 1886 one professor delivered only 13% of his lectures and others barely 30%. This led to a protest by the student body. After the walkout, a ruling was made that a professor who did not give 75% of his lectures must resign. Part of this lack of enthusiasm was due to teachers not receiving a regular salary but being credited $6.00 for each student in a class that year. Those same financial problems also plagued the university in general and it became necessary to consolidate all the Faculty of Arts into one building, and to sell vacated land in order to maintain the budget. This closed down the teaching facilities in the Boys' College, and all medical teaching returned to the one five-room cottage.

In the 1885-1886 session there were 53 matriculants with 7 graduates and the numbers rose over the next few years. The Royal College of Physicians and Surgeons in Edinburgh gave recognition to Western's degree in 1886, but the increasing enrollment meant a greater strain on the physical facilities. To remedy the situation, an application was granted by the Senate of the university to erect a suitable building, but no funds were made available. So, the faculty formed themselves into a syndicate to raise money on individual bonds to purchase and maintain a medical school building. This resulted in the erection of a new building, at the corner of Waterloo and York Streets, in which first lectures were given in October 1888, to 64 registered students. Some of those who registered came from east of Toronto. The medical school was owned and governed by the medical faculty which continued to serve without any compensation from the university, the only source of income being from student fees and two contributions of $500. each from two local benefactors, Adam Beck and Thomas Beattie. At the end of each year the books were balanced, and any surplus of funds was distributed to the teaching staff by the tally sheets which showed the number of lectures they had given. This precarious state of financial affairs continued and eventually the school became insolvent. It was put up for sale in 1890 and was purchased by a "friend" who then resold it to the Dean at a nominal price. What was bought was a single room, called the laboratory of pathology, bacteriology and histology, with equipment consisting of some microscopes and some labelled specimens. There was a "wretched chemical laboratory" and an ordinary dissection room with a few hundred books locked in cases to which the janitor carried the key. Most of the books were the gift of Dr. A.G. McCallum, who led a delegation to the government in 1902 asking for financial aid to the faculty. The request was not granted that year; but, five years later, at the urging of Adam Beck, M.L.A. (later Sir Adam, creator of the Hydro-Electric Power Commission of Ontario), the legislature passed a vote of $50,000 for the construction of a hygienic institute building.

The teaching arrangements in the wards of Victoria Hospital were initially satisfactory, but when medical teaching ceased during the summer months, it was necessary for non-university staff to care for indigent patients. This led to some friction, and physicians who were not connected with the school, demanded that there be a fair division of labour and that the staff for the indigent ward should alternate every three months. This meant that teaching on the wards would be limited to just three months. The friction grew with the school men being supported by G. Reid, and the town men by Adam Beck. The issue became more heated and led to a mass public meeting where Beck, an adroit politician and minister without portfolio, maneuvered the speaking timetable so that he was able to speak until midnight on Saturday without giving Dr. McCallum a chance to rebut, for the sabbath had come. The result of this discussion was that the three months' alternating service went into force, causing the school some difficulties. These were solved by the threat of the school men to make private arrangements to send their private patients to St. Joseph's Hospital. Beck's role in this incident was strange since he was a strong supporter of the school and was later instrumental in the financial arrangements which put the medical faculty on its financial feet.

Even though financial problems gave grim portents, lectures proceeded. The first Dean, C. J. Moore, lectured on the Principles and Practices of Surgery, and he was supported by J.M. Fraser, Professor of Medicine; and R. M. Bucke, Professor of Nervous and Mental Diseases. Mr. W. Saunders, an established druggist in the city of London and head of a manufacturing and distribution firm for drug products, taught Materia Medica and Pharmacy, and many of the drugs used in the teaching programme were samples from his factory. He was President of The Ontario College of Pharmacy and was a world-renowned entymologist, who made major contributions in the hybridization of apples and the development of Marquis wheat. Therapeutics and Toxicology were taught by J.A. Stevenson, and J. Bowman was Professor of Theoretical and Practical Chemistry. F.R. Eccles, who gave the surgical lectures and who had graduated from Toronto and had spent some time in England with Dr. Lawson Trait, was a Canadian authority on abdominal surgery.

The herculean attempts by the Western faculty to keep the medical school open with private funding was an echo of what had been tried and had failed at Victoria. Queen's too, had been unsuccessful. Trinity's private stock company had been dealt a mortal blow by the results of the inquiry into the use of government funding for the biological building. It was quite apparent private funds could not compete against public funds. But Trinity still had a few shots left in the locker. In March of 1900 an Act, Related to Medical College and Schools in Affiliation With The University of Toronto, Bill No. 136, was introduced into the House by Dr. Angus McKay. He was a graduate of Trinity who practised in Ingersoll and had been elected M.L.A. in 1883. The Bill proposed that there be a medical department consisting of all the teaching medical colleges or medical schools which were or might be affiliated with the University. It also proposed that the examiners for University be drawn from all the affiliated schools. The reaction to this by the University of Toronto physicians was loud and immediate. Dr. Alexander Primrose saw a Trinity hand in the Bill, which would lead to the abolition of the teaching faculty. What is more, he pointed out, this was a continuation of Dr. Geikie's objection to the methods of instruction to medical students in scientific medicine, which included teaching of biology. Dr. I.H. Cameron, Professor of Surgery, clearly saw this as a means to bolster the Trinity Medical School, and objected that it was the first incidence of American-style lobbying introduced into Canadian educational matters, where a joint stock company (Trinity) had planned for months and then mounted a campaign against the University by introducing the Bill. Part of the justification for the Bill, put forward by McKay and others in Trinity, was that Trinity students had been denied access to the University of Toronto examinations. This constituted a negation of the "vested rights" of the private medical colleges which had been ensured that fair competition would continue. Further the new Bill would finally sweep away the fear aroused by Sir William Meredith, Chancellor of the University, when he said:

... the creation of a Medical Faculty in the University would be regarded as a standing menace to the other medical colleges of the province ...

Drs. George Peters and A.B. McCallum, of the University, argued that the university examinations were quite open to all students who were affiliated, including Trinity, but not more than one percent of the Trinity men knew about this since the information had been concealed by Geikie. Part of the reason Trinitarians did not appear for the examinations was that they had little or no preparation in zoology or biology for those studies had, in effect, been "doled out [to] the very minimum of medical education."

Geikie, backed up by the graduates and undergraduates of Trinity, had an answer to that argument. "Biology", they stated, "was a subject on which there was not total agreement in the medical fields". In view of the heavy load imposed by the large subjects of medicine such as physiology and anatomy, to require study of another area was just too much. They countered, having culled *The British Medical Journal* for 1897, that there was a grave defect in the educational model that used elementary biology to teach the different forms of life in order to give the student a greater grasp of man. Trinity's argument was that students should be given a greater grasp of man and less about earth-worms or dogfishes which, though interesting, were quite dispensable. While biology was a grand study, so was astronomy, and on that basis might have as much bearing as the former upon medicine. In addition, Trinity stated that the full intent of the McKay Bill was to provide a larger and better medical department. To this the medical faculty replied in several pamphlets and broadsides that it would mean the end of the University of Toronto Medical Faculty if the Bill was passed. They also produced facts and figures to show that the medical faculty was not only paying for itself in the University of Toronto but was turning over a profit to the university, and the old claim that it occupied special status was denied. Many of the arguments took place on the pages of the Toronto papers claiming that the Bill would deprive the 1,800 graduates of the university of the right to elect members to the University Senate and thus disfranchise them from an active part in directing medical education in the province. The pressure mounted against Trinity particularly when it was realized that the Bill, purposely or not, effectively turned the direction of medical education over to Trinity and the Women's Medical College. Eventually the Bill was withdrawn from the Order Paper.

Looming behind all the argument surrounding the McKay Bill was a much larger concern — amalgamation. Various universities and colleges such as Victoria, St. Michael's and Knox had entered Federation with the University of Toronto. Now feelers were put forward to Trinity Medical College to amalgamate during the nineties and in 1900 a subcommittee appointed to investigate amalgamation with the medical college began to look at the broader question of amalgamation with Trinity University. In 1900 Provost Welch, of Trinity, resigned and was replaced by the Rev. T.C.S. Macklem, who undertook with his appointment to work towards Federation with the University of Toronto. In doing so, he included Dean Geikie in the discussions and requested from him a nomination of representatives who would confer with a Commission on Federation. In March of 1901 Geikie responded, with the full backing of the medical college, that he was heartily in favour of amalgamation provided it was on equal terms. The problem was that the Medical Faculty of the Toronto University had taken a strong stance, in that they would not permit any additions to the present teaching staff of the primary departments of the University of Toronto. The large number of cross-appointments in Arts and Medicine which were already present at the University of Toronto school precluded the addition of a large number of teachers if amalgamation was carried out with Trinity. Geikie noted that his equal-terms-provision had been well known to the university group for some time, yet within the past year eleven appointments had been made to the medical staff of the Toronto University by the Senate, further compounding the staff problem. In the same statement, Geikie recommended that the government should not endow chairs in anatomy, pathology, sanitary science, preventive medicine, jurisprudence and toxicology in the university school as this would be unfair to Trinity and other private schools.

The Calendar for Trinity Medical College 1901-1902 stated clearly that Federation proposals were not making any progress and that the corporation of the Trinity Medical College had finally and definitely decided against amalgamation. However, the medical college was once again threatened with financial problems. The University of Toronto had begun building a new modern medical building, complete with scientific laboratories, while Trinity still occupied a second-rate structure.

To overcome this problem it was suggested that the college should be reinstated as the Medical Faculty of Trinity with the hope that funds could be provided through Trinity University. A series of meetings with Geikie and Dr. C. Sheard acting as medical representatives led to a resolution that the Medical College would once again become part of Trinity University. At the same time a fund of $50,000 was offered towards the erection of a new building. These negotiations continued into April of 1903 when the Charter of the Medical College was surrendered to Trinity University to hold in trust. Final arrangements were completed and on the 9th of July the Medical Faculty of Trinity University was announced. On the same day the federation of Trinity and Toronto Universities was decreed. Thus the Medical Faculty of Trinity was amalgamated with the Medical Faculty of the University of Toronto.

This abrupt change of policy rested upon a number of factors. In a letter to Provost Macklem on October 30, 1900, Geikie had mentioned an "Honorary Deanship" if the amalgamation went through. This would have satisfied some of the requirements for equality. In addition, none of the students suffered from the amalgamation, and the erection of a new building, a considerable expense, was no longer necessary since facilities could be shared in the University of Toronto building.

Geikie had already made his case against amalgamation and when it was announced, there was little more to be said. His last hurrah, in June of 1903, had pointed out that it was difficult for him to understand how the corporation could proceed to amalgamation after all of the protestations which had been made over the past three years. He concluded his letter with:

> ... I could not be a party to take any share in sending the Faculty in which I have so long been a member over the Niagara Falls of Amalgamation ...

All members of the Trinity Medical Faculty received new appointments in the University of Toronto — except Geikie.

Chapter XIX
An Emerging Order

It was his own affair if a man chose to forsake recognized
medical practitioners...

The World 1890

The Medical Act of Upper Canada, 1865, set, for the first time,
the standards of education required to be a doctor. Prior to this, the
Upper Canada Medical Board had been the sole arbiter and as the
composition of the Board varied, so did the standards. W.T. Aikins
had tried for many years to create a single portal of entry into the
profession as he was fully aware of the differences and discrepancies
of courses and examinations in each of the schools, and he shared
with some of his colleagues the overwhelming conviction that there
was a right way and a wrong way to do medicine. The poorly-trained
regular physician, the quack or the irregulars who practised in
Ontario were the living denial of all for which the profession stood
— if they were allowed to care for the sick, the physician's right to
status, justification and reward was questionable.

But first it was necessary to clean the medical Augean stable.
The 1865 Act appointed a Registrar, whose duty it was to licence
those who qualified by satisfactory completion of a course at
medical school. But this power did not fully control the content of
the curriculum of the school, although the General Council could,
if dissatisfied, make recommendations for change. This was rectified
by amendments in 1869 with the appointment of a College of
Physicians and Surgeons in which was vested the authority to hold
examinations for licensure, which was the exclusive doorway into
medical practice. The College also set matriculation examinations
— a qualification at the secondary school level before entering a
course in medical instruction, which applied only to medical school
candidates and was the first uniform matriculation examination in
the province.

The final examination required a pass mark in medical
diagnosis, pathology, surgical anatomy, practical chemistry,
sanitary science, operative midwifery, operative surgery and

surgical anatomy, materia medica and therapeutics, the theory and practice of medicine and medical jurisprudence. To prepare for these examinations, for the first time in the province, certain textbooks were recommended by the College, including *Gray's System of Anatomy*, which became a standard textbook for many years. The other textbooks changed gradually. For surgery, *The Science and Art of Surgery* (1853) by Sir John W. Erichsen, who had Lister as his house surgeon, remained a required text until the twentieth century, and to it was added *A System of Surgery* (1859) by Samuel D. Gross (1805-1884), who was professor at Jefferson Medical College; and *The Surgeon's Vade Mecum* (1870) by Robert Druitt (1814-1883). Carl Rokitansky (1804-1878) whose text on *Pathological Anatomy* was translated into English in 1849, was the accepted textbook author in pathology during the 70's but was dropped in the 80's. This textbook was replaced by C.H. Jones' (1818-1890) *Manual of Pathological Anatomy* (1875).

Sir Michael Foster's (1836-1907) *Textbook of Physiology*, published in 1877, was recommended in 1880 to students in addition to S.P. Yeo's (1845-1900) *Manual of Physiology* (1884), written in Philadelphia. *Principals in Practice of Medicine*, published in 1866 by Austin Flint (1812-1886), was the main text until displaced by Osler's *Textbook of Medicine* in 1894. Fleetwood Churchill's (1808-1878) *Theory and Practice of Midwifery*, which first appeared in 1843 with several new additions, was the standard text and was accompanied by several publications of Eustace Smith (1853-1914) on diseases of infants and children.

Although the College was the examining board for the three different sections, allopathic, homeopathic and eclectic, there was not as much change in textbooks in the homeopathic section as in the allopathic department. Hahnemann and Hering were the two main texts which remained until the twentieth century, although the homeopaths shared Jacob DeCosta (1883-1890), Flint and Gross at later dates. In general, all references and textbooks were drawn equally from U.K. and American authors.

In 1880 the College increased the length of medical courses from three to four years, which led to more lecturing but, it was noted in 1890, not to an increase in practical experience. A change in time-tabling adjusted this imbalance. By 1895, the entry qualification to medicine was raised to the provincial junior matriculation level and Greek was no longer required.

There was also a parallel gradual up-grading of examinations. In 1856 the third-year examination in Practical Chemistry asked about the usual impurities of sulfuric acid and the wet-test for mercury. This general type of question continued, and by 1860 the fourth-year examination in Physiology asked the candidate to "explain the general plan of the circulation and state the causes which assist the heart in its production". In addition, it asked the cause of animal heat and how it was affected by disease. The 1865 paper on Surgery asked to name the distinguishing characteristics between caries and necrosis, stating the causes and treatment of each. The 1873 Surgery paper asked for the clinical history and treatment of cases of psoas abscess. But this general type of question was gradually phased out to be replaced by more searching, specific questions, with the entry of the College into the examining field.

The 1880 candidate in medicine was required to know the symptoms of acute rheumatism, its complications and treatment, and another question asked about the symptoms of scarlet fever. The medical pathology paper had a question which asked for the causes of hyperemia in the arterial and venous vessels. Operative surgery asked, "How would you pass a catheter in the male? Where may hitches occur, and how are they to be overcome?" Train wrecks and resultant trauma led to many questions on the surgical examinations well into the 90's, usually dealing with amputation and its care. The first question on the treatment of a fracture was asked in 1890. In 1889 exopthalmic goiter and its treatment, the pathology of infantile paralysis, and the interpretation of sphygomagraphic tracings tested clinical and the newly developed laboratory skills were queried in medicine.

By 1900 part of the examination of physiology (which was combined with histology) asked for an account of the mechanism employed in the accommodation of the eye for near vision; another question asked the effects produced by a destructive lesion of the upper fourth of the Rolandic area. The chemistry paper asked the methods of preparation and properties of aldehydes. The medicine paper questioned on (a) malignant endocarditis (b) paroxysmal tachycardia (c) pathological bradycardia and treatment of palpitation of the heart. Surgery, in 1894, asked for the diagnosis and treatment of the most common dislocations of shoulders, elbow and hip. By 1900 it was asking for a description of the operation for cholecystostomy, which had been described by M. Sims in 1878.

The examinations, in general, were on par or above those given in Montreal, London, Philadelphia or Boston. They were a trial to the applicants, and it was reported at the College annual meeting in 1876 that there was some "misbehaviour" on the part of the candidates, which led in 1879 to notification that:

> *any pupil at any exam detected using any notes, giving or receiving any assistance, under the influence of liquor, using insolent language to examiners ... shall lose his examination and have not less than one year added to the length of his curriculum ...*

It is apparent that a medical course did not automatically turn out scholars and gentlemen, all of which showed the urgent need of a disciplinary force. Early attempts to charge doctors with unprofessional actions were not successful. Dr. R. Hornby, in 1839, shrugged off a charge on the basis that the College could not enforce its by-laws. In 1842, the Board was informed it could not pursue a prosecution of a practitioner, even though he had presented bogus diplomas. *The Streetsville Review*, in 1854, reported of a new doctor:

> *... since his arrival the demands for coffins has enhanced 50 percent and every sexton has compassed a new suit of sables. These functionaries have presented the excellent medical with a snuff-box, fabricated out of a skull, bearing the following gracefully apposite motto — kill and let live*

Even after the 1865 Act, which set up the Register, there were difficulties. Dr. Clement of Bradford refused to pay his one dollar fee to be registered. He was convicted of practising medicine without being registered and fined .25¢, which he refused to pay. Two months later, he was served with a warrant of committal, but it was withdrawn and he continued to practise, although unregistered. Such was not the case with another doctor. When the College brought a charge against him of practising medicine without a licence, the local judge refused to consider a prosecution or issue a warrant.

In order to make its position firmer the College, in 1877, circulated to all of its members a copy of the Penal Clauses accompanying the Act, which outlined that on the laying of information by a doctor, or for that matter any respectable person, a charge could be made of a breach of the Ontario Medical Act:

> *... go to the nearest or most intelligent Magistrate ... so that a summons could be issued.*

However, this was not satisfactory as Magistrates did not seem to follow up complaints in many cases, and in most instances they did not have constables who were available to go out and collect evidence. The College then appointed an official prosecutor, whose duty was to collect evidence and present it to the appropriate authorities. He received $15.00 for each conviction obtained against unregistered practitioners, or the amount of the fine levied minus the court cost. The prosecutor could be alerted to infractions by the deposition of four medical practitioners, and following the initial investigation, he was to report back to the College which decided whether to proceed with laying a charge.

In the 1889 report Dr. John McEown and Dr. James Cook Bright were named by four practitioners and an investigation was launched. The following year it was reported that John McEown could not be found, and therefore, could not be served with his summons. Bright had been found guilty in a court of providing a drug with intent to procure a miscarriage, and was erased from the Register, which meant he could no longer practise, legally. In that year Dr. B.H. Lemon and Dr. Nelson Washington were investigated. Washington was charged with advertising extensively in the papers in Ottawa and Kingston, and that he had made unreasonable claims for curative powers. He had given a receipt to a patient in Kingston, stating "this is to certify that Thomas Cochrane of Kingston is to be treated until cured of Catarrhal Bronchitis, for the sum of $25.00". He repeated this action, in exchange for cash paid, on many occasions throughout the province. He also advertised his activities by hand bills, which were distributed on public streets.

The doctor was notified by the College that receiving fees on the promise of a cure was considered unethical and furthermore his advertisements were unprofessional. He promised to stop. But the ads continued and Washington was called before the Discipline Committee of the College in June 1892. His lawyer pointed out that the main problem was in advertising and that if Washington was gagged, the demands of the profession would be fully satisfied. Although Washington had entered into an agreement with the College the previous year that he would cease advertising, he had continued because the College had allowed other specialists "without demur or bringing them up, to go on advertising". After a good deal of discussion, the Committee resolved that Washington's name should be erased. His lawyer objected that the proceedings were ultra vires of the College, and that he planned to appeal the decision to the courts. He found some sympathy, for his major thrust was that the College was concerned chiefly with professional misconduct in treating a patient, not in whether he advertised or not.

224

The decision of the College was appealed to the courts and the case was tried at Osgoode in June of 1893. The action of the Council was sustained, and Washington then registered a higher appeal, which was dismissed in October of that year. Meanwhile, he continued to practise. The College prosecutor, Detective Thomas Wasson, tried to catch up with Washington to give a cease-and-desist order in Kingston and Cornwall, with a great deal of difficulty. Finally Washington was apprehended, brought before a Magistrate and fined $50.00. His excuse was that all of his advertisements had been withdrawn and he was simply treating his old patients.

Actually Washington must have been a popular physician — so popular that Dr. William E. Bessey was charged in 1898 with impersonating Washington and carrying on in the same manner. The prosecutor alleged that Bessey had represented himself as Washington, had put up one of Washington's cards in a hotel in Kingston and had made improper and fraudulent bargains for the cure of "numerous patients". Bessey maintained in his defence that it was entirely a coincidence, and that he was not very good at treating catarrhal conditions in any case. He explained that before he got his medical degree he was totally blind with cataracts and had never expected to see again. The question was "how to make a living". As he had no capital, and was unable to invest in a practice, he had circulars made with his name advertising his presence. However, the circulars were unsatisfactory, one called him a "great Canadian specialist", so he had them burned and kept one as a sample. This had come into the hands of the College detective.

The Discipline Committee voted to erase Dr. Bessey from the Register.

Electricity was the downfall of Dr. Benjamin Heaton Lemon of Thorold. He graduated from Victoria in 1867, and 22 years later he was asked to appear before the College of Physicians and Surgeons on charges of unprofessional conduct. This charge was consequent to an advertisement which publicized his "esoteric Hypno-Magnetic Force". This force was supposed to be sufficient to treat patients from a distance, in some cases many miles, and it enabled him to claim remarkable cures. He himself admitted, in the advertisement, it was a "Strange and Mysterious Beneficient Healing Influence ...". The College agreed that it was strange, but Dr. I.H. Cameron, who testified at the hearing, pointed out there was "no such thing as Esoterism in medicine, and treatment of the absent was humbug". However, Miss Haslett, a patient, testified that she had been cured of neuralgia of the spine and stomach through Dr. Lemon's "laying on of hands". Lemon was erased from the College Register, and the newspapers headlined the story as a "Lemon Squeezed".

The Committee spent many hours investigating the dozens of claims, which were made of improper, infamous or disgraceful conduct in a professional respect. Many of them dealt with improper advertising, where large multi-coloured posters were circulated announcing the "most celebrated European and American physicians, surgeons and specialists", which would be "here today. Consultation free . . .". One of these was circulated by Dr. John Robert McCullough in Strathroy, London, Bradford, Ingersoll and other small towns. He usually received $15.00 on condition that he would guarantee cure of a female (suffering from a disease which could not be cured). On being charged by the College, McCullough responded with a letter of apology, confessing that he had been wrong, and was sorry for it. He pointed out in his letter:

> I am an ageing man and out of the past years of my life, I have served the public to the best of my ability as physician and surgeon, accoucher and specialist, having received my licences as such from Lord Elgin, Earl of Elgin and Kincardine, then Governor of Upper and Lower Canada, in 1851. And now in old age and declining years, I have a wife and helpless family who have no other way of support or living to keep them alive, but what I can make now in my declining years by my profession, and so, Mr. Chairman and gentlemen of this honourable body, I beg leave to submit myself to your mercy in this case, and I undertake and agree not to offend in the future . . .

He followed this letter with a heartrending, personal address to the Discipline Committee. Council opinion was summed up by Dr. C.T. Campbell, who admitted he was disposed as much as anybody to take into consideration the age and circumstances of the offender, but on the other hand, it was necessary to consider the character of the offence which had been committed. McCullough had consistently made false claims, such as having been a surgeon in one of the branches of the United States Army, and being a European-trained physician. None of these were true. In the past leniency had been shown to some offenders, in that they had not been erased, but had been suspended. However, that policy had not been effective, and the Committee decided that J.R. McCullough was to be erased from the Register.

A policy of leniency had prevailed for some years, but reached its demise with Dr. Samuel Edward McCully.

The newspaper reader was a target for many medical sharpshooters, as can be seen in the March 26, 1892 issue of the *Toronto World*, where a letter was addressed to Dr. McCully. The letter came from a grateful mother, whose child had recovered from catarrhal bronchitis. Dr. McCully was not self-effacing. He followed this information, in the same column, with a report of a cure of a woman with a uterine tumor, diagnosed by a professor at Trinity Medical College. A confrere was called in to confirm the diagnosis, and:

> *the lady was thereupon sent to the Old Mill for vivisection. The faiths were agin these two long haired gentlemen, B and T, and one delay followed another until one night the house surgeon assistant was called, and the uterine tumor manifested itself in the good old way. For the benefit of these gynecologists and teachers of medicine we are pre-warning to others not to take too much stock in the men who called Dr. McCully, Quack, and failed to make good the assertion.*

He went on to say, "the doctors, as a body, are now on the level of street hucksters, they can only peddle with a yearly licence in their pockets. We can only practise medicine after dropping $2.00 into the Inquisition Slot".

The individual ability of the doctor did not count, according to McCully: "Come down with your $2.00 a year, you medical huckster, and your head is in the basket and the whole town may die from want of your skill. In such a case who does the killing? Was this law made pro bono publico?"

Dr. McCully claimed that he now treated abdominal tumors by sterilization, which saved an operation. He also went on to list his cure of diseases of the skin, pimples, piles, and ended up saying, "young man, why go to druggist, quacks and irresponsible Medical Companies?"

He had an office at the corner of Yonge and Gerard Street, Toronto, gave free consultations, and flooded the newspapers with letters:

> *The Medical Council has for years been engaged in the delectable task of dog eat dog. They were called into existence to protect you from these Rampant Soul-less*

Vampires: they live now but to degrade the profession and harrass and tax honest men to create an irresponsible monopoly.

In addition to "infamous advertisements in Toronto newspapers", he advertised in detail the names of his patients, the particulars of their disease and statements regarding alleged cures for treatment. He claimed that he was better qualified for the practice of the medical profession than other registered practitioners and that he cured patients when others failed to do so. He made patients believe they were curable, whether the ailments they were suffering from were curable or not. In the city of London, he guaranteed to cure a female patient, and took her into his home in order to give treatment. She died in his house, and he refused to give up her body to her husband, until his bill had been paid. In Whitby he promised to cure a patient of paralysis on receiving payment of a fee. The Board found him guilty of unprofessional conduct, but Dr. McCully appeared before them and pleaded his case. He signed an undertaking to cease advertising and pointed out:

> *I am a man raising a family in Toronto, and I have practised medicine to earn bread and butter, and keep my children comfortable. Under these circumstances it would be a little bit hard on me to take my name off the roll, but of course, I must leave the matter to you ...*

The Board relented and suspended McCully. However, he violated his promise and the advertisements reappeared. The College prosecutor was unable to locate him to serve an order, because he was in Milwaukee. In that city he published large advertisements, with his portrait, pointing out that he was a Canadian physician, but was "none of your doctors that were ever exflunkeyfied by medical councils ...". His advertisements asked, "Young men have you sapped your vitality by vicious habits ... old men, have you burned the wick of life at both ends — has your sexual life gone? We bring it back, we guarantee our work". The College finally removed his name from the Register.

Frequently prosecutions by the College were countered by the defendant asking for more time so that he could get some money together and go to the States. This was reasonable, as the doctor still had his diploma — even though he did not have a licence to practise in Ontario — and the Statue of Liberty still stated she would accept the "homeless and tempest-tossed".

The public read of these matters either in the news columns or advertisements. However, the quack problem continued. A good deal of it was laid at the door of advertising. Dr. J.N. Grant of Ottawa wrote in *The Canadian Practitioner* of 1883, that the solution was to tax every quack advertisement as to make advertising impractical. Dr. Geikie proposed that quacks should be taxed in the same way as peddlers or circuses. On the other hand, Dr. Lavell of Kingston felt there should be free trade in medicine, holding it to be the "inalienable right of every British subject to be fooled to the top of his bent when so inclined." But Dr. James McCammon of Addington strongly recommended that the Medical Act was the most effective way to stop quackery. Those who were not registered physicians should have their name erased from the Register for any conduct "infamous in a professional respect".

The disciplinary power of the College of Physicians and Surgeons specifically to erase the practitioner's name from the Medical Register due to "infamous or disgraceful conduct" was established in 1887, but the actions which constituted infamous or disgraceful conduct were prone to change over time. During the 1890's the annual report showed fifty to sixty prosecutions annually. The Council spent many hours agonizing over the decision to say a doctor should practise no longer. With McCully the final judgment was clear, but on the route to that pronouncement there were many misgivings. Dr. D. Bergin, in 1894, stated:

> *The name of Dr. McCully for years past has been really a stench in the nostrils of the profession ... Now I see that man in the decline of his life ... I think we can do no better than treat him with some sort of merciful consideration ...*

Merciful consideration was employed with Albert William Sovereen, a graduate of Victoria, who initially practised in Delhi, but later acted as a medical representative of the Kamama Hindoo Remedies. In a letter to the College, written from Rat Portage (now Kenora) c/o Mikado Mines, he apologized that he did not have enough money ($65.00) to appear before the Discipline Committee as he had only two mines to attend which meant, at the rate of fifty cents per month for each of 60 miners, his take-home pay was barely $30.00. The Committee considered many letters, including a testimonial to his honesty from the people of Delhi, in examining whether he should be erased, and deliberated:

> *... let it be clearly understood, first, that it is not a duty sought by the profession: secondly, that the benefit of this work is not for the profession, but largely and almost entirely for the public.*

This was written into the record before the vote to erase his name was carried.

Whether it was a case against the Kickapoo Indians (case dismissed in Stevensville, but upheld in Tilbury) or a conviction against Carmina Sarlo for practising witchcraft in Toronto, the prosecutor worked hard. His pay was a combination of keeping the fines, less cost of prosecution, plus part-time janitorial work at the College building. His net income suffered frequently when after considerable time and expense to secure a conviction, the accused skipped the country. Further losses were incurred with prosecution of "five year men", who had graduated from a medical school and started practice although not properly registered, because the Discipline Committee usually took a lenient view and declined prosecution.

Some of the lenience was held by the newspapers in considering prosecutions. *The World* in 1890 editorialized:

> *The action of the grand jury in throwing out the charge of manslaughter against Mrs. Stewart, who is called a Christian Scientist, will be generally approved. Quacks and fanatics are supported in their imposition and delusions by the credulity of a section of the public. As a rule they work no direct injury to the body politic, and if occasionally someone comes to grief in their hands, it is no more then we might expect. The deceased, John Kent, placed himself under the woman's care and died. There was nothing to show that the same result might not have been ensued had Kent never heard of Mrs. Stewart. It was his own affair if a man chooses to forsake recognized medical practitioners and put himself under the care of this Christian Scientist. The judge in concurring in the acquittal of the woman, fairly interpreted the law.*

In part, this editorial reflected current legal opinion, which explains the difficulty in obtaining convictions and the consequent perseverance by the College. To the College, medicine was enshrined in the cathedrals of the medical schools as prescribed by the College. To the legal opinion, wrote R. Vashon Rogers, Jr., a barrister at Osgoode Hall in 1884:

> *The common law knows nothing of systems or schools of medicine. In its eyes, eclectic, botanic, physio-medical, electrical, Thomsonian, homeopath, reformed, Indian doctor, cancer doctor, Indian opathist, clairvoyant doctor and regular physician are alike.*

Chapter XX
The Blooding of Medicine

... the profession does not forbid differences of opinion. Indeed such differences may be the only safe pathway to truth...

Varied Operations, Dr. H.A. Bruce

While Ontario drew most of its physicians and surgeons from the ranks of the regimental medical officers in the early 1800's, there was no need to develop a military medical service until the end of the century. Dr. Widmer, who had had extensive experience in the Peninsula War, found that his military experience fitted him well for a civilian life as did Dr. William Dunlop of Galt. Dunlop had arrived in Canada in time to be Medical Officer for the assault on Fort Erie, in 1812, when the British forces were ordered to remove the flints from their muskets to prevent an alarm being given by a premature shot. The result was that the British lost 905 men and the Americans 17. "Tiger", his sobriquet from a campaign in India, was a six-foot-three giant of a man with bear paws for hands who had little trouble carrying wounded like potato sacks on his back to an improvised dressing station. Following his military duties he acted as right-hand man to John Galt in the Canada Company and aided in the settlement of Southwestern Ontario. He was never at a loss for words or action and when the City of Guelph was founded, he broke the funereal pause of the dignitaries by toasting the new city from a flask of whiskey. The flask was one of the notorious Twelve Apostles, jugs of hard liquor, that he kept mounted on a dumb waiter in his home. They served as useful companions while he wrote his famous will, which included a legacy of a silver cup to a person as a "token of my gratitude for the service he had done the family in taking my sister, no man of taste would have taken". In fact, Dunlop did very little medical practice as a civilian.

Although Canada sent a regiment to the Indian mutiny in 1858, no doctors were required in this organized expedition to a foreign country. But the many Canadians who fought in the American Civil War (53,532) did not go as organized units. Many medical men volunteered their services. Their political ideals sometimes got in the way of their surgical knives. Dr. Ross served as a spy for the north; Canniff doctored with the Army of Potomac; Alfred S. Oliver was at Fredericksburg; and Dr. Francis Moses Wafer was constantly in action with Hancock's Division of the Northern armies. After putting himself through Queen's Medical School as a Surveyor's Assistant, Wafer signed up in the Union forces. Originally there was wide sympathy in Canada for the anti-slavery forces but as the battle over states rights became the issue, idealism yielded to self-interest and sympathy turned in favour of the confederacy. Wafer, while on leave in Kingston, was the target of an editorial in *The British Whig* which deplored "the barbarities on the part of the north which have characterised the present war ... no Canadian can support the cause of the north consistently with his duties as a British subject ...". Wafer returned to the fighting and records in his diary show that at Gettysburg, in the course of an hour, he was surrounded by a quarter of an acre of wounded.

Ironically, sympathy with the American forces in the Civil War was followed closely by resistance to the invading Americans during the Fenian raids. The Volunteer Force of Canadian Militia was called up for an important battle at Ridgeway in 1866 and The University of Toronto Battalion, including students from the medical school, were soon in action. One, William Tempest, recorded his experiences in attending the Toronto School of Medicine. In a letter to his father in Oshawa, he wrote of the difficulties getting to clinics at the General Hospital on Gerrard Street and of the Dean warning him that he must wear his cap and gown or be fined. Tempest wore his uniform to Ridgeway and was one of the three casualties in the fighting. His corpse was found by Drs. Thorburn of Queen's University and by his father, William Tempest. Another physician, Captain R.S. King, was wounded in the fighting and sustained an amputation of his leg.

The troops that were sent to deal with Louis Riel in the Northwest Rebellion were largely Canadians with the exception of the British commanders. Regimental surgeons provided the only medical services available at that date. A Royal Commission on the Health of the Army had been established in 1857 to investigate and recommend changes in the British medical services. This led to the founding of an army medical school in 1860, which amalgamated in 1883 with the Army Hospital Corps, comprised of assistants and stretcher bearers, to form the Medical Staff Corps. But similar action had not taken place in Canada.

This caused considerable discontent among army and medical men, for the medical service was "without a head to direct. They have withered to occupy the position of an ornamental appendage", charged a "Volunteer Surgeon of Many Years" in a letter to the editor of the *Montreal Gazette* in March of 1885. He went on to state that instruments in medical stores were never sufficient for even a ten-day camping trail. These charges may have led the minister of militia to appoint Dr. Darby Bergin of Cornwall to organize a medical service for the campaign and bestow on him the rank of Surgeon General.

There were many problems associated with the birth pangs of the service and the Honourable Adolph Caron, Minister of Militia, was called upon to decide the amount of pay which should be offered to Surgeons, Dressers and Ward Orderlies, and to obtain provisions, blankets, hospital beds and settle many other details. Surgeon Major Campbell Douglas, V.C., who had been born in Quebec in 1841, had initial responsibility for Bergin's appointment. He became exasperated with the amount of money and the little time available to organize a medical department and sarcastically suggested to the Honourable Caron that Canada should apply to the U.S. Medical Department for help, on the ground of common humanity. Further exasperation was shown by Dr. G.T. Orton, of Fergus, who was so incensed over the appointment of an "incompetent" medical superior that he wired Caron "I hold you responsible for deaths occurring by neglect . . .". Orton, later, devised horse-drawn ambulances to transfer casualties over a 68-km stretch.

On May 14, 1885 after the engagement at Batoche, surgeon James Bell and three other surgeons "carried on" under fire when their hospital tent was pierced many times by bullets. Two weeks later Dr. William Canniff arrived with a detachment of seven nurses from Toronto.

But to many of the volunteer physicians such as John Cavan of Toronto, most of the campaign was spent in taking care of medical stores, pulling teeth, "best sport we have", or taking care of horses' tongues, as the result of damage caused by furious riding.

Following the medical activities in the Northwest Rebellion, the medical service which had been organized under Dr. Bergin disappeared.

This caused discontent in a certain Dr. George Sterling Ryerson, who was the nephew of Egerton Ryerson, and whose father had been married at one time to John Rolph's sister. Dr. Ryerson had been appointed Professor of Ear, Eye and Throat Disease at Trinity in 1883, and subsequently he served in the Riel Rebellion. Later he became a co-founder of the Canadian Red Cross and the St. John Ambulance Association. Following his return from the North-West and the dissolution of the medical service, he organized the Association of Medical Officers of the Canadian Militia. One of its purposes was to discuss matters relating to the Medical Department of the Militia and another to discuss military matters from a medical point of view. An enthusiastic group of doctors held the first meeting and listened to papers which advocated reform in the Militia Medical Service and to accounts of experiences on active service. A short time later notice was received from the General Office commanding Canadian Militia that the discussion was subversive to discipline and that "the medical officer's duty was to obey, and not to protest." Although Ryerson wanted to take the matter to the public, others refused and the Association went into limbo.

When Dr. Frederick Borden became Minister of Militia in 1896, he appointed Colonel J.L.H. Neilson as Director General of Medical Services. The latter had served as Medical Officer with the Canadian Voyageurs, 378 men who had been raised for the Imperial Forces to assist in the relief of General Gordon in Khartoum. This Soudan Campaign used Canadians who were not recruited as soldiers and did not wear uniforms, yet were a military contingent with a Canadian medical officer. Neilson used the Royal Army Medical Services as a model for the establishment of the Canadian Army Medical Corps which was organized by Order-in-Council in 1899. Although the Corps organization was not in time to send any formal units to the Boer War in South Africa, there were some regimental medical officers organized under Dr. G. Carleton Jones in that conflict.

All of these moves were made in collaboration with the Imperial Forces which remained resident in Canada until 1906. But in 1904 Sir Frederick Borden omitted the King's Regulations for the British Army in establishing that "we should rely in future upon the regulations made in Canada for the administration of the militia of Canada".

Two years later Dr. Jones was promoted to Director of Medical Services and prepared a plan for the mobilization of an Army Medical Corps under the direction of Borden. When Borden was succeeded by Colonel (later Lieutenant General Sir Sam) Hughes in 1911, the plan was relegated to a top shelf, and so, when World War I broke out, Hughes presided over what has been described as "spontaneous mobilization". Colonel George Naismith of Toronto was put in charge of one of the first units and he and Dr. J.T. Fotheringham of the same city, who had organized a Medical Reserve Corps some years prior to the war, were soon in France.

By August 21, Colonel Jones, feeling the Royal Army Medical Corps should be relieved of the responsibility of the care of Canadian casualties, urged the formation of two stationary hospitals, two general hospitals and a casualty clearing station. Number Two General Hospital was formed under the command of Dr. J.W. Bridges and drew on Toronto and the rest of Ontario for staff. Number one Casualty Clearing Station, under Lieutenant Colonel F.S.L. Ford, was recruited in Toronto and dispatched to Taplow in England and eventually to Wimereux in France. Early problems at the hospitals consisted mainly of combatting mud and the disorganization on the Salisbury Plain. However, when the Number Two Stationary Hospital, under Lieutenant Colonel A.T. Shillington, reached France in November of 1914, they had, amongst the gun-shot wounds resulting from enemy action, major casualties with "trench foot", from prolonged exposure in water and mud. A simple treatment was designed consisting of rubbing the feet and legs with whale oil and providing roomy boots.

One of the volunteers in the Reserve was H.A. Bruce of Toronto, who had founded The Wellesley Hospital. He travelled to England at his own expense to offer his services as surgeon to the Director of Medical Services. But the D.M.S. was in France, so Bruce arranged a posting to France. On meeting Jones, he was informed there was no need for a surgeon. Bruce, miffed, declared he would return to Canada where there was need for surgeons but he was instructed to remain in France until order papers came through. However, regardless of this instruction, Bruce, wearing his Lieutenant Colonel's uniform of the Medical Reserve Corps, wangled his way back across the channel and back to Canada before Surgeon General Jones was aware of his absence. Bruce brought with him some x-ray plates showing interesting fractures with the intention of using them as teaching material in Toronto. Jones charged that he had stolen Government property, which, according to Bruce, caused Sir Sam Hughes to be highly amused when he heard of the charge. Sir Sam was in need of some amusement just then as he was under heavy fire for the conduct of the Medical Services. After the second battle of Ypres, in April 1915, rumours were heard that suggested Canadian casualties were not receiving the best of care.

The original plan had been to care for Canadian casualties in Canadian medical establishments. But with the landing of British and Anzac troops in Gallipoli in April of 1915, a tremendous increase in allied casualties led to a request from the British for assistance. Major-General Jones decided to withdraw Number One Stationary Hospital from France and dispatch Number Three Stationary Hospital, recruited mainly in London, and Number Five, recruited at Queen's, to the Gallipoli area. The London unit set up on the island of Lemnos and the Queen's unit, which was converted to Number Seven General Hospital, went to Cairo. Here, in addition to the military casualties, they had to treat malaria and dysentery in the summertime and trench-foot and pneumonia in the colder weather. In October 1915, the Number Four General Hospital, University of Toronto, was set up in Salonika with Major J.J. Mackenzie, Professor of Pathology, as a member of the staff, and Private Lester B. Pearson, as one of the medical orderlies.

These moves meant that Canadian casualties from the western front were not being seen by Canadian doctors, which caused much rumbling on the home front. The result of this criticism was the appointment by Sir Sam Hughes on July 31, 1916 of Dr. Bruce to act as Special Inspector General, "... to make an inspection of all the Canadian hospitals and Medical Institutions to which the Canadian Government in any way contributes and to report on your observations with any recommendations deemed advisable ...".

Sir Andrew MacPhail, who wrote an official medical history of the Canadian Forces remarked, "... it would be interesting to inquire into the mental process by which the Minister arrived at the conclusion that he selected the proper person for so exacting a task ..."; however, Bruce was appointed and with him five other officers whom he chose to assist in the inspection, including Dr. F.W.A. Wilson of Niagara Falls, Dr. Wallace Scott, Surgeon, University of Toronto and Dr. Walter McKeown, Chief Surgeon, St. Michael's Hospital. Within seven weeks the Inspector General had visited numerous medical installations in Great Britain and brought down a report on September 20th. The report was a wide-reaching document which looked at all aspects of care provided to Canadian soldiers in Britain. It pointed out that too many soldiers were arriving in England from Canada medically unfit, and it documented some cases who were suffering from tuberculosis or other diseases. Several special "unfit" cases were cited including one of a soldier sixteen years of age, who weighed 80 lbs., and had suffered from infantile paralysis with under-developed and weak muscles in the right hip and thigh. In addition, the report charged that the system of distribution of casualties on the front to the Imperial hospitals was highly unsatisfactory and stressed that Canadian soldiers should be cared for in Canadian hospitals. Part of the objection was that the receiving hospitals were scattered over so wide an area that it was impossible for proper medical inspections to be carried out by the Canadian Medical Services. This resulted in unnecessary detention in hospitals, and, frequently, failure to send back to Canada those who were to be invalided from the service. These, and many other findings, led Bruce to charge the D.M.S. with failure to provide sound and economical management. In addition to the economy, Bruce was concerned about inefficient, expensive and unsatisfactory use of Voluntary Aid Hospitals in Britain. These were hospitals which were operated by civilian practitioners and a large number of volunteer nurses, who, while very welcome and hard working in their dedication, did not provide the high level of medical care to which Bruce felt the Canadian soldier was entitled. In particular Bruce felt that the administration of 57 Voluntary Aid Hospitals under the Shorncliffe Military Hospital in Southern England was unsatisfactory and expensive.

The report was highly critical of the system of handling patients with venereal and other infectious diseases and of the treatment of rheumatics. It also charged that failure to maintain proper medical records would inevitably lead to an inability on the part of the Pension Board to properly evaluate fair pensions, which would cost the Canadian taxpayer heavily in the future.

The appointment of Bruce as Inspector General, over the heads of many others in the service, and without consultation with Surgeon General Jones, caused considerable consternation. Sir William Osler, who by now was in Oxford and was acting as consultant to Canadian Hospitals, queried Bruce, whom he knew, as to the advisability of continuing the inquiry in view of those factors. Bruce did not answer, on the advice of Sir Sam. Osler felt that the commission would see only the inevitable problems which were part of a rapid mobilization, and hear only "stories of disgruntled people".

However, Bruce and his fellow investigators felt they had uncovered so many serious problems that they recommended a reorganization of the Canadian Army Medical Services "from top to bottom". This report marked "Confidential, for official use only" was sent to Sir Sam Hughes. Although marked confidential, it quickly became public, raising the ire of the Imperialists in Canada, for it was interpreted as anti-imperial. It was also seen as a strong criticism of the Voluntary Aid Hospitals. Bruce maintained that neither of these had been intended, and that his chief intention was to improve the quality of care. The report was voluminous in citing the evidence to support the committee's recommendations. In listing the large number of operations which produced no increased military efficiency, the procedure of "loose semilunar cartilage" was classed as a "fool operation". Canadian practice, which resulted from the teaching of Dr. John B. Murphy of the U.S. stressed that drainage tubes should not be left in the joint, since it usually led to infection and amputation.

Dr. R.J. Manion of Toronto recorded in his book "Surgeon in Arms", the terrible problems associated with sepsis:

> ... I have given 150 inoculations hypodermically for the prevention of typhoid in a tent in which men and myself stood ankle deep in mud ... After the battle of Vimy Ridge my boys and I dressed our men for four days in an open, muddy trench, with shells dropping about all the time ...

Dr. Manion was closer to the front than Number One General Hospital (Montreal) which was selected for the care of fractured femurs. Unlike the casualties in the South African War, the wounds in World War One were mostly from high explosives, resulting in many compound and comminuted fractured femurs with excessive laceration. The mortality from these cases had been 14 percent in the early years of the war, but Number One C.G.H. was able to reduce this to 8 percent by more effective wound, toilet, and traction treatment. However, when it was stationed at Etaples, they received a heavy bombing from the enemy with many casualties amongst the staff and patients. Number Seven (Queen's) General Hospital which had returned from Lemnos was also hit severely during the raid.

Venereal cases, which the commission reported were alarmingly high, totalled 7,223 for 13 months between July 1915 and August 1915. Bruce was concerned that these soldiers were not organized into "venereal battalions" and maintained at top physical fitness level while awaiting a cure. He strongly condemned that hospital beds should be used for these patients rather than caring for them in a tent hospital, thus freeing more beds for front-line casualties. Actually a tent hospital had been used until nearly the end of 1915 when recommendations were made to admit those patients to various English hospitals throughout the country.

Surgeon General Jones had his reply to the Bruce Committee ready in an interim report within eight days. The gist of the reply was that many of the things that Bruce had observed were well known to himself and his proposals were impossible to carry out or were outside the accepted philosophy of the medical department. Jones' answers also contradicted the feasibility, accuracy or necessity of many of the points made by Bruce. In the course of reporting the cases, Bruce admitted that he had inadvertently included the name of a surgeon, which caused considerable embarrassment. Both documents were put before the Sub-Militia Council, consisting of staff officers of the Canadian Overseas Army, and the arguments were summarized by Major John Lash, who was Deputy Judge, Advocate General of The Canadian Forces in England. He summed up that Jones concurred with eleven of the recommendations, but he felt that it would be too expensive to treat Canadian casualties as far as was possible in Canadian hospitals, and disagreed in part with the re-organization scheme put forward, and absolutely did not concur that the Canadian Medical Services should be re-organized from "top to bottom". In spite of these differences the Sub-Militia Council passed a resolution that Bruce should implement the recommendation, and at the same time General Jones should proceed to Canada to co-ordinate Canadian Medical Services in England and France. This recommendation received the approval of Sir Sam Hughes who sent confirmatory messages to the Secretary of the War Office in London.

Bruce went quickly into action. He arranged with British Authorities to take over the administration of the 57 V.A.D. Hospitals as an economy measure, and to re-organize and increase the Canadian bed capacity in England. At the same time he arranged for an increase in the number of beds at Taplow, in collaboration with Dr. Hodgetts of The Canadian Red Cross. He also saw to it that Canadians were sent directly to Canadian Hospitals, if beds were available.

Dr. Bruce was spurred on by the statements made by Sir Sam Hughes, in a Toronto speech, that thousands of Canadians had lost months and sometimes a year, in hospitals that were not under Canadian control, when they should have been back in the trenches, and that Canadian soldiers were allowed to go under the knife of first-year medical men while the services of experienced surgeons from Canada were not being utilized.

However, the work of reorganization came to an acute stop two days after that statement, when General Sir Sam Hughes, the Minister of Militia and Defence for Canada, resigned his portfolio and was replaced by Sir George Perley as Overseas Minister for The Military Forces of Canada. One of Perley's first actions was to cancel the arrangements made for the return to Canada of Surgeon General Jones. Hector Charlesworth, introducing the Bruce publication in 1919 of *Politics and the C.A.M.C.*, characterized Perley as one who "played a sinister role". Correspondence between Sir George and Bruce shows that within the first few weeks the two were at loggerheads. Bruce was ticked off for writing directly to Sir George rather than going through normal administrative channels. Bruce noted that while Sir George admitted the urgency of the problems he "proclaimed his devotion to red tape, which would ensure needless delay". Within four weeks Sir George appointed a Board of Inquiry to examine the criticisms made by Colonel Bruce and his recommendations. The Board of Inquiry was made up of Surgeon General Sir William Babtie, K.C.M.G., C.B., V.C.; and four doctors, Colonel E.C. Ashton; Colonel J.T. Fotheringham; Colonel A.E. Ross and Colonel J.M. Elder.

Bruce vehemently objected to this step on several grounds. He cabled the Prime Minister of Canada that he had received authority to proceed with the reorganization, and now it appeared Sir George "intends to whitewash effective my report instead of facing issue". He objected to the content of Board of Inquiry which was to look at his report rather than the actual problems that were facing the medical services. But his major objections concerned the personalities who made up the Board. Colonel Ashton was not a member of the Canadian Army Medical Corps and had been continuously engaged as a combatant officer; Colonels Ross and Fotheringham were administrative officers at the front and with Lieutenant Colonel Elder had little or no experience of what was happening in Britain. Bruce's greatest concern was with the President of the Board, Sir William Babtie, who was an Imperial Officer, unfamiliar with conditions in the Canadian Service and possibly "keenly interested, from an adverse point of view, in the Voluntary Aid Detachments Hospitals, owing to the fact that, as a member of the

British Medical Service, he shared the responsibility for the employment of many thousands of these hospitals by this service".

In addition, Bruce was vociferous in protesting that he would be called to present evidence but would not be allowed to be present during the inquiry to hear other evidence or to take part in the proceedings. He strongly suspected that the result of the inquiry was a foregone conclusion, and this suspicion was borne out by the *British Medical Journal* which printed in its November 25 issue that "the tenor of the report will be such as to lead to the reinstatement of General Jones." Part of Bruce's suspicion that this would be the case rested on the knowledge that Colonel Fotheringham had issued a memorandum to the Second Canadian Division, on 18th November, in which he stated that his division wished no further recognition or desired any segregation from the rest of the Medical Services of the empire. The memo had also pointed out there was "evidence of what one may term over-engrossment in their own affairs of the Canadian Medical Services in England, and failure fully to appreciate the fact that we at front are the main item of importance."

The Babtie report stated that the dominating idea of the Inspector General had been that the Canadian Expeditionary Force was something separate and apart from the Imperial Army — a water-tight-compartment policy in matters medical. The Board disagreed with this and felt it would be inadvisable to attempt separation on the return of the sick and wounded to the United Kingdom. It added that the Inspector General had ignored the good work done by Surgeon General Jones and his staff under circumstances of novelty and great difficulty. Babtie did not agree with Colonel Bruce's view that a complete re-organization "from top to bottom" of the Medical Services was necessary. This information was communicated quickly to the press of London by Sir George Perley, but Bruce's reply was not carried in the same manner, with the result that he had to wait until he was demobilized to put his objections before the public. On December 30, 1916 Bruce received a notice that there was no further need of a special Inspector General of Medical Services, with a final line "thanking you for the attention which you have given to your duties", signed by George H. Perley.

Bruce attempted to resign from the service but was seconded to the Imperial Army in France with the understanding that he would not have any care of Canadian servicemen. This was irksome to the doctor, who later became Lieutenant-Governor of Ontario;

who strongly proposed better housing for the poor while his Majesty's representative; and who then served in the Federal House as a Member of the Progressive Conservative Party. However, he bided his time and published his side of the argument in 1919. He wrote that twenty-three of the twenty-eight improvements which he suggested had been put into effect.

What may have been lost to the antagonists and the other viewers was the magnificent growth, from a handful of men to a Corps of 20,000 medical personnel in response to the demands of war. Sir Andrew McPhail commented on the entire situation "one cannot help feeling that it was more or less of a tempest in a teapot ..." (certainly between the liberals and conservatives, a political event) "really nothing more Gilbertesque had ever happened in the profession." But to Dr. William F. Feasby of Toronto, it was a demonstration of the democratic system whereby armed forces must remain subordinate to civil authority. The echo of this sentiment was seen in Dr. Wilson's opinion that the Bruce Report was "too advanced for the type of man such as Sir William Babtie."

Bruce himself may have summed up the whole matter in *Varied Operations* in stating:

> ... *the profession does not forbid differences of opinion. Indeed such differences may be the only safe pathway to truth ...*

But the fighting on the home front never reached the desperation seen in the real war. Number Three Canadian Stationary Hospital (London) established an enviable record in the treatment of "shell shock", and Surgeon General Jones established a rehabilitation centre for these patients at Ramsgate. By 1916, only a few cases had to be transferred to the United Kingdom as most were treated in stationary hospitals closer to the front line. The front line was a site of a baffling disease, "trench fever", which incapacitated large numbers of men. It was eventually found to be caused by the body louse which was endemic in the front line troops. Major J.A. Amyot, former Professor of Hygiene at the University of Toronto, developed the "Amyot disinfestor" which rid clothing of lice. His previous assistant, George G. Naismith, designed an effective mask against chlorine gas.

While Bruce was with the British Medical Services, and other Canadians were in the medical aid posts or dressing stations or serving on hospital ships or with mobile operating rooms, the medical officer of the First Brigade Canadian Field Artillery, Dr.

242

John McCrae of Guelph, was setting up his post for the second battle of Ypres. He had prepared for casualties before many previous battles and as part of this preparation had come to terms with death — by referring to it as honoured peace. About this time he wrote "In Flanders Fields", which remains a memorial to all soldiers.

McCrae and twenty-one other Ontario medical officers died in the war.

Chapter XXI
The Twentieth Century Promise

... for the first time in history a patient going to a doctor had better odds that 50:50 of profiting by his visit ...

Dr. E.P. Scarlett

The names of the many Ontario doctors who lost their lives during the war are marked by plaques throughout the province. There is one in the Academy of Medicine of Toronto, which lists those Fellows who died — Andrew Gordon, Robert Holm, Herbert Jones, W.J.O. Mallock, H.R. Smith, J.H. Todd and N.J.I. Yellowlees. Dr. Robert Nobel, who unveiled it, was one of the many physicians who, while fighting the war, was preparing for peace. In the same year he opened Osler Hall and said:

> ... the growing multiplicity of specialists constitutes a dangerous evil. The man who specializes because of the financial return which such a practice would make, and not because of his fitness for some particular line, is an unworthy member of the profession ...

He was voicing the ongoing concern of various members of the Ontario Medical Association, which had begun in 1897 when Dr. John Coventry of Windsor claimed that the role of the family physician had changed in the previous twenty-five years, during which he had been as much a social as a professional force in family life. But now the specialist was usurping that place — and he may have been usurping a larger share of the general practice income. A Select Committee of the House of Lords in England had heard general practitioners, in the early 1890's, state that specialists robbed the generalists, and in 1900 *The General Practitioner* stated that the specialist knew nothing of "... constitutional idiosyncrasies of the individual" which were necessary for the correct diagnosis.

This opinion was echoed in 1914 when Dr. Charles F. McGillivary of Whitby, pointed out that the general practitioner, who was removed from the teaching hospital centres, was regarded as the wisest counsellor, the truest of friends, and a sort of intellectual beacon. While he agreed that the generalist might not be abreast of all the recent advances in medical science, he did have the necessary knowledge to carry out minor surgery, therapeutics and a general practice. Possibly McGillivary was expressing some of the questioning about the continuing thrust towards "scientific" medicine. This drive had been given considerable impetus in 1903 with the opening of the new medical building at the University of Toronto, which was constructed for the departments of physiology and pathology, and was patterned closely on the most modern laboratory facilities seen at Harvard University. To its opening were invited the full hierarchy of medicine from both sides of the Atlantic; William H. Welch (1850-1934) from Johns Hopkins; Thomas S. Roddick (1846-1923) M.P., Dean of the Medical Faculty of McGill; William Osler of Johns Hopkins and Sir Charles Scott Sherrington (1857-1952) of Liverpool University:

> ... Science — especially medical science — is growing in importance to the community. We must have organization in science as in industry ... These laboratories prove a cornerstone for the upbuilding of a temple of knowledge and a touchstone for the best of the intellects within the bounds of this great land ...

One of the people on the platform was Dr. Archibald Byron Macallum. He had been the chief planner of the building which represented the 20th century scientific spirit in medicine. Born in Belmont, he spoke and heard only Gaelic as a child, and after qualifying as a teacher in that small town, he saved his money to go to the University of Toronto. He completed his undergraduate studies under Ramsay Wright, taught high school at Cornwall and then went to Johns Hopkins to prepare for the first chair of physiology on his return to Toronto. From that time forward his driving spirit transformed the philosophy of the medical school to put it on a sound foundation of biological science. Seaborn reports that, as a young man:

> He never lost a moment from his books, even taking them to the table with him to conserve the moment or two it took others to be seated. He was not disliked by us, but we were afraid to ask him questions, afraid to make a noise. He just seemed to be sitting there thinking.

In 1917 Macallum was appointed Chairman of The First National Research Council. He issued a perceptive report which "expressed its embarrassment having undertaken to co-ordinate scientific research in a country so backward in scientific matters". He found that there was little to co-ordinate. But the opening of the laboratories at Toronto was the first of a series of research facilities in Ontario medical schools which would lead to magnificent results some 20 years later.

His special interest was in the chemical changes between animal tissues and the blood, and in particular the homeostasis that was established between different electrolytes. Sherrington, in commenting on the dynamic steady state which characterized life, as seen from a chemical viewpoint, acknowledged Macallum's contribution to solving the riddle of how salts remained dissolved in the blood.

A. Bruce Macallum, his son, became Dean of The School of Medicine at the University of Western Ontario.

One of the workers in the laboratories was Dr. John G. FitzGerald, who, as Associate Professor of Hygiene at Toronto, was responsible for the setting up of antitoxin laboratories in the sub-basement of the medical building to aid in the development of preventive medicine facilities.

The high hopes for research development expressed at the inaugural ceremonies had to await the presence of a corps of researchers. When William Osler moved to Johns Hopkins he was followed by the MacCallum brothers from Dunnville, John and Thomas McCrae, and Dr. Thomas Cullen. He, as Professor of Gynaecology at Johns Hopkins Hospital, worked for many years to establish the specialty of gynaecology in order to improve the quality of teaching in that area. The British Medical Journal described him as "a great gynaecologist, an inspiring and generous leader and a man whose genius is excelled only by his humanity...". Dr. J.B. MacCallum died at an early age after showing brilliant promise, but his brother Dr. W.G. MacCallum went on to show the complete cycle of the malarial parasite in the blood. This elite of young scientist-physicians, who served medicine well, made their contributions outside of Ontario.

Another who took the path to Johns Hopkins was Dr. L.E. Rowntree of London. In addition to an appointment as Director of Clinical Research at the Mayo Foundation in Minnesota, he published many articles on Addison's disease, kidney and liver function tests and experimental tumours.

However, not all the brilliant doctors took that course. Many, among them Alexander Primrose, Clarence L. Starr of Newmarket and George Bingham, remained and became renowned teachers in Toronto. One of these was Dr. George Armstrong Peters of Fergus, who showed his inventiveness in many fields. He described a new method for making fracture casts, was the first surgeon to transplant the ureters into the rectum for extrophy of the urinary bladder, and designed many surgical instruments. His inventiveness was matched in part at a later date by Dr. Norman Bethune of Gravenhurst, who, before becoming a national hero in China, designed many instruments for chest surgery.

Bethune, during the Spanish Civil War, became interested in direct blood transfusions in the early treatment of war injuries. This work had been pioneered in 1913 by Dr. Bruce Robertson of Toronto, who introduced a method of transfusion which avoided the problem of clotting when stored, by transferring the blood rapidly in small amounts with 20 c.c. syringes. This method was used by the Number Two Canadian Casualty Clearing Station in World War I and was documented in one of the earliest reports on the use of blood transfusion in the treatment of battle wounds.

His namesake, Dr. D.E. Robertson of Toronto, and Dr. W.E. Gallie of Barrie, were pioneers in the emerging field of surgery, beginning about 1911, in the use of tissues in transplantation. This preceded the work of Dr. A.B. Lemesurier who applied tissue transplantation as a living suture in the repair of hernias and shoulder dislocations and published *Hare-Lips and Their Treatment*. Much of this interest in surgery resulted from the work of Mr. I.H. Cameron, who was Professor of Surgery at Toronto at the end of the 19th century. Trained in the early principles of aseptic surgery by Dr. Lister, he never wore gloves but meticulously scrubbed his hands in water and mustard before operating.

His colleagues included John T. Fotheringham who was apt to appear at the Toronto General Hospital in his dog cart with coachman, while Starr would be arriving in his White Steamer from the other direction. Meanwhile, Herbert Bruce would arrive at The Wellesley in his electric phaeton. Toronto, Hamilton, Ottawa and all the other cities had grown since those early days when it was a four-day coach ride from Kingston to London. There were now 2,523,274 people in Ontario and a new land north and west of the Kawartha and Muskoka Lakes had opened, bringing new problems in medical care.

But in spite of the aggressiveness of research, there were still many unexplained diseases. Dr. E.P. Scarlett, a historian of medicine from Calgary, Alberta, stated that at the beginning of the twentieth century although medicine was improving, "for the first time in history a patient going to a doctor had better odds than 50:50 of profiting by his visit".

And that applied in country or city. In Sault Ste. Marie that patient might be seen by Dr. Edward Bromley. He arrived after practising in Toronto, Beeton, Woodstock and after two years in the mines of the Klondike goldrush and he followed Dr. John Kelly, who was the first to use chlorohydrate for puerperal fever, according to *The Lancet*. Kelly practised in the Sault but he had the "gold bug" and always carried a prospector's hammer and eventually he left the settlement. There was no gold. Bromley most likely had some of his patients examined by Dr. Robert James Gibson who had arrived at the Sault from Guelph. He had the distinction of having the first x-ray machine in Northern Ontario. It was powered by a nearby stream. Dr. Thomas L. Gray of Clinton, Ontario, who practised in St. Thomas, was not so fortunate since his early machine had to be operated by turning a crank. He practised in the same years as Dr. Charles Duncombe in St. Thomas, who was the nephew of Dr. Charles who had fled the country in the 1837 Rebellion.

While many general practitioners were quick to adopt technological developments and acquire scientific equipment, Dr. Arthur Sutton of Port Credit was not so anxious. While practising in that area about the turn of the century, he installed a telephone, but it was found years later shut behind a heavy oaken door, which was kept carefully closed at all times.

The quality of medical care became of greater significance to medical organizations at the beginning of the century. In 1902 the Canada Medical Act was proposed which would standardize registration across the country, but it was not passed until 1912 as it had to be ratified by the provinces individually under the terms of the British North America Act. The Canadian Medical Association had been forewarned of this when Workman in the Presidential Address of 1878 urged, along with Canniff, that all efforts be made to avoid legislative ineptitudes. He was drawing on the strong sentiment expressed earlier by Dr. J.P. Rottot who had said, "the sympathies of legislators generally, and especially the unscientific who comprise the majority, are in favour of quackery and free trade in medicine".

That there was lack of quality in medical care in 1910 was

clearly detected by Abraham Flexner. He toured and inspected Ontario schools under the aegis of the Carnegie Foundation for the Advancement of Teaching which had been endowed to appraise the quality of professional education in the United States. While his visit to Ontario confirmed many of the observations and criticisms made by Osler in 1885, it was possible to find many improvements that had been made in Toronto, particularly with the opening of the new Medical Science building and an improved relationship with the Toronto General Hospital.

But this was not the case in Kingston. There it was noted that clinical facilities were limited, that there were too few obstetrical cases and the postmortem material was mainly obtained from the insane asylum. Dean of the Medical Faculty, Dr. James C. Connell of Ayr, had not had time to bring in the reforms he was anxious to carry out, nor had Dr. Walter T. Connell, the Professor of Pathology and Bacteriology. Both of these men were quick to protest that Flexner had visited the school for barely half a day and there had been no opportunity to make a proper inspection.

Nor was London acceptable to Flexner. Here there was no equipment for physiology, pharmacology or clinical microscopy, and no museum "deserving the name". The University of Western Ontario was equally rapid to point out the inadequacy of the inspection.

The visit of Flexner and his subsequent report eventually led to re-organizations and upgrading of teaching facilities in the province. The professional associations such as Academies of Medicine and County Medical Societies of the Ontario Medical Association were already leading the way. By 1906 the Association announced its success that had resulted in the opening of the Hospital for Epileptic Patients in Woodstock. In the following year the Association urged that the medical profession should use its influence with both levels of government to curtail the sale of habit-forming drugs such as opium, heroin, codeine, cocaine and morphine. At this same meeting, while noting that many Ontario graduates were going overseas, it was urged that a committee be established to consider and enforce adequate measures for a campaign to guard against the "ravages of cancer by early diagnosis and treatment". Three years later Dr. Fredrick William Marlow, of Port Perry, was President of the Ontario Medical Association. He developed, in association with Dr. Gordon Richards of Toronto, a treatment for carcinoma of the cervix incorporating radiotherapy.

But in spite of the many stories of successful treatment that were being reported throughout the province, the 1918 OMA meeting repeated the continuing question: "Do we as a profession adopt adequate means for safeguarding the public from incompetency among ourselves?" The answer by the profession was that the best safeguard was thorough teaching and careful clinical training.

The same meeting called upon the profession to co-operate at an early date in some system of state medicine for the treatment of the poor. Marlow was Chairman of the Meeting which at a later date suggested that some form of state medicine should be provided whereby the poor might receive adequate medical attention. Looking back one century to the early announcements of "the poor treated gratis", it was possible to realize the sweep of medicine over a hundred years.

By the beginning of the 1920's the medical profession was poised on the brink of a breath-taking quarter of a century which would see new ideas in hospitals and universities with the reorganization of teaching facilities in university-affiliated hospitals. There would be the opening of new psychiatric facilities. The age of antibiotics was only a few years away. The triumphs of preventive medicine, seeded at the beginning of the century, would see the eradication of many of the diseases which had plagued the 19th century doctors. Pediatric medicine would be brought to new heights by doctors such as Alan Brown, Fredrick Tisdall and T.G.H. Blake. Research into the causes of disease was about to live up to the promises which had been made by those who fought for scientific medicine, in the persons of Dr. Banting, Dr. Best, Dr. Collip and many others.

The previous century had been marked indelibly by the presence of strong figures who shaped the course and practice of medicine in their image. But behind those figures who seized the imagination and merit mention in any history were the hundreds of family physicians who lived and died in a life of service. They are not cited by historical studies. They have been remembered for a few years, then marked by a simple stone on their graves.

They were the persons who put into practice those principles for which the educators fought. They used the best of contemporary knowledge and applied it with their utmost competence. To the inoculator, prevention of smallpox was practised in the most modern manner. It was part of the medical model that cholera resulted from eating shell-fish. Most insanity resulted from self-abuse or could be treated by amputation of the cervix. Pain in the abdomen suggested perityphlitis and any operation to treat it was a dangerous procedure. And each of these disease concepts or treatment procedures was validated by the medical school teachers, with scientific evidence.

In their practice those century-ago doctors left notes and records which, today, tempt the historian to scoff — just as will the historian be tempted to scoff at our ways fifty years hence. In their philosophy they forged associations dedicated to raising levels of competence and protecting the public. In their dreams they sought a better country and frequently took up public life to that end. In their lives they remained sensitive, fallible and human in providing medicine for Ontario.

TABLE A

A Schematic Chronology of Medical Education in Ontario

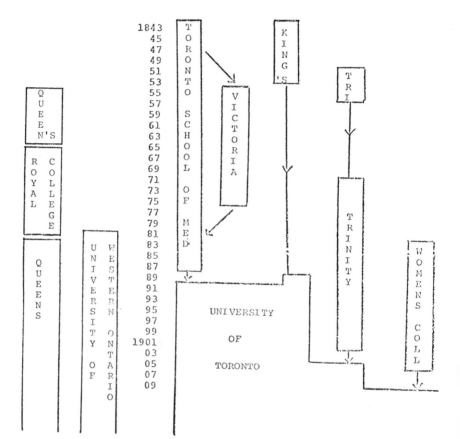

TABLE B

Death from Typhoid in Ontario
(Mortality Rate per 100,000)

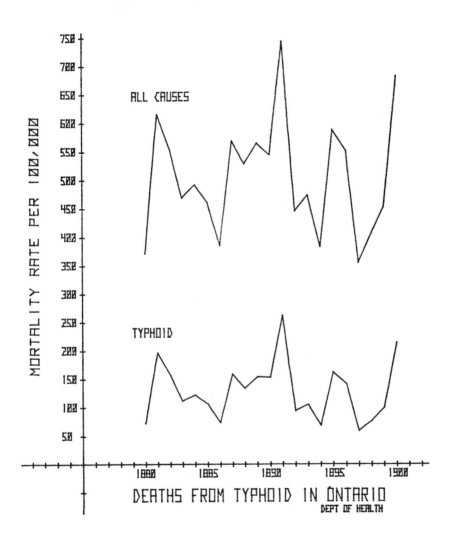

TABLE C

The following is a Record of the Ten Highest Causes of Death for the years 1871, 1872, 1873, 1874, 1876, 1877, 1878, 1879, 1880, 1881, and 1882

1871.		1872.		1873.		1874.		1876.	
Whole number of Deaths registered	9182	Whole number of Deaths registered	10745	Whole number of Deaths registered	11069	Whole number of Deaths registered	10352	Whole number of Deaths registered	18623
Phthisis	1042	Phthisis	1120	Phthisis	1217	Phthisis	1143	Phthisis	2259
Scarlatina	650	Scarlatina	642	Old Age	778	Pneumonia	642	Old Age	1405
Pneumonia	508	Old Age	545	Lung Disease	533	Old Age	536	Diphtheria	864
Exhaustion	467	Pneumonia	514	Typhoid Fever	401	Typhoid Fever	369	Pneumonia	786
Old Age	454	Diarrhœa	407	Heart Disease	399	Heart Disease	351	Lung Disease	662
Heart Disease	353	Heart Disease	350	Cerebro-spinal Meningitis	324	Diarrhœa	334	Convulsions	569
Typhoid Fever	291	Dysentery	342	Stomach Disease	321	Enteritis	283	Diarrhœa	644
Dropsy	241	Exhaustion	332	Brain Disease	278	Convulsions	267	Typhoid Fever	456
Convulsions	209	Typhoid Fever	329	Pneumonia	276	Dropsy	239	Dropsy	381
Diarrhœa	207	Brain Disease	318	Cholera Infantum	276	Lung Disease	231		

No Report in 1875.

1877		1878		1879.		1880.		1881.		1882.	
Whole number of Deaths registered	20053	Whole number of Deaths registered	17808	Whole number of Deaths registered	17958	Whole number of Deaths registered	19802	Whole number of Deaths registered	22821	Whole number of Deaths registered	21800
Phthisis	2157	Phthisis	1999	Phthisis	2065	Phthisis	2154	Phthisis	2397	Phthisis	2464
Old Age	1661	Old Age	1722	Old Age	1749	Old Age	1658	Old Age	1972	Anæmia	1895
Infantile Debility	1164	Infantile Debility	1100	Infantile Debility	955	Infantile Debility	1300	Infantile Debility	1481	Old Age	1841
Pneumonia	1050	Diphtheria	986	Pneumonia	942	Pneumonia	1257	Diphtheria	1171	Pneumonia	1322
Diphtheria	964	Pneumonia	826	Heart Disease	784	Diphtheria	822	Pneumonia	1137	Diphtheria	1239
Scarlet Fever	717	Heart Disease	621	Diphtheria	574	Heart Disease	760	Heart Disease	886	Heart Disease	753
Heart Disease	697	Convulsions	454	Convulsions	445	Convulsions	518	Diarrhœa	818	Typhoid Fever	555
Diarrhœa	666	Enteritis	415	Dropsy	400	Bronchitis	438	Typhoid Fever	616	Scarlatina	543
Convulsions	573	Diarrhœa	401	Enteritis	393	Croup	429	Croup	533	Diarrhœa	497
Enteritis	497	Typhoid Fever	379	Diarrhœa	340	Congestion of Lungs	419	Convulsions	509	Convulsions	492

Registration Reports, 1882

TABLE D

Death from Tuberculosis by Cities, 1889-1893

Report relating to Registration of Births, Marriages and Deaths in
the Province of Ontario for the Year ending 31, October, 1898.

Printed by Order of Legislative Assembly of Ontario

*Table showing deaths from Tuberculosis in certain Counties in 1871 and 1898, with
Population, illustrating periods of permanent settlement.*

County.	Year.	Population.	Death rate.
Brant	1871	32,239	1.0
	1898	39,169	1.0
Welland	1871	25,761	1.5
	1898	32,369	1.1
Leeds and Grenville	1871	57,918	1.22
	1898	65,339	2.0
Prince Edward	1871	20,336	1.0
	1898	20,965	1.2
Huron	1871	66,165	0.54
	1898	91,664	1.0
Bruce	1871	48,515	0.20
	1898	69,328	1.2
Simcoe	1871	64,248	0.40
	1898	76,974	1.4
Waterloo	1871	40,251	1.5
	1898	54,168	1.0
Oxford	1871	48,247	0.93
	1898	53,493	1.35
Middlesex	1871	83,595	0.6
	1898	109,417	1 25
Norfolk	1871	30,763	1.20
	1898	53,256	1.10

DEATHS IN CITIES.—The total deaths in the cities from tuberculosis are seen in the
following table to have increased in absolute numbers during the ten year period by 40 per
cent. Whether this represents an actual increase depends, however, on the relative
completeness of returns in the earlier years of the period, with the inclusion of deaths
under one year in the returns for 1898. An additional allowance must be made for an
increased population, estimated at 25.6 per cent in the ten years.

Deaths from Tuberculosis by Cities, 1889 to 1898

	1889.	1890.	1891.	1892.	1893.	1894.	1895.	1896.	1897.	1898.
Toronto	303	387	450	477	512	442	430	442	467	483
Hamilton	80	88	90	73	88	80	104	100	83	109
Ottawa	102	106	83	80	111	98	91	109	131	148
London	27	38	52	43	42	54	51	61	52	64
Kingston	61	39	42	39	35	33	27	41	54	45
Brantford	18	15	22	26	32	19	26	31	25	23
St. Thomas	11	12	15	13	9	12	15	19	17	13
Guelph	11	8	10	16	23	17	15	15	14	21
So. Catharines	26	27	12	27	18	23	21	17	15	21
Belleville	25	16	14	25	17	13	24	11	20	15
Stratford	15	16	8	9	11	16	8	12	13	19
Windsor	16	16	28	13	17	21	21	21	17	23
Chatham	16	22	17	11	14	13	7	18	12	14
Total	**701**	**790**	**792**	**852**	**920**	**841**	**840**	**857**	**923**	**908**

There certainly has been no decrease in Ontario such as has marked the cities of
Great Britain during the past thirty years, which have made in spite of their enormous
populations, such great advances in the problem of the housing of the poorer classes. As
yet no systematic steps have been taken by local boards in the cities of Ontario to maintain
a supervision of houses where consumptives are resident, nor to disinfect the premises after
death.

REPORT RELATING TO REGISTRATION
OF BIRTHS, MARRIAGES AND DEATHS
IN THE PROVINCE OF ONTARIO FOR
THE YEAR ENDING 31, OCTOBER 1898.

PRINTED BY ORDER OF
LEGISLATIVE ASSEMBLY
OF ONTARIO.

TABLE E

Graduates from Ontario Medical Schools

QUEEN'S UNIVERSITY

1855 - 9	1870 - 10	1885 - 13
1856 - 5	1871 - 12	1886 - 36
1857 - 10	1872 - 5	1887 - 27
1858 - 11	1873 - 9	1888 - 28
1859 - 12	1874 - 7	1889 - 36
1860 - 11	1875 - 9	1890 - 32
1861 - 17	1876 - 6	1891 - 38
1862 - 20	1877 - 12	1892 - 30
1863 - 30	1878 - 11	1893 - 24
1864 - 16	1879 - 15	1894 - 20
1865 - 15	1880 - 12	1895 - 23
1866 - 11	1881 - 17	1896 - 25
1867 - 11	1882 - 15	1897 - 28
1868 - 14	1883 - 13	1898 - 34
1869 - 18	1884 - 15	1899 - 23

UNIVERSITY OF WESTERN ONTARIO

1883 - 1	1896 - 6
1884 - no grad class	1897 - 10
1885 - 2	1898 - 16
1886 - 8	1899 - 19
1887 - 4	
1888 - 11	
1889 - 13	
1890 - 20	
1891 - 17	
1892 - 23	
1893 - 4	
1894 - 13	
1895 - 11	

UNIVERSITY OF TORONTO

1844 - 4	1864 - 21	1884 - 12
1845 - 1	1865 - 23	1885 - 16
1846 - 0	1866 - 32	1886 - 16
1847 - 0	1867 - 22	1887 - 27
1848 - 1	1868 - 22	1888 - 61
1849 - 1	1869 - 26	1889 - 51
1850 - 3	1870 - 25	1890 - 52
1851 - 2	1871 - 19	1891 - 55
1852 - 0	1872 - 17	1892 - 66
1853 - 6	1873 - 19	1893 - 54
1854 - 0	1874 - 18	1894 - 59
1855 - 0	1875 - 20	1895 - 65
1856 - 2	1876 - 16	1896 - 59
1857 - 1	1877 - 28	1897 - 39
1858 - 3	1878 - 41	1898 - 56
1859 - 10	1879 - 42	1899 - 53
1860 - 8	1880 - 40	
1861 - 7	1881 - 36	
1862 - 4	1882 - 31	Degrees added by Victoria
1863 - 14	1883 - 11	at Federation = 917

Degrees added by Trinity
at Federation = 1,809

GENERAL BIBLIOGRAPHY

Burwash, N.
The History of Victoria College. Toronto 1927.

Canniff, W.
The Medical Profession in Upper Canada. William Briggs. Toronto 1894.

Douglas, J.
Medical Topography of Upper Canada. 1819.

Ermatinger, C.O.
The Talbot Regime. The Municipal World. St. Thomas 1904.

Firth, F.G.
The Town of York, 1815-1834. Champlain. University of Toronto Press. 1966.

Gimby, W.E.
History of The Medical Profession. Sault Ste. Marie 1922.

Gourlay, R.
Statistical Account of Upper Canada. London 1822.

Halpenny, F.G.
Dictionary of Canadian Biography. University of Toronto Press. Vol. IX: Vol. X.

Heagerty, J.J.
Four Centuries of Medical History in Canada. MacMillan 1928.

Heagerty, J.J.
The Romance of Medicine in Canada. MacMillan 1940.

MacDermott, H.E.
Medicine in Canada, 1867-1967. McClelland & Stewart. Toronto 1967.

Robertson, J.R.
The Diary of Mrs. John Graves Simcoe. William Briggs. Toronto 1911.

Scadding, H.
Toronto of Old. Hunter & Ross. Toronto 1873.

The Librarian,
The University of Toronto and Its Colleges, 1827-1906. Toronto 1906.

PAPERS & MANUSCRIPT COLLECTIONS

Academy of Medicine — *Collection of original letters and documents of Rolph, Aikins, Canniff and Geikie.*

Public Archives Ontario — *Collections of papers of Rolph, Canniff, Ryerson and Geikie.*

Victoria University Library — *Caniff's Papers.*

CHAPTER BIBLIOGRAPHY

Chapter I

Cherniak, E.A.
Statutory Enactment Relating to Hospitals, Doctors, Dentists and Pharmacists in Law Society of Upper Canada Special Lectures. 1973.

MacNab, E.
A Legal History of Health Professions in Ontario. Queen's Printer. Toronto 1970.

Chapter II

Henry, W.
Trifles from my Portfolio by a Staff Surgeon. 1838.

Chapter III

Angus, M.
Kingston General Hospital. McGill-Queen's Press. Montreal 1973.

Barr, M.
Century of Medicine at Western. U.W.O. London 1977.

Brien, J.W.
The Medical Men of Essex County. Windsor 1945.

Curtis, J.D.
St. Thomas and Elgin Medical Men of the Past. St. Thomas 1956.

Guilley, E.C.
The Valley of the Trent. The Champlain Society. Toronto 1957.

Kaiser, T.E.
History of the Medical Profession of the County of Ontario. Oshawa 1934.

Lauriston, V.
A Centennial Chronical of Kent Doctors. Chatham 1967.

Leavitt, T.W.H.
History of Leeds and Grenville. Recorder Press. Belleville 1879.

Lewis, E.N.
Early Medical Men of Elgin County. Sutherland Press. St. Thomas 1931.

Lizars, R.and K.
In the Days of the Canada Company. Briggs. Toronto 1896.

McTaggart, J.
Three Years in Canada: an account of the actual state of the country in 1826-27-28. London 1829.

Moodie, S.
Roughing It in the Bush. London 1852.
Muir, R.C.
The Early Political and Military History of Burford. Quebec 1913.
Small, H.R.
Medical Memoirs of By-Town. Ottawa 1903.

Chapter IV

Duncombe, C.
Report on the Subject of Education. Reynolds. Toronto 1836.

Chapter V

Dent, J.C.
The Story of The Upper Canada Rebellion. Blackett Robinson.
Toronto 1885.
Geikie, W.B.
An Historical Sketch of Canadian Medical Education. The Canadian
Lancet. 1901.
Guillet, E.C.
The Lives and Times of the Patriots. Nelson. Toronto 1938.
Gwyn, N.
*Details Connected with the Evolution of Medical Education in
Toronto*. University of Toronto Medical Journal. Vol. 8, 1930, pp.
224-9.
Hodgkins, J.G.
The Establishment of Schools and Colleges in Ontario, 1792-1910.
1910.
Kinchen, O.A.
The Rise and Fall of the Patriot Hunters. Bookman Associates. New
York 1956.
Link, E.G.
Doctors and Democracy. N.Y. State Journal of Medicine. V 70. 1970.
Reid, D.B.
The Rebellion of 1837. Robinson. Toronto 1896.

Chapter VI

Bull, William Perkins.
From Medicine Man to Medical Man, McLeod, 1934.
Careless, J.M.S.
Brown of the Globe, 1959.
Godfrey, C.M.
King's College: Upper Canada's First Medical School. Ont. Med.
Review, Jan. 1967, pp. 19-22.

Macara, J.
Origin, History and Management of the University of King's College, Toronto, 1844.
Moss, T.
An Interview with Dr. W.W. Ogden. Rare Book Room. University of Toronto.
Richardson, James H.
Letter to President Loudon, June 27, 1899. Academy of Medicine.
Thomas, C.
Ryerson of Upper Canada. Ryerson Press. 1969.

Chapter VII

Clark, C.K.
A History of the Toronto General Hospital. Toronto 1913.
Godfrey, C.M.
Trinity Medical School. Applied Therapeutics. December 1966.
Hodgkins, J.G.
Documentary History of Education in Upper Canada. Toronto 1902.
Spragge, G.W.
Trinity Medical College. Ontario History. Vol. LVIII #2. June 1966.

Chapter VIII

Godfrey, C.M.,
Dr. John Rolph — *Bull. Acad. Med.* Feb. 1966, p. 80.
Montague, J. and A.
Impressions of Some Canadian Medical Institutions in 1837. Canadian Psychology Association Journal. Vol. 21. No. 2. 1976.
Poole, T.W.
A Sketch of the Early Settlement of the Town of Peterborough. Peterborough 1867.
Roland, C.G.
Diary of a Canadian Country Physician. Medical History. Vol. I. April 1971.

Chapter X

Hacker, C.
The Indomitable Lady Doctors. Clark & Irwin. Toronto 1974.
Jameson, A.
Winter Studies and Summer Rambles in Canada. London 1838.
MacDermot, H.E.
The History of the Canadian Medical Association. Toronto 1935-1958.

Routley, T.C.
Routley's History of the Ontario Medical Association. Ontario Medical Review. 1963-1967.

Smith, W.L.
The Pioneers of Old Ontario. Morang. Toronto, 1923.

Chapter XII

Peer, F.T.
A Nineteenth Century Physician of Upper Canada and His Library. Bull Cleveland Medical Library XIX. July 1972.

Chapter XIII

DeFries, R.D.
Development of Public Health in Canada, Toronto, 1940.

Godfrey, C.M.
The Cholera Epidemics in Upper Canada, 1832-66. Seccombe House, Toronto, 1968.

Guillet, E.A.
Cobourg 1778-1848. Goodfellow Printing. Hamilton 1848.

Hassal, A.E.
The Microscopic Anatomy of the Human Body in Health and Disease. Vol. I. New York. Pratt, Woodruff & Company. 1851.

Herepath, W.B.
On the Employment of Injections of Milk or Milky Water. Association Medical Journal. September 1, 1854.

Hodder, E.M.
Transfusion of Milk in Cholera. Practitioner 10:14, 1873.

Milton, Ross Alexander
Memoirs of a Reformer, 1832-92. Toronto. Hunter, Ross & Company. 1893.

Patterson, M.A.
The Cholera Epidemic 1832, In York, Upper Canada. Bull Medical Library Association. April 1858.

Seaborne, E.
The March of Medicine in Western Ontario. 1944.

Chapter XV

Agnew, G.H.
Canadian Hospitals 1920-1970. University of Toronto Press. Toronto 1974.

Braithwaite, M.
  The Story of the Hospital for Sick Children in Toronto. McClelland & Stewart. Toronto 1974.

Brink, G.C.
  Across the Years: Tuberculosis in Ontario.

Elliott, J.H.
  Results Already Achieved at the Muskoka Cottage Sanitarium. Philadelphia Monthly Medical Journal. October 1899.

Greenlands, C.
  Three Pioneers of Canadian Psychiatry. JAMA. Vol. 200, No. 1, June 1967. Page 833-842.

Groves, A.
  All in a Day's Work. MacMillan. Toronto 1934.

Ontario Department of Health
  The Hospitals of Ontario. Toronto 1934.

Runnalls, J.L.
  A Century with the St. Catharine's General Hospital. St. Catharines 1974.

Wherrett, G.J.
  The Miracle of the Empty Beds. University of Toronto Press. Toronto 1977.

Chapter XVI

Godfrey, C.M.
  The Origins of Medical Education of Women in Ontario. Medical History, Vol. XV-I, #1, pp. 89-93. January 1973.

Hacker, Carlotta
  The Indomitable Lady Doctors. Clarke, Irwin and Company. Toronto 1974.

Shortt, E.S.
  Historical Sketch of Medical Education of Women in Kingston. Osler Club. Queen's University. September 14, 1916.

Chapter XVII

Ameke, William
  History of Homeopathy; Its Origins, Its Conflicts. The British Homeopathic Society. 1885.

Bruce, H.A.
  Varied Operations. Longman & Green. Toronto 1958.

Campbell, C.G.
  Medical Legislation in Ontario; The annual address at the meeting of the Canadian Institute of Homeopathy. Hamilton June 14, 1892.

Cochran, E.W.
  Men of Canada. Brantford 1893.
Cushing, H.
  The Life of William Osler. Oxford 1904.
Kaufman, Martin
  Homeopathy in America. The Johns Hopkins Press. 1971.
Kett, Joseph K.
  The Formation of the American Medical Profession. Yale University 1968.
Osler, W.
  Aequanimitas. Blakiston. Philadelphia 1904.

Patterson, G.R.
  Canadian Pharmacy and Brief Confederation Medical Legislation. JAMA June 5, 1967. Vol. 200, No. 10, pp. 149-852.

Chapter XVIII

Calvin, D.D.
  Queen's University of Kingston. 1841-1941. Trustees of University. Toronto 1941.
Gundy, H.P.
  Growing Pains: The Early History of the Queen's Medical Faculty. Historic Kingston. 1955.
Patterson, G.R.
  The History of Pharmacy in Ontario. Canadian Pharmaceutical Journal. February 1967.
Sullivan, M.
  Retrospect To Fifty Years of the Medical School of Kingston.
Talman, J.J. and R.D.
  Western, 1878-1953. 1953.

Chapter XIX

Canadian Medical Journal, Vol. 6, p. 17, 1913.
LaValley, R.
  What is the Practice of Medicine, 1979. Unpublished mss.
Macnab, Elizabeth
  A Legal History of Health Professions in Ontario. Queen's Printer, 1970.
Minutes of C.P.S.O. 1869-1900.
Rogers, R. Vashon, Jr.
  Law and Medical Men. Published Coswell, 1884.

Seaborne, E.
The March of Medicine in Ontario, 1944.

Chapter XX

Bruce, H.A.
Politics and the C.A.M.C. Briggs. Toronto 1919.
Feasby, W.R.
Official History of the Canadian Medical Services, 1939-1945. Ottawa 1956.
MacPhail, A.
Official History of the Canadian Great War, 1914-1919. Ottawa 1925.
Nichols, C.S.
Seventy Years of Service. Borealis. Ottawa 1977.
Ryerson, G.A.S.
Looking Backward. Toronto 1924.

Chapter XXI

Flexner, A.
Medical Education in the United States and Canada. New York. Carnegie Foundation. 1910.
Lockwood, T.M.
A History of Medical Practice In and Around Port Credit, 1789-1963. Ontario Medical Review. October 6, 1963.

APPENDIX

Ontario doctors mentioned in this history, listing

1. Birth and death dates.

2. Birthplace, if in Ontario the town is cited; if not in Ontario the country is cited.

3. Graduate of medical school; if Ontario the following abbreviations are used:

    Queen's University — Queen's
    University of Western Ontario — Western
    University of Toronto — U. of T.
    King's College — King's
    Victoria College — Vic.
    Trinity College — Trin.
    Toronto School of Medicine — Tor. Sch. Med.
    Upper Canada Medical Board — U.C.M.B.
    Ontario Women's Medical College — O.W.M.C.

4. Major area of practice — pract.

5. Posts held:

    Canadian Medical Association — CMA
    Ontario Medical Association — OMA
    College of Physicians and Surgeons — CP&S
    Academy of Medicine — Acad. of Med.
    Medical Council of Ontario — Med. Counc.
    Royal College of Surgeons — R.C.S.

6. Editor — ed.
    Author — auth.

7. Political Offices:
    Member of Federal Parliament — M.P.
    Member of Ontario Parliament — M.L.A.

Other academic degrees are not cited.

Other than Ontario physicians are described in the text but are not shown in this section.

In some cases the information is incomplete, due to loss of records or the physician was in transit.

BEST, Charles Herbert
1899-1978 b. U.S.A.; grad. U. of T.; pract. Toronto; auth. — *Diabetes & Insulin and the Lipotropic Factor;* co-auth. with N.B. Taylor *The Human Body & Its Functions: An Elementary Textbook of Physiology;* co-auth. *The Living Body, A Text in Human Physiology,* ed. with N.B. Taylor *The Physiology Basis of Medical Practice: A Text in Applied Physiology*; co-discoverer of Insulin (with Banting).

BESWICK, Christopher
1721-1839 b. England; pract. Stouffville & Aurora ; Friend of Samuel Lount; died at 118.

BETHUNE, John G.
1834-1911 b.   ; grad. Queen's Univ.; pract. Wingham; member of Ontario Medical Council.

BETHUNE, Norman
1899-1939 b. Gravenhurst; grad. U. of T.; pract. Detroit & Montreal; Surgeon to Loyalist forces in Spain, 1936-37; Eighth Route Army, China.

BETHUNE, Norman
1822-1892 b. Moose Factory; grad. Edinburgh, London; pract. Toronto; dean — Trin. Medical Faculty; co-founder of the U.C. School of Medicine 1850.

BILLINGS, W.
1805-1891 b. England; grad. Apothecaries Hall; pract. Nottingham & Hamilton; memb. of City Council (Hamilton).

BINGHAM, George S.
1860-1923 b.   ; grad. Trin.; pract. Toronto; prof. of clinical surgery, U. of T.; Surgical Staff of T.G.H., St. Michael's & Hospital for Sick Children.

BIRK, Patrick
Circa. 1800, U.E. list.

BLAKE, Charles
Circa. 1800 b. England; grad.   ; pract. Montreal; U.E. List Surgeon 34th Regt.

BOVELL, James
    1817-1880 b. Barbados; grad. London, Edinburgh and Dublin; pract. Toronto; dean — Trin.; co-founder U.C. Medical School; lect. in Tor. Sch. Med. (physiology & pathology).

BOWMAN, David J.
    1800-1848 b. Niagara; grad. U.S.A.; pract. St. Thomas.

BOWMAN, James H.
    1853-1936 b. Hamilton; grad. Ontario Coll. of Pharmacy; pract. Univ. of Western Ontario; Prof. Theoretical Chemistry.

BOYES, Henry
    1775-1868 b. England; grad. Edinburgh; pract. Whitby; Bursar King's; Fellow Linnean Society.

BRITTON, William
    1862-1915 b.   ; grad. U. of T.; pract. Toronto; President of O.M.A. (1898).

BROMLEY, Edward
    1855-1839 b. Ottawa Valley; grad. Tor.-Vic. Sch. Med.; pract. Toronto, Beaton, Woodstock, and in the mines of the Klondike goldrush and The Sault.

BROWN, Alan
    1887-1960 b. Clinton; grad. U. of T.; pract. Toronto; auth. *Common Procedures in the Practice of Paediatrics — The Normal Child*; Physician-in-Chief, Hospital for Sick Children.

BROWSE, William Henry
    1824-1881 b. Matilda; grad. McGill; pract. Prescott; pres. Med. Counc.; senator.

BRUCE, Herbert A.
    1873-1963 b. Blackstone; grad. U. of T.; pract. Toronto; auth. *Politics & C.A.M.C.; Our Heritage and Other Addresses; Varied Operations; Friendship, The Key to Peace.*

BRYCE, Peter Henderson
    1855-1932 b. Brant County Mt. Pleasant; grad. U. of T.; pract. Toronto & Guelph; sec. Board of Health Ontario.

BUCHANAN, George
    1843-1937 b. Zurich; grad. U. of T.; pract. Zurich; CP&S; memb. CP&S of Ontario, 1871.

BUCKE, Richard Maurice
    1837-1902 b. England; grad. McGill; pract. Sarnia, London; supt. Hamilton and London Asylums; auth. *Cosmic Consciousness, a study in the evolution of the human mind;* prof. of Mental & Nervous Diseases at Western, London.

BULL, Edward
> 1823-1894 b. York Twp.; grad. Vic.; prac. Lloydtown, Bond Head, Weston & Toronto.

BURDETT, David Earl
> 1838-1895 b. Prince Edward County; grad. Trin.; pract. Belleville.

BURGESS, J.W.
> 1849-1926 b. Toronto; grad. U. of T.; pract. London & Quebec; supt. London, Hamilton, and Verdun Asylums; memb. of Faculty of Medicine at Western, London and McGill; auth. *The Lake Erie Shores as a Botanising Ground.*

BURNS, David
> Circa. 1806; pract. York; Surgeon, Queen's Rangers; Clerk of the Crown Chancery of Upper Canada; U.E. Loyalist.

BURNS, James H.
> 1845-1898 b. Oshawa; grad. Tor. Sch. Med.; pract. Priceville, Collingwood and Toronto; Vice-Pres. Ontario Medical Council.

CALCAGNO, Dr.
> Circa. 1840 b.   ; grad.   ; pract. Palermo.

CAMERON, Irving Howard
> 1855-1933 b. Toronto; grad. Tor. Sch. Med.; pract. Toronto; prof. of Surgery, U. of T.

CAMPBELL, C.T.
> 1843-1923 b. Seaforth; grad. Cleveland Homeopathic Medical College; pract. London, Ont.; Mayor — London, Ontario.

CAMPBELL, Duncan
> 1811-1879 b. Scotland; grad. Uni. of Edinburgh; pract. Toronto; Pres. of the Homeopathic Board; Pres. Medical Council of Ontario.

CANNIFF, William
> 1830-1910 b. Thurlow; grad. Tor. Sch. Med.; pract. Belleville and Toronto; Dean — Vic. Medical Faculty; Medical Health Officer in Toronto; memb. "Canada First" Party; Pres. of the CMA 1880; auth. *A History of The Early Settlement of Upper Canada - The Medical Profession in Upper Canada — An Historical Narrative — Historical Sketch of the County of York — A Manual of The Principles of Surgery.*

CARSAW, G.A.
> Circa. 1868; pract. Whitby.

CASSIDY, John J.

1843-1914 b. Toronto; grad. Tor. Sch. Med.; pract. Toronto; ed. *Canadian Journal of Medicine and Surgery.*

CATHCART, James

1798-1832 b. Ireland; grad. Dublin; pract. York; died of Cholera.

CAVAN, John

1860-1914 b. St. Mary's; grad. Victoria; pract. Toronto; Prof. of Pathology, U. of T.

CHAMBERLAIN, Theodore F.

1838-1927 b. Farmersville; grad. Queen's; pract. Leeds, Morrisburg, Prescott, Chaffey's Locks.

CHISHOLM, Archibald

1795-1830 b. St. Thomas; grad. pract. London (first to practise in London).

CHRISTIE, Alexander James

1778-1843 b. Scotland; grad. Edinburgh; pract. By-Town; established *The By-Town Gazette*; ed. the first *Canadian Magazine.*

CHRISTOE, William G.

1824-1904 b.   ; grad. Vic.; pract. Flesherton, Orono.

CLARK, Ernest Alexander

1897-1964 b. Smiths Falls; grad. Queen's; pract. Woodstock, Toronto; supt. of Toronto General Hospital.

CLARK, Robert Whichelo

1811-   b. Scotland; grad. Edinburgh, Glasgow; pract. Whitby, Ottawa, Hastings; Northwood and England.

CLARKE, Charles Kirk

1857-1924 b. Elora, Ont.; grad. U. of T.; pract. Hamilton Asylum, Rockwood, Kingston, and Toronto General Hospital; supt. Toronto Asylum; dean — Faculty of Medicine, U. of T.; auth. *A History of the Toronto General Hosp.*

CLARKE, Daniel

1835-1912 b. Scotland; grad. Vic.; pract. Oxford County; surgeon U.S. Army of the North; med. supt. Toronto Asylum; Pres. Ont. Med. Council; auth. *Heredity, Worry and Intemperance; Mental Diseases; Pen Photographs of Celebrated Men and Noted Places; An Animated Molecule.*

CLARKE, Edward

-1856 b. Ireland; prac. Toronto; Resident physician & surgeon to T.G.H.

CLEMENT, Lewis
   b.   ; grad. Vic.; pract. Bradford.

COLLIP, James Bertram
   1892-1965 b. Belleville; grad. U. of T.; pract. Toronto; chairman Dept. of Biochemistry McGill; dean — Western; founding member Can. Physiological Society.

COMFORT, William Mingle
   1822-1899 b. Pelham; grad. Western Reserve, Ohio; pract. Fonthill, Ridgeville.

CONNELL, James Cameron
   1863-1947 b. Ayr, Ont.; grad. Queen's; pract. Kingston; prof. Eye, Ear, Nose and Throat; dean — Medical Faculty in Kingston.

CONNELL, Walter Thomas
   1873-1964 b. Spencerville; grad. Queen's; pract. Kingston; prof. of Pathology and Bacteriology in Kingston; founding member & vice-president CP&S; prof. of Medicine, Queen's (pathology & bacteriology).

CONNOR, James
   Circa. 1815; Surgeon's Hospital Mate Military Surgeon; U.E. List.

CORNISH, William K.
   Circa. 1840 b. England; grad.   ; pract. London; also a lawyer.

CORSON, John W.
   Grad. Victoria, 1857; pract. Brampton.

COVENTRY, John
   1836-1902 b. Scotland; grad. Buffalo Medical College & Vic.; pract. Windsor.

COVERNTON, Charles William
   1813-1901 b. England; grad. St. Andrews; pract. Simcoe & Toronto; pres. Council CP&S; OMA; memb. Provincial Board of Health; prof. Hygiene — Trin.

COVERNTON, Selby
   1854-1908 b.   ; grad. U. of T.; pract. Hamilton, Cambridge; lect. on Sanitary Science, Women's Medical College & Trin.; chief of staff of Medical Inspectors for the Ontario Government.

CRAIGIE, William
   1799-1863 b. Scotland; grad. Aberdeen; pract. Ancaster; educator, meteorologist.

CROFT, Lawrence Victor
    1877-1941 b. Middleville; grad. McGill; pract. Middleville, London; prof. of Chemistry, Tor. Sch. Med.

CULLEN, Thomas Stephen
    1868-1952 b. Bridgewater; grad. U. of T.; pract. Baltimore; prof. of Gynaecology, Johns Hopkins Hospital; auth. *Cancer of the Uterus — Adenomyoma of the Uterus — Myomata of the Uterus.*

DAVISON, Myers
    1839-1891 b. Nuberg; grad. Queen's; pract. Florence.

DEAZELEY, Thomas
    1826-1854 b. Ireland; grad. Dublin; pract. Grahamsville; prof. of Surgery Trin.

DEFRIES, Robert Davis
    1889-1955 b. Toronto; grad. U. of T.; pract. Toronto; dir. Connaught Laboratories; pres. Canadian Public Health Association; ed. *Canadian Public Health Journal* 1928-64; C.B.E.

DEIHL, Peter
    1787-1868 b. Quebec; grad. Edinburgh; pract. Montreal and York; member Royal Coll. of Surgeons, London, Eng.; member of Medical Board, York.

DICK, R.
    Circa 1840 b.   ; grad.   ; pract.   ; ed. *The Unfettered Canadian*, a journal of the Thomsonites in 1849.

DICKSON, John Robinson
    1819-1882 b. Ireland; grad. New York; pract. Kingston; founder Medical Dept. Queen's; pres. CP&S.

DIGBY, Alfred
    1806-1866 b. Ireland; grad. Dublin; pract. Brantford; Reeve.

DOUGLAS, John
    1788-1861 b.   ; grad.   ; pract. Upper Canada — Assist. Surg. 8th Regiment; auth. *Medical Topography of Upper Canada,* 1819.

DOWDING, John
    Circa 1800 b.   ; grad.   ; pract. Ancaster, Brantford & Dundas.

DRAKE, Theodore G.H.
    1892-1959 b. Webbwood; grad. U. of T.; pract. Toronto; Paed. at H.S.C.; Assist. prof. of Paed. U. of T.; headed research inst. H.S.C. One of three who devised baby "Pablum food".

DUNCOMBE, Charles
1792-1858 b. U.S.A.; grad. Med. Sch. City of New York; pract. St. Thomas, Sacramento, California; auth. *Report Upon The Subject of Education,* 1836; M.P. State Representative (California); memb. U.C.M.B.

DUNLOP, William
1792-1848 b. Scotland; pract. Galt; founder Mechanics Institute; M.P. Huron; editor & publisher; auth. *Statistical Sketches of Upper Canada.*

DURIE, William (Lucius O'Brien)
1779-1871 b. Scotland; grad. Edinburgh; pract. Toronto, Thornhill; memb. of U.C.M.B. reconstructed in 1838.

ECCLES, Friend Richard
1843-1924 b. Sarnia; grad. Tor. Sch. Med.; pract. London; authority on abdominal & gynecological surgery; dean — Faculty of Medicine Western, London.

EDMONSON, Robert
1802-1871 b. Ireland; grad. Glasgow; pract. Brockville; elder in the Presbyterian Church; pres. Bible Society.

ELLIOTT, Jabez Henry
1873-1942 b. Hampton; grad. U. of T.; pract. Toronto; pres. American Assoc. of History of Medicine; Academy of Medicine; American Climatological and Clinical Assoc.; Canadian Tuberculosis Assoc.; Est. the Muskoka Cottage Sanitorium.

FEASBY, William Richard
1915-1970 b. Listowel; grad. U. of T.; pract. Toronto; auth. *Medical Manual; Official History of the Canadian Medical Services;* co-author *The Story of Insulin;* ed. *Modern Medicine of Canada, Canadian Medical Directory.*

FENWICK, Thomas Makins
1844-1901 b. Kingston; grad. Queen's; pract. Kingston; staff of the Women's Medical College in Kingston.

FIFE, Joseph
Circa. 1867 b. Peterborough; grad. Victoria; pract. Hastings, Brampton & Peterborough.

FISHER, Andrew
1826-1898 b.   ; grad. Uni. of New York; pract. Amherstburg.

FITZGERALD, John G.
 1882-1940 b. Drayton; grad. U. of T.; pract. Buffalo; prof. Hygiene and Preventive Medicine; worked with Amyot in Connaught Laboratories; dean — Faculty of Medicine, U. of T.; auth. *An Introduction to The Practice of Preventive Medicine.*

FOOT, Jonathan
 1804-1885 b. U.S.; grad. Vermont; pract. Whitby.

FOOTE, Ezra
 -1875; pract. Aylmer.

FORD, Frederick Samuel Lampson
 1869-1944 b. Milton, N.S.; grad. Univ. of Maryland; pract. Toronto; assist. director of Medical Services, 1st Can. Div. (France & Belgium); mem. Acad. of Med.

FORSTER, James Moffatt
 1864-1941 b. Brittania; grad. Tor. Sch. Med.; pract. Toronto, Whitby and Brockville; supt. Ont. Hospital Brockville, Toronto, and Whitby; assistant to C.K. Clarke & R.M. Bucke.

FOTHERINGHAM, John Taylor
 1860-1940 b. Kirkton; grad. Trin.; pract. Toronto; Org. a Medical Reserve Corps before World War I; pres. Acad. of Med.; mem. CMA.

FOWLER, Fife
 1823-1903 b. Scotland; grad. Edinburgh; pract. Kingston & Queen's; pres. Ont. Med. Council; dean — Faculty of Medicine, Queen's.

FRASER, John
 1806-1882 b. Scotland; grad. Glasgow; pract. Niagara.

FRASER, John Martin
 1836-1891 b. London, Ontario; grad. Queen's; pract. London; prof. of Medicine, Western, London; member R.C.S., England; dean — Fac. of Western, 1888.

FULTON, James
 1851-1909 b. England; grad. Trin.; pract. St. Thomas; chairman — Board of Health, St. Thomas.

FULTON, John
 1836-1885 b. Elgin County; grad. U. of T. 1855 (Rolph); pract. Toronto; prof. Physiology (Rolph); Trin.; ed. *Canada Lancet*; auth. *A Manual of Physiology — A Textbook of Physiology.*

GALLIE, William Edward
 1882-1959 b. Barrie; grad. U. of T.; pract. Toronto; prof. Surgery; dean — Faculty of Med. U. of T.

GAMBLE, John
> 1755-1811 b. Ireland; grad. Edinburgh; pract. Kingston; asst. surgeon to the Queen's Rangers.

GEIKIE, Walter Bayne
> 1830-1917 b. Scotland; grad. Tor. Sch. Med. and Jefferson Coll, Pa.; pract. Toronto, Bondhead & Aurora; prof. Materia Medica and Therapeutics-Medical Faculty Vic.; dean — the second Trinity College; member, Acad. of Med.

GIBSON, Robert James
> 1866-1919 b. Guelph; grad. McGill; pract. Sault Ste Marie; Had first x-ray in Northern Ontario; pres. Ont. Medical Council.

GILCHRIST, James Eikin
> -1871 b. U.S.A.; grad. Dartmouth; pract. Cobourg.

GILCHRIST, John
> 1792-1859 b. U.S.; grad. Dartmouth; pract. Otonabee, Peterborough; M.P. for Colborne district; active in founding of Victoria College.

GILCHRIST, Mathew
> - b. U.S.; grad. Dartmouth; pract. Colborne; M.P.P. for Northumberland.

GILCHRIST, Samuel
> -1849 b. U.S.A.; grad. Dartmouth; pract. Port Hope.

GILMOR, William R.
> 1838-1872 b. Three Rivers; grad. Trin.; pract. Penetanguishene.

GILPIN, William
> 1858-1929 b. Barrie; grad. Victoria; pract. Brechin for 48 years; Medical Officer to Rama Reserve.

GOODHUE, Josiah Cosmore
> Circa 1840; grad. U.S.A.; pract. London and St. Thomas.

GORDON, Andrew
> 1863-1917 b. Glengarry; grad. U. of T.; pract. Toronto; Prof. Clinical Medicine (Tor.); Fellow of the Academy of Medicine (Tor.).

GRAHAM, John Rolph
> b. Garafraxa; grad. Tor. Sch. Med. Rolph's School; pract. Tillsonburg.

GRANT, James Alexander (Sir)
> 1831-1920 b. Scotland; grad. McGill; pract. Ottawa; pres. CMA, St. Andrews Society; Mechanics Institute; M.P. for Ottawa.

GRASETT, George Robert
1811-1847 b. Portugal; grad.   ; pract. Amherstburg and Toronto; Health Officer; Med. Supt. Emigrant Hospital, 1847; died of typhus.

GRAY, Jennie Wildman
-1953 b. Dundas; grad. Trin.; pract. Barrie; In charge of the first clinic for women in Toronto, 1898.

GRAY, Thomas
1872-1930 b. Clinton; grad. Western; pract. St. Thomas.

GROSS, Pitkin
1791-1873 b. England; grad. Hanover; pract. Brighton.

GROVES, Abraham
1791-1873 b. Fergus; grad. Tor. Sch. Med.; pract. Fergus; 1883 using a kitchen table in a farmhouse at Fergus performed the "first" appendectomy in North America; auth. *All in the Day's Work — Stray Thoughts.*

GUNN, Robert John
1815-1900 b. Scotland; grad. Edinburgh; pract. Whitby; mayor Whitby.

GURIA, Williams
1779-1871 b. Scotland; grad. Edinburgh; pract. Thornhill; memb. U.C. Medical Board.

GUTHRIE, Anselm
Circa. 1820; pract. Clearville.

GUTHRIE, Robert
Circa. 1800; grad.   ; pract.   ; Surgeon; Butlers Rangers.

GWYN, Norman
1875-1952 b. Dundas; grad. U. of T.; pract. Toronto.

GWYNNE, William Charles
1806-1875 b. Ireland; grad. Trin.; pract. Kingston and York; prof. of Anatomy & Physiology at Kings Coll. (1843); memb. CP&S's of Upper Canada and U.C.M.B.

HALLIWELL, William
1814-1873 b. Quebec; grad. Edinburgh; pract. Kingston and Toronto; co-founder of the U.C. School of Medicine, 1850.

HAMILTON, James
1797-1887 b. Scotland; grad. Edinburgh; pract. Montreal, Ancaster; memb. Medical Board; M.P.

HAMILTON, Joseph
   1798-1847 b. Niagara; grad. Edinburgh; pract. Queenston and Toronto; memb. U.C.M.B.

HAMILTON, Robert D.
   1783-1857 b. Scotland; grad. Edinburgh; pract. Scarborough; auth. *Canadian Literary Magazine; Currier Harold — British Colomnist; Principles of Medicine on the Plan of Baconian Philosophy* (1882); Memb. U.C.M.B.

HANSON, Henry
   1823-1885 b. England; grad. Rolph's School; pract. St. Thomas, London.

HARRIS, William T.
   1852-1896 b.   ; grad.   ; pract. Brantford; memb. CP&S, Ont.; Pres. Ontario Medical Council (1895).

HARVEY, William
   Circa. 1800; Garrison surgeon at Fort Malden & Amherstburg.

HASKINS, James
   1805-1846 b. Ireland; grad. Dublin; pract. Belleville, Trenton, Frankford; auth. *The Practical Works of James Haskins.*

HASTINGS, Charles John
   1858-1931 b. Markham; grad. Dublin; pract. Toronto; Medical Officer of Health (Tor.); Stressed the importance of preventive medicine and pasteurization.

HENRY, Thomas
   -1878 b. Ireland; grad. Edinburgh; pract. Sandhill and Toronto.

HENRY, Walter
   1791-1874 b. Ireland; grad. London; pract. Kingston & Ottawa; auth. *Trifles from the Portfolio of a Staff Surgeon, Events of a Military Life.*

HENWOOD, Edwin
   1819-1882 b. England; grad.   ; pract. Hamilton; U.C.M.B.; apothecary at Toronto General.

HERRICK, George
   1789-1856 b. Ireland; grad. Dublin; pract. York; memb. U.C. Medical Board.

HILLARY, James Jager
   1831-1885 b. Ireland; grad. Dublin; pract. Uxbridge.

HILLARY, Michael

1840-1884 b. Ireland; grad. Dublin; pract. Stouffville; surgeon U.S. Army Civil War.

HILLARY, Robert William

1833-1894 b. Ireland; grad. Dublin; pract. King Township and Aurora; memb. Med. Council 1872-75.

HODDER, Edward Mulberry

1810-1878 b. England; grad. Paris, Edinburgh, London, King's; pract. Kingston, Toronto: dean — Trin.; pres. U.C.M.B.; pres. CMA; founder — Royal Canadian Yacht Club; auth. *The Harbours and Ports of Lake Ontario.*

HODGETTS, Charles Alfred

1860-1952 b. Toronto; grad. Queen's; pract. Ottawa & Toronto; First Medical Inspector Board of Health (Ont.); founder Can. Red Cross Society; charter memb. St. Johns Ambulance Assoc.; pioneer public health field.

HOME, Robert

1890-1917 b. Toronto; grad. U. of T.; pract. Toronto; memb. Acad. of Med.

HORNBY, Robert

1813-1869 b. England; grad. Edinburgh; pract. Cleveland, Toronto; memb. U.C.M.B.

HORNE, Robert Charles

1880-1945 b. England; grad.   ; pract.   ; Military Surgeon; Printer to His Most Excellent Majesty; ed. Official Gazette; chief teller Bank of U.C.

HUME, Rowenna

1877-1966 b. Galt; grad. O.W.M.C.; pract. Toronto; founder Women's College Hospital, Tor.; memb. C.M.A., O.M.A., Life fellow Acad. of Medicine.

HUNTER, James

1790-1850 b. England; grad. Fairfax Medical College; pract. Niagara & Whitby.

HUTCHISON, John

1797-1847 b. Scotland; grad. Glasgow; pract. Cavan and Monaghan and then Peterborough; 1818 settled at Port Hope; died of typhus.

HYDE, John

1816-1878 b. Stratford; grad. Glasgow; pract. Stratford; memb. Med. Council (1869-75).

JOHNSTON, Robert James
1832-   b. Ireland; grad. Trin.; pract. Thorold.

JONES, Ernest
1879-1958 b. England; grad. Univ. Coll. Hosp.; pract. Toronto; Freud's disciple; Medical Director of the out-patient clinic at the Toronto General; auth. *S. Freud Life and Work, Free Association, Memoirs of a Psychoanalyst;* co-editor with C.K. Clarke *Bulletin of the Ontario Hospital for the Insane.*

JONES, Guy Carleton (Sir)
1864-1928 b. Halifax, N.S.; grad. London; pract. Ottawa; M.R.C.S. 1906 Dir. General of Medical Services.

JONES, Herbert
1874-1917 b. Hamilton; grad.   ; pract. Hamilton; fellow of The Academy of Med., Toronto.

JONES, Solomon
1756-1822 b. U.S.A.; grad. Albany; pract. Brockville; Surgeon's Mate Loyal Rangers; M.P.

JUKES, Augustus
1821-1905 b. Bombay; grad. Trin. (1865); pract. St. Catharines; pres. Med. Assoc. St. Catharines.

KAISER, Thomas E.
1863-1940 b. Edgely; grad. U. of T.; pract. Oshawa; auth. *Historic Sketches of Oshawa — A History of the Medical Profession of the County of Ontario;* M.P.P.

KELLY, John
Circa. 1890 b.   ; pract. The Sault.

KERR, Robert
1755-1824 b. Scotland; grad.   ; pract. Niagara; Principal of Surrogate Court, called the "Boxing Magistrate".

KERR, William
Circa. 1872 b. Scotland; grad. Glasgow; pract. Galt.

KERR, William
1859-1940 b. Galt; grad. Dublin; pract. Cayuga, Dunnville, and Toronto.

KING, John
1806-1857 b. Ireland; grad. Trin. and Dublin; pract. Quebec & York; Chairman — Board of Health.

KING, Richard S.
1817-1885 b. Ireland; grad. Ireland; pract. Stonebridge.

KINGSTON, J.J.
 1845-1915 b. Coburg; grad. Vic.; pract. Aylmer and Vienna.

KIRKLAND, Archibald
 1845-1905 b. Scotland; grad. Vic.; pract. Collingwood, Duntroon, Co. Simcoe.

KNIGHT, Archibald (Patterson)
 1849-1935 b. Renfrew; grad. Vic.; pract. Kingston; auth. *Hygiene for Young People — The Ontario Public School Hygiene — Introducing Physiology and Hygiene.*

LAMBERT, Walter
 Circa. 1868 b. Niagara; grad. Trin.; pract. Amherstburg.

LANCASTER, Joseph J.
 1813-1884 b. Oxford County; grad. U.C.M.B.; pract. London, Norwich.

LANDER, A.
 Circa. 1867; pract. Brockville.

LANGSTAFF, James
 1825-1889 b. Thornhill; grad. Guys Hospital, Rolph's School; pract. Unionville, Richmond Hill.

LATHAM,
 Circa. 1800; surgeon to the King's Regiment of Foot; skilled in the new procedure of smallpox inoculation.

LAVELL, M.
 1825-   b. Quebec; grad. Queen's; pract. Kingston; dean of Royal Medical College of Kingston; pres. of CP&S, Ont. (1874-75); fellow, R.C.P.S., Kingston; memb. Medical Council, 1866-75; surgeon, Kingston Hospital.

LEE, Hiram David
 1791-1847 b. Connecticutt; grad. Rolph's School, St. Thomas's; pract. Southwold; Government Medical Officer for London 1833.

LEE, William
 1763-1833 b.   ; grad.   ; pract. Home District; Surgeon's Mate to the 49th Regiment; App. to the Indian Dept.; moved to York in 1807; Gentleman Usher of the Black Rod to the Legislative Council; secretary of the U.C.M.B.

LEITCH, Archibald
 1846-1925 b. Elain Co.; grad. Trin.; pract. St. Catharines, St. Thomas; secretary of the St. Thomas Medical Assoc.

LEMESURIER, A.B.

1889-   b. India; grad. U. of T.; pract. Toronto; surgeon-in-Chief, Hosp. for Sick Children; auth. *Hare Lips & Their Treatment.*

LOW, George Humphry

1790-1865 b. Ireland; grad. Trin. College; pract. Whitby, Bowmanville & Darlington.

LYND, Ida

1857-1943 b. Bondhead; grad. O.W.M.C.; pract. Toronto; in charge of the first clinic for women in Toronto 1898.

LYONS, William

1780-1834 b.   ; grad. Edinburgh; pract. York; Military Surgeon, War of 1812; memb. Medical Board.

MACALLUM, Archibald B.

1859-1934 b. Belmont; grad. U. of T.; pract. Toronto; prof. of Physiology, U. of T.; Chairman of the Honorary Advisory Council for Scientific and Industrial Research; First Prof. of Biochemistry in Canada.

MACCALLUM, George

1843-1947 b. Toronto; grad. Vic.; pract. Whitevale and Dunnville; Lect. psychiatry, Western.

MACAULAY, James

1759-1822 b. Scotland; Surgeon — Queen's Rangers; Inspector General of Hospitals.

MACDONALD, James

1803-1849 b. U.S.A.; grad. New York; pract. New York City.

MACDONALD, John D.

1819-1901 b. Scotland; grad. Vic.; pract. Hamilton; pres. Ontario Med. Council; pres. OMA; memb. Provincial Board of Health.

MACK, Theophilus

1820-1881 b. Ireland; grad. Geneva College, U.S.A.; pract. St. Catharines; founded a spa at Springbank in London; founder — the St. Catharines Marine and General Hospital; established the first training school for nurses in Ontario.

MACKELCAN, George L.

1835-1909 b. Guelph; grad. McGill; pract. Hamilton; co-founder of the OMA.

MACKENZIE, A.K.

Circa. 1837; pract. Hamilton; Patriot physician.

MACMURCHY, Helen
1862-1953 b. Toronto; grad. O.W.M.C.; pract. Toronto; auth. *The Almosts, a study of the feeble-minded — Sterilization? Birth Control?;* C.B.E.; Life Fellow of the Acad. of Med., Tor.

MALLOCH, William John Ogilvie
1872-1919 b. Clinton; grad. U. of T.; pract. England, Toronto; Fellow of the Acad. of Med., Tor.

MANION, R.J.
1881-1943 b. Toronto; grad. Trin.; pract. Fort William; Minister of Railways & Canals for Canada; auth. *Surgeon in Arms — Life is an Adventure.* National Leader of Conservatives.

MARLOW, Frederick William
1877-1936 b. Port Perry; grad. Trin.; pract. Toronto; Pioneer gynecologist and radiotherapist; pres. OMA.

MCCAMMON, James
1833-1885 b. Addington; grad. Queen's; pract. Toronto, Montreal; memb. of Ontario Council; mayor of Kingston.

MCCRAE, John
1872-1917 b. Guelph; grad. U. of T.; pract. Montreal; auth. *In Flanders Fields; A Textbook of Pathology for Students of Medicine;* co-author with John George Adam; memb. Royal Coll. of Physicians, London Assoc. of American Physicians.

MCDERMOT, James
1845-1920 b. Bond Head; grad. Vic.; pract. Sunderland.

MCGILL, William
1806-1883 b. Scotland; grad. McGill; pract. Oshawa; helped establish the Ontario College of Pharmacy; M.L.A.

MCGILLIVARY, Charles F.
1857-1945 b. Audley; grad. U. of T.; pract. Whitby.

MCINNIS, Thomas Robert
1840-1904 b. Nova Scotia; grad. Chicago Rush Med. School; pract. Dresden, Vancouver; Lieut.-Governor, British Columbia; mayor of Ingersoll.

MCKAY, Angus
1852-1916 b. Oxford County; grad. Trin.; pract. Ingersoll.

MCKENZIE, Andrew
1810-1901 b. Quebec; grad. Glasgow; pract. St. Thomas, London.

MCKEOWN, Walter P.

1866-1925 b. Toronto; grad. Trin.; pract. Toronto; medical service Riel Rebellion; chief surgeon in St. Michael's Hospital; pres. Acad. of Med. (Tor.).

MACLEAN, Donald

1839-1903 b. Seymour; grad. Edinburgh; pract. Kingston; staff memb. of the Royal College; ed. — American edition of *Syme's Surgery.* fellow — Royal Coll. of Surg., Edinburgh; pres. of American Medical Association (1894).

MCQUEEN, Thomas Fraser

1805-1860 b. Edwardsburg; grad. Glasgow; pract. Ottawa, Cornwall and Brockville.

MEADE, Letitia K. (Sirrs)

1857-1943 b. Haltonville; grad. O.W.M.C.; pract. Haltonville.

MELVILLE, Henry

1816-1868 b. Barbados; grad. Edinburgh; pract. Niagara, Toronto; founder — U.C. School of Medicine.

MITCHELL, James

1793-1861 b. London; grad. Rolph's School; pract. North Cayuga.

MONTGOMERY, John W.

1827-   b. Newtonbrook; grad. Rolph's School; pract. Sutton; supt. Insane Asylum, Hamilton.

MOORE, Charles Greenwood

1817-1886 b. London, England; grad. McGill; pract. London; first dean of the Faculty of Medicine at Western.

MOORE, Charles S.

1852-1923 b. London; grad. McGill; pract. London; memb. of the Faculty of Medicine, Western; prof. Obstetrics & Diseases of Women and Children.

MOORE, George

Circa. 1840 b. Ireland; pract. London and Toronto.

MOORE, Vincent Howard

1848-1904 b. Brockville; grad. Queen's; pract. Brockville; pres. of CP&S (1889-90); memb. of Medical Council.

MOORHOUSE, Walter Hoare

1842-1921 b. Tyrconnel; grad. Trin.; pract. London; dean — Faculty of Medicine at Western; pres. C.M.A.

MORDEN, John Howell
Circa. 1860 b.   ; grad. Queen's; pract. Brockville.

MORRISON, Thomas Davis
1796-1856 b. Quebec City; grad. U.C.M.B.; pract. York; M.P.; mayor of Toronto, 1836.

MUIRHEAD, James
1765-1834 b. Scotland; grad.   ; pract. Newark; prisoner of war 1812; surgeon general 1822; Surgeon's Mate, 64th Reg't.

MULLIN, John A.
1835-1899 b. U.S.A.; grad. Vic.; pract. Toronto and Hamilton.

MUTTLEBURY, James
-1832 b. England; grad.   ; pract. York; died — cholera epidemic 1832.

NASMITH, George Gallie
1877-   b. Toronto; grad. U. of T.; pract. Toronto; auth. *Canada's Sons and Great Britain During the Great War, Timothy Eaton, Smith's of a Better Quality;* advised Use of first preventative gas mask, later adopted by British Army.

NEISH, James
1834-1908 b. England; grad. Roy. Coll. of Physicians; pract. Kingston; publisher *The Canadian Medical Times,* published in Kingston for the first half of 1873; memb. CP&S.

NEVITT, Richard Burrington
1850-1928 b. U.S.A.; grad. Trin.; pract. Toronto; surgeon — North West Mounted Police; dean — Women's Medical College (Tor.).

NICOL, William Bulmer
1812-1886 b. England; grad. London; pract. Bowmanville; prof. Materia Medica, King's.

NIVEN, James
1847-1916 b. Ireland; grad. Trin., Dublin; pract. London; memb. of Faculty of Medicine at Western, London; chief of staff of London General (Victoria) Hospital.

NOBLE, Robert Thomas
1870-1958 b. Norval; grad. U. of T.; pract. Brampton and Toronto; pres. of O.M.A. & C.M.A.; pres. of Tor. Acad. of Med.; pres. CP&S; pres. Medical Council of Canada; registrar, treasurer of CP&S.

OGDEN, Uzziel
1827-1909 b. Toronto Township; grad. Tor. Sch. Med. (Rolph) and Vic.; pract. Toronto; prof. Gynecology, U. of T.; ed. *Canadian Practitioner.*

OGDEN, William W.
1837-1915 b. Toronto; grad. Vic.; prac. Toronto; prof., Forensic Medicine.

OLDRIGHT, William
1842-1917 b. West Indies; grad. U. of T.; pract. Toronto; prof. Hygiene Tor. Sch. Med.; Influential in establishing the new Museum of Hygiene in the U. of T., 1896; memb. Ontario Medical Council.

OLIVER, Alfred Sales
1845-1900 b.   ; grad. Queen's; pract. Kingston; memb. the staff of the Women's Medical College in Kingston.

O'REILLY, Gerald
1806-1861 b. Ireland; grad. Dublin; pract. Hamilton, St. Catharines, Brantford and Oakville.

ORONHYATEKHA,
1847-1901 b. Brantford; grad. Tor. Sch. Med., Oxford; pract. Frankfort and Stratford; Supreme Chief I.O.O.F.; Right Worthy Grand Templar.

ORTON, G.T.
1837-1901 b. England; grad. Univ. of St. Andrews; pract. Guelph and Fergus; memb. Royal Coll. Surgeons, Eng.; M.P.; Chief Medical Officer in C.P.R. (1884-5).

OSLER, William (Sir)
1849-1919 b. Bondhead; grad. McGill; pract. Montreal; prof. Clinical Medicine, Uni. of Philadelphia; prof. of Medicine, Johns Hopkins Uni. of Baltimore; Regius Prof. Medicine, Oxford; auth. *Principles and Practice of Medicine; The System of Medicine; Science and Immortality; Equanimitas and Other Addresses; Councils and Ideals; Thomas Linacre; An Alabama Student; A Way of Life; The Student Life and Other Essays.*

PARKE, George
1826-1849 b.   ; grad.   ; pract. Simcoe and Ancaster; supt. Toronto Lunatic Asylum; lect. Tor. Sch. Med.

PARKER, Thomas Sutherland
1829-1868 b.   ; grad. U.S.A.; pract. Guelph; Legislated a General Council of Medical Education and Registration in U.C. in 1866; M.L.A.

PEMWARDEN, John M.
1844-1892 b. Elgin County; grad. Vic.; pract. Fingal and St. Thomas.

PETERS, George Armstrong
1859-1907 b. Fergus; grad. U. of T.; pract. Toronto; prof. Surgery, U. of T.; Lt. Col. Toronto Light Horse.

PHILBRICK, Cornelius J.
1816-1885 b. London; grad. London, Dublin, Edinburgh; pract. Yorkville; prof. of the Principles and Practice of Surgery; fellow — Royal Coll. Surg., Eng.; prof. — Trinity Coll.

POOLE, Thomas W.
1831-1905 b.   ; grad. Vic.; pract. Norwood and Peterborough; Mayor of Lindsay; ed. *Peterborough Weekly Review;* auth. *A Sketch of the Early Settlement and Progress of the Town of Peterborough — Physiological Therapeutics.*

POWELL, Grant
1779-1838 b. England; grad. Guy's Hospital and Apothecary's Hall; pract. York; Judge — Home District Court; Clerk — Legislative Council; memb. U.C. Medical Board; founder — York General Hospital.

PRESTON, R.H.
1840-1927 b. Smiths Falls; grad. Queen's; pract. Newborne, M.P.P.

PRIMROSE, Alexander
1861-1944 b. Nova Scotia; grad. Edinburgh; pract. Toronto; prof. Anatomy, Clinical Surgery U. of T.; dean — Faculty of Medicine; pres. Pathological Society; Toronto Medical Society; American Surgical Assoc.; CMA.

RAE, John
1813-1893 b. Scotland; grad. Edinburgh; pract. N. Ontario & Canada; Explorer and Surveyor.

REAUME, Joseph Octave
1865-1933 b. Essex County; grad. Trin.; pract. Windsor; M.L.A.; Minister of Public Works.

REES, William
1801-1874 b. England; grad.   ; pract. Toronto; first Supt. of Provincial Lunatic Asylum; founder Toronto Club.

REEVE, Richard Andrews
1842-1919 b. Toronto; grad. Queen's; pract. Kingston; pres. Tor. Acad. of Med.; C.M.A.; prof. of Chemistry, R.C.P.&S., Kingston.

REID, John B.
    -1931 b. Orangeville; grad. Trin.; pract. Tillsonburg.

RICHARDS, Gordon
    1885-1949 b. Toronto; grad. U. of T.; pract. Toronto; fellow — Royal
    Coll. Phys. & Surg.; head — Ont. Inst. of Radiotherapy, Tor. Gen.
    Hos.; prof. Radiotherapy, U. of T.; hon. memb. Royal Soc. of Med.;
    set up first high voltage x-ray treatment machine in Canada, early
    1920's.

RICHARDSON, James W.
    1823-1909 b. Presqu'Isle; grad. King's; pract. Toronto; prof.
    Anatomy, U. of T., Tor. Sch. Med.; pres. OMA.

RICHARDSON, Robert
    -        b. Scotland; pract. Niagara; stationed in York in 1794; Fort
    Malden 1802; Military Surgeon.

RICHARDSON, Samuel R.
    1842-1919 b. Toronto; grad. Vic.; prac. Toronto; memb. CP&S, Ont.;
    Prof. of Diseases of the Mind, Vic.

RIDLEY, George Neville
    1794-1857 b. England; grad. Guy's and St. Thomas's; pract. Kingston
    and Cobourg.

ROBERTSON, David E.
    1884-1944 b. Milton; grad. U. of T.; pract. Toronto; Surgeon-in-
    Chief, Hosp. for Sick Children.

ROBERTSON, Lawrence Bruce
    1885-1923 b. Toronto; grad. U. of T.; pract.   ; pioneer in blood
    replacement for burn patients.

ROLPH, John
    1793-1870 b. England; grad. St. John's College, Cambridge; pract.
    York; dean — Tor. Sch.; Vic. — Faculty of Medicine; est. a medical
    school at St. Thomas; memb. U.C. Medical Board; M.P.

ROLPH, John Widmer
    Circa. 1860; b.   ; grad. Vic.; pract. Kuanton, Pelang.

ROLPH, Thomas
    1768-1814 b. England; grad. London; pract. Ancaster; Immigration
    Agent for Government of Canada; auth. *Statistical Account of Upper
    Canada — Emigrating and Colonization.*

ROSEBRUGH, Abner Mulholland

1835-1914 b. Galt; grad. Vic.; pract. Toronto; Inventor of many electrical devices; founder of the Toronto Eye and Ear Dispensary; auth. *An Introduction to the Study of Optical Defects of the Eye,* 1866; *Chloroform and a New Way of Administering It,* 1869; *A Handbook of Medical Electricity,* 1885; *Recent Advances in Electro-Therapeutics,* 1887.

ROSS, Alexander Milton

1832-1897 b. Belleville; grad. N.Y.; pract. Toronto; founder — The Soc. for the Diffusion of Physiological Knowledge; auth. *The Truth About Vaccination — Memories of a Reformer; Memorial of Fifty Years in the Life of A.M. Ross — Letters of Marshall S. Bidwell; The Birds of Canada; The Butterflies of Canada.*

ROSS, Arthur E.

1871-1953 b. Cobden; grad. Queen's; pract. Toronto; M.P.; Ontario Health Minister.

ROUTLEY, Clarence

1889-1963 b. Lindsay; grad. U. of T.; pract. Toronto; hon. pres. C.M.A.; auth. *History of the Ontario Medical Association;* founding memb. World Med. Assoc.; man. ed. Can. Med. Assoc. Jour.

ROWNTREE, Leonard C.

1883-1959 b. London; grad. U.W.O.; pract. Mayo Clinic, Philadelphia, Institute for Medical Research and Uni. of Miami.

RUDOLF, R.

1865-1941 b. Picton, Nova Scotia; grad. Edinburgh; pract. Toronto; auth. *Notes on Medical Treatment of Diseases;* fellow — R.C.P.&S.; F.R.C.P. (C) of London, Eng.; Emeritus Prof. of Therapeutics U. of T.

RUSSELL, Francis M.

1825-1860 b. Dublin; grad. Edinburgh; pract. Toronto; lect. Medical Jurisprudence, Trin.

RUSSELL, Peter

1733-1800 b.   ; grad. Cambridge; pract. York.

RYERSON, George Ansel Sterling

1855-1925 b. Toronto; grad. Trin.; pract. Toronto; prof. Eye, Ear, Throat at Trin.; founder Canadian Red Cross; founder St. John Ambulance; pres. United Empire Loyalist Assoc.; auth. *Looking Backward,* 1924; M.P.P.

SAMPSON, James
1790-1861 b. Ireland; grad. Trin., Dublin; pract. Kingston; pres. Faculty of Medicine in Kingston; Mayor 1839-40-44; founder — Kingston General Hospital.

SAUNDERS, Herbert J.
1847-1896 b. England; grad. Queen's; pract. Kingston; prof. Clinical Med.

SCHOFIELD, James
1753-1828 b. U.S.A.; grad.   ; pract. Upper Canada.

SCHOFIELD, Peter
1790-1860 b. U.S.A.; grad. New York; pract. Brockville.

SCHULTZ, John (Sir)
1841-1896 b. Amherstburg; grad. Queen's; pract. Winnipeg; Sailor, fur trader; taken prisoner during Red River Rebellion and escaped; Senator; M.P.

SCOTT, Wallace Arthur
1873-1949 b. Ottawa; grad. U. of T.; pract. Toronto; F.R.C.S. (England); prof. U. of T.

SCOTT, William James
1792-1875 b.   ; grad. Dublin; pract. Prescott; Army Medical Staff; physician North-West Company.

SHEARD, Charles
1856-1929 b. Toronto; grad. Trin.; pract. Toronto; prof. Trin.; pres. CMA; M.P.; memb. City Council; Health Officer of Tor. (1893-1911); examiner Can. Branch of Royal Sanitary Instit.; Vice-Pres., prof. Prev. Med. U. of T.

SHILLINGTON, Adam Tozeland
1870-   b. Prospect (Co. Lanark); grad. McGill; pract. Ottawa.

SHUTTLEWORTH, Edward Buckingham
1842-1934 b. England; grad. Trin.; pract. Toronto; first prof. Pharmacy; dean Ontario College of Pharmacy; founder — Canadian Pharmaceutical Soc.; ed. *Canadian Pharmaceutical Journal.*

SMITH, H.R.
1890-1919 b. Leamington; grad. Vic.; pract. Toronto; fellow of the Acad. of Med. of Tor. Worked Re-educational staff at Hart House with soldiers to recover use of limbs.

SMITH-SHORTT, Elizabeth
1859-1949 b. Winona; grad. Queen's; pract. Kingston; a founding memb. of the Victorian Order of Nurses, The Women's Canadian Club, The Ontario Council of Women, Ontario Mother's Allowance Board.

SMYTHE, George
Circa. 1800; pract. Albany; Surgeon, Loyal Rangers.

SPARHAM, Eric Benzel
Circa. 1865; grad. McGill; pract. Brockville.

SPARHAM
Circa. 1812; Hospital Mate Reduced.

STARR, Clarence Leslie
1868-1928 b. Newmarket; grad. U. of T.; pract. Toronto; first prof. of Surgery at U. of T.

STEVENSON, John A.
1851-1883 b. Niagara; grad. McGill; pract. London; Prof. of Therapeutics and Toxicology, Western, London.

STEWART, Alex
1855-1911 b. Palmerston; grad. Vic.; pract. Palmerston. By 1885 had established the Ontario Vaccine Farm to produce good quality smallpox vaccine.

STEWART, James
-1848 b. Ireland; grad. Dublin; pract. By-Town; Surgeon's Mate.

STEWART, John
1811-1891 b. Scotland; grad. Edinburgh; pract. Kingston; dean — Royal CP&S, Kingston; ed. *The Argus.*

STIMSON, Elam
1792-1869 b. U.S.A.; grad. Med. Institute of Yale; pract. London; auth. *The Cholera Beacon.*

STOWE, Ann Augusta (married name: Gullen)
1857-1943 b. Norwich, Oxford County; grad. Vic.; pract. Toronto; daughter of Dr. Emily Stowe; prof. Dis. of Children; OMAC.

STOWE, Emily
1831-1903 b. Norwich; grad. New York; pract. Toronto Medical College and Hospital for Women; founder of the Toronto Women's Library Club, 1877; Canadian Suffrage Assoc. memb.; CP&S (1880).

STOVELL, Thomas
　　1761-1832 b. U.S.A.; grad.　　　　; pract. York.

STRATFORD, Samuel John
　　1798-1868 b. England; grad. St. George's and Westminster Hospital;
　　pract. Woodstock and York; prof. Trin.; ed. *Upper Canada Journal
　　of Medical, Surgical and Physical Sciences.*

SULLIVAN, Henry
　　1805-1850 b. Ireland; grad. Dublin; pract. Toronto; memb. CP&S of
　　Upper Canada; memb. Med. Board; prof. Practical Anatomy, U. of
　　King's Coll.; surgeon, Royal Forestors.

SULLIVAN, Michael
　　Circa. 1880; b.　　　　; grad. Queen's; pract. Kingston; fellow —
　　Royal Coll. Phys. & Surgeons, Kingston; memb. the staff of the
　　Women's Medical College, Kingston; prof. Anatomy, R.C.P.&S.;
　　memb. of Medical Council, Co. Frontenac.

SUMNER, Cyrus
　　1772-1846 b. U.S.A.; grad.　　　　; pract. Clinton, Grimsby; served
　　with General Brock at Detroit.

SUTTON, Arthur
　　1882-1958 b. U.S.A.; grad. U. of T.; pract. Port Credit; Coroner for the
　　County of Peel.

TELFORD, Walter
　　　-1857 b. Scotland; grad. Edinburgh; pract. Niagara, Toronto;
　　supt. Lunatic Asylum; memb. U.C.M.B.

TEMPEST, William
　　1819-1871 b. England; grad. U. of T.; pract. Toronto; M.O.H.
　　Toronto; auth. *The Abortive Treatments of Cholera;* memb. R.C. of
　　Surgeons (Eng.); L.R.C.P. (London); fellow — R.C.P. (Canada).

THOM, Alexander
　　　-1845 b.　　　　; grad. Aberdeen; pract. Perth; Staff Surgeon to
　　General Brock.

THORBURNE, James
　　1830-1905 b. Queenston; grad. Tor. Med. Sch.; pract. Toronto; pres.
　　C.M.A.; pres. Ontario Medical Council; auth. *Manual of Life
　　Insurance Examinations.*

TIMS, John E.
　　　-1839 b. Ireland; grad.　　　　; pract. Toronto; alderman.

TISDALL, Frederick
    1893-1949 b. Clinton; grad. U. of T.; pract. Toronto; prof. of
    Paediatrics of U. of T.; auth. *The Home Care of the Infant Child —
    Your Food and Health in the North;* Physician & Director of
    Research Lab., Dept. of Paediatrics, Hosp. for Sick Children.

TODD, James Harvey
    1883-1918 b. Georgetown; grad. Tor. Sch. Med.; pract. Toronto;
    fellow of the Academy of Medicine of Toronto; Charge, x-ray dept.
    Duchess Connaught, Red Cross Hosp.

TROUT, Jennie Gowanlock
    1841-1921 b. Scotland; grad. Tor. Sch. Med.; pract. Pennsylvania; the
    first licensed female practitioner in Canada, 1875; est. the
    Therapeutic and Electrical Institute in Toronto.

TUCKER, David
    -1871 b. Ireland; grad. Trin. Coll. Dublin; pract. Pickering
    (1853-1871).

TUZER, Charles
    -1861 b. Aylmer; grad. U. of T.; pract. Kent County.

WADE, William
    1863-1896 b. Cobourg; grad. Trin.; pract. Parry Sound.

WAFER, Francis Moses
    1831-1876 b.   ; grad. Queen-s; pract. Kingston.

WAUGH, William Ebenezer
    1891-1936 b. London, Ont.; grad. McGill; pract. London; founding
    memb. of the Faculty of Medicine at Western; sec. Board of
    Governors, Western.

WEIR, William
    1834-1882 b. Merrickville; grad.   ; pract. Merrickville.

WHITE, J.E.
    1848-1894 b. Beaverton; grad. U. of T.; pract. Toronto; founder
    OMA.

WIDMER, Christopher
    1780-1858 b. England; grad. Guy's and St. Thomas's; pract. York;
    founding memb. Upper Canada Medical Board; pres. U. of T.; dir.
    Bank of U.C.; founding memb. of the Toronto General Hospital;
    chairman of the Board of Trustees of the Toronto Hosp.; M.P.

WILSON, John T.

    Circa. 1837; pract. Sparta; Patriot physician.

WISHART, John
-1926 b. Guelph; grad. Trin.; pract. London; prof. Clinical Surgery, Western University, London.

WOOLVERTON, Jonathan
1811-1862 b. Grimsby; grad. Philadelphia; pract. Grimsby; Surgeon of 4th Regiment Lincoln (1839).

WORKMAN, Joseph
1805-1894 b. Ireland; grad. McGill, 1835; pract. Toronto; prof. Midwifery Tor. Sch. Med.; supt. Toronto Lunatic Asylum; pres. CMA.

WORTHINGTON, Edward
1820-1895 b. Ireland; grad. St. Andrew; pract. Sherbrooke; claimed to have performed first capital operation under ether in Canada.

WRIGHT, Adam
1846-1930 b. Georgetown; grad. Rolph's School; pract. Colborne and Toronto; prof. Obstetrics and Diseases of Women and Children, Tor. Sch. Med. and Tor. Women's College Hosp.; auth. *A Textbook of Obstetrics.*

WRIGHT, B.
1816-1882 b. Prince Edward County; grad.   ; pract. Dundas, Markham, and Toronto; pres. CP&S; chairman — Public School Board, Tor. Exiled during 1837 Rebellion.

WRIGHT, Henry Hover
1816-1899 b. Prince Edward County; grad. Rolph's School; pract. York, Dundas, and Markham; prof. Medicine Rolph's School; Medical Dept. U. of T.; memb. Council of CP&S.

WRIGHT, Thomas
Circa. 1812; Surgeon, 1st Batallion.

YATES, Horatio
1821-1873 b. U.S.A.; grad. Uni. of Philadelphia, London; pract. Kingston; faculty memb. Kingston; supt. Lunatic Asylum near Liverpool.

YELLOWLESS, N.J.I.
1886-1916 b. Toronto; grad. U. of T.; pract. Toronto; fellow of the Acad. of Med. Toronto.

INDEX

A

abortion 87, 88, 89

Adamson, Dr. Joseph 31

advertising 191-92, 224, 225, 226, 227-28, 229

ague 27, 28, 149, 200

Aikins, James C. 94, 195

Aikins, Dr. William Thomas 25, 50, 57, 62, 63, 73, 74, 75, 76, 77, 78, 81, 94, 95, 99, 101, 164, 173, 204, 208, 220

alcohol 22, 28, 68, 91-3, 191, 231

"Alien Question" 35

Allison, William 30, 31, 32

allopaths 18, 192, 193, 194, 197, 198, 221

American Civil War 232

American invasion of Canada, 1838 44-5

American Revolution 11, 12, 13

amputation 22, 86, 222, 238

Amyot, Major J.A. 242

anatomy 51, 52, 58, 212

Anglican church (Church of England) 19, 25, 35, 36, 40, 49, 53, 55, 59, 60, 61, 209, 213

Anthony, Dr. George 27

antitoxin 161, 205-06

apothecaries 199

appendectomy 180

Army Hospital Corps 232

army medical school 232

Arnott, Henry 213

Arthur, Sir George 46

Ashton, Colonel E.C. 240

Association of Medical Officers of the Canadian Militia 234

Ault, Dr. H.T. 160

B

Babtie, Surgeon General Sir William 240, 241, 242

Badgley, Dr. F. 56, 60, 61

Bagot, Governor General Sir Charles 47, 48

Baldwin, Robert 39, 41, 46, 151

Baldwin, William Warren 15, 69

Baldwin Act, 1849 53, 59

Ball, Dr. Jerrald 201

Banting, Dr. 250

Barrett, Dr. Michael 25, 73, 74, 77, 188-89

Barry, Dr. James (Miranda) 86-7

Beattie, Miss 189

Beaumont, Dr. Charles 52

Beaumont, Dr. William R. 48, 75, 76, 77, 78, 85, 101

Beck, Adam 214, 215

Bell, Dr. 61

Bell, James 233

Belleville 29, 30, 65, 97, 179, 200

Bergin, Dr. Derby 233

Berryman, Dr. C.B. 95, 96, 101

Bessey, Dr. William E. 225

Best, Dr. 250

Beswick, Dr. Christopher 17

Bethune, John G. 85

Bethune, Dr. Norman (Sr.) 56, 60, 61, 63, 64, 65, 85

Bethune, Dr. Norman 247

Billings, W.C. 177

Bingham, Dr. George 247

biological buildings 168-72, 216

biology 216, 217

Blake, Dr. T.G.H. 250

bleeding 23, 24, 61-2, 67, 68, 71, 98, 99, 152, 193

blood transfusions 247
Boer War 234, 238
Bond Head, Sir Francis 40, 41, 44
Borden, Sir Frederick 234, 235
Bovell, Dr. James 25, 50, 56, 60, 61, 62, 63, 65, 76, 77, 80, 93, 101, 152, 153, 179, 207, 209
Bowman, J. 216
Boys, Dr. Henry 54
Brant, Chief Joseph 13, 14
Bright, Dr. James Cook 224
"Brockville Abortion Case" 87-9
Bromley, Dr. Edward 248
Brouse, Dr. J.E. 88
Brown, Dr. Alan 250
Brown, George 53, 54, 55, 80
Browse, William Henry 67
Bruce, Inspector General Dr. Herbert A. 203-04, 205, 235, 236, 237, 238-39, 240-42, 247
Bruce, William 44
Bryce, Dr. Peter 185, 202
Buchanan, Dr. George 84
Bucke, Richard Morris 213, 215
Bull, Edward 67
Burdett, Dr. David 65
Burgess, Thomas J.W. 213
Burnham, Sofia 87, 88
Burns, David 14
Burnside Hospital 164

C
Caledonia Springs 176
calomel 22-3, 68, 91, 152
Cameron, Dr. I.H. 216, 225, 247
Campbell, Dr. C.T. 194, 197, 226
Campbell, Dr. D. 193
Canada First Party 105
Canada Lancet 86, 147, 153, 205
Canada Medical Act, 1912 248
Canada Medical Journal 85, 86
Canadian Army Medical Corps 234, 235, 237, 238, 239, 241, 242

Canadian Medical Association (C.M.A.) 90, 101, 106, 107, 157, 182, 248
Canadian Pharmaceutical Society 102
cancer 249
Canniff, Dr. William 19, 20, 25, 30, 49, 68, 90, 96, 97, 99, 101, 102, 103, 104, 105-06, 145, 157, 161, 162, 202, 232, 233, 248
Caron, Hon. Adolph 233
Carsaw, Dr. G.A. 191
Cathcart, Dr. James 151
Cavan, John 233
charcoal powders 24, 66
Charity Act, 1874 184
Chisholm, Dr. Archibald 27
chloroform, 86, 87, 179
cholera 28, 29, 43, 51, 71, 149-52, 153, 154, 193
Christie, Dr. Alexander James 28, 84
Christie, William 172
Christoe, Dr. W.S. 84
Church University 59, 60, 64, 65
cinchona 22, 66, 147, 192
Clark, Dr. Daniel 206
Clark, Dr. E. 64
Clark, Dr. R. Whichelo 30, 78, 79, 84
Clarke, Dr. Charles 184
Clergy Reserves 35, 40, 49
Colborne, Sir John 25, 26, 36, 38, 40, 151
College of Physicians and Surgeons of Ontario 46, 47, 161, 166, 186, 187, 196-97, 198, 220, 221-26, 228, 229, 230
College prosecutor 224, 225, 228, 230
Collip, Dr. 250
Comfort, Dr. William 143-45, 148
Connell, Dr. James C. 249
Connell, Dr. Walter T. 249
contraception 145

Cornish, William J. 27
Coventry, Dr. John 244
Covernton, Dr. Charles W. 85, 90, 91, 161
Covernton, Dr. Theodore Selby 161
cowpox 19
Croft, Professor H. 48, 53, 77
Crouse, Dr. J. 32
Cullen, Dr. Thomas 246
Cullen, William 23

D

Davison, Dr. Myers 31
Deazley, Dr. Thomas 51
Diehl, Peter 39, 46
Department of Health and Mortuary Statistics 161
Dick, Dr. R. 85
Dickon, Dr. John R. 209, 211
Digby, Dr. Alfred 69
diphtheria 84, 160, 202, 205, 206
Discipline Committee of College of Physicians 224, 225, 226, 228, 229-30
dissection 51, 52, 71, 180, 187, 212
Dixon, John 79, 80, 85
Dominion Medical Journal 86
Douglas, Surgeon Major Campbell 233
Dowding, Dr. John 69, 70
druggists 199, 200
duels 68, 69, 70
Duncombe, Dr. Charles 32, 34, 43, 44, 48, 70, 248
Duncombe, Dr. Charles (nephew) 248
Dunlop, Dr. William 32, 91, 231
Durie, Lucius O'Brien 46

E

Eastwood, Dr. 74
Eccles, F.R. 216
eclectics 18, 22, 103, 189, 190, 191, 192, 196, 197, 198, 221, 230

Edmonson, Dr. Robert 67-8
education system 44, 50, 59, 91, 206
Elder, Colonel J.M. 240
electricity 195, 200, 225
Elliot, Dr. Jabez H. 157, 184
ether 48, 86, 179
examinations 216, 217, 220, 221, 222-23

F

Family Compact 19, 40, 41, 44
Feasby, Dr. William F. 242
fees 197, 202-03
female physicians 186-90
Fenian raids 232
Fever Hospital 46
Fife, Dr. Joseph 191
Finwick, Dr. Thomas N. 189
Fisher, Dr. A. 62
Fitzgerald, Dr. John G. 246
Flexner, Abraham 249
Foot, Jonathan 18
Foote, Dr. Ezra 160
Fotheringham, Dr. John T. 234, 240, 241, 247
Fowler, Dr. Fife 210, 211
Fraser, John M. 213, 215
Friendly Botanic Society 21, 22
Fulton, Dr. James 161
Fulton, Dr. John 85

G

Gallie, Dr. W.E. 247
Gamble, Dr. John 13
Gamble, William 13
Geikie, Dr. Walter Bayne 25, 37, 56, 81, 96, 97, 101, 102, 163, 165, 166, 167, 168, 169, 170, 171, 172, 188, 216, 217, 218, 219, 229
General Council of Medical Education and Registration in Upper Canada 195
Gibson, Dr. Robert James 248

Gilbert, Dr. 32
Gilchrist, Dr. John 29, 67
Gilmon, Dr. W.P. 65
Goodhue, Dr. 32
Gourlay, Robert 16, 21
government 12, 13, 15, 16, 17, 18, 25,
    31, 62, 165, 167, 168, 170, 171, 172,
    173, 216, 248, 249
Graham, John Rolph 67
Grant, Principal George 188, 212,
    213
Grant, Dr. James Alexander 67
Grant, Dr. J.N. 229
Gray, Dr. Jennie 189
Gray, Dr. Thomas L. 248
Gross, Dr. Pitkin 17
Groves, Dr. Abraham 180
Grow, George 32
Gullen, Harriet Stowe 105
Guthrie, Dr. Anselm 31
Gwyn, Dr. Norman 37
Gwynne, Dr. William C. 46, 48, 51,
    53, 54

H

Halliwell, Dr. 56
Hallowell, Dr. W. 60, 61, 65
Hamilton 45, 93, 149, 151, 175, 247
Hamilton, James 46
Hamilton, Joseph 46
Hamilton, Robert D. 46
Hamilton City Hospital 177
Hansen, Henry 69
Harby, Dr. William 27
Haskins, Dr. James 30
Hastings, Dr. Charles J. 157, 205-07
Henry, Dr. Thomas 45
Henry, Dr. Walter 24, 28-9
Herrick, Dr. G. 48, 76, 77
Herring, Dr. Constantine 193
Hincks, Hon. Francis 57, 58, 77
Hincks Act 58, 62, 63, 75
Hind, Dr. Henry Y. 61

Hodder, Dr. Edward M. 25, 55, 60,
    61, 62, 65, 75, 76, 77, 79, 85, 95,
    152, 153, 163
Hodgetts, Dr. Charles A. 201, 202
Holmes, Dr. Oliver Wendell 193,
    208
homeopaths 18, 103, 176, 192-95,
    196, 197, 198, 208, 221, 230
Hornby, Dr. R. 223
Horne, Dr. Robert C. 15, 46
Hospital for Sick Children 177,
    178, 179
hospitals 10, 174, 175, 176-79, 181,
    184, 185, 250
Hospitals and Charitable Institu-
    tion Act, 1912 185
Hotel Dieu, Montreal 70
Hughes, Sir Sam 235, 236, 237, 238,
    239, 240
Hume, Dr. Rowena 189
Hunter, Dr. James 23, 45
Hunter Lodges 45
Hutchison, Dr. John 66-7
Hyde, Dr. John 204, 205
hydropathy 176, 177
hygiene 161, 179, 180

I

Indian Mutiny 231
Indians 13, 14, 15, 31, 157, 230
"In Flanders Fields" 243
inoculation 14
insanity 52, 70, 158, 159, 181-82,
    250-51
Inspector General's Report 236-37,
    238, 239, 242
intravenous milk 152, 153
Isolation Hospital 205

J

Jenner, Edward 19
Jones, Surgeon General Dr. G.
    Carleton 234, 235, 236, 237, 239,
    240, 241, 242

Jones, Dr. Solomon 28
Johnston, Dr. R.J. 65

K

Kaiser, Dr. T.E. 30-1
Kelly, Dr. John 248
Kermott, Dr. J.W. 72
Kerr, Dr. Robert 11, 14, 174
King, John 39, 46, 48
King, Captain R.S. 232
King's College 25, 26, 35-7, 38, 46, 47, 48, 50-3, 54, 55, 58, 59, 80, 175
Kingston 13, 15, 25, 28, 29, 149, 150, 151, 152, 154, 175, 177, 188, 189, 209, 210, 224, 225, 229, 247, 249
Kingston General Hospital 29, 175, 177, 213
Kingston Penitentiary 44
Knight, Dr. A.P. 187, 188, 189

L

Lambert, Sir Walter 145-46
Lancaster, Dr. Joseph L. 193, 194, 195
Langstaff, James 73
laudanum 23
Laurier, Sir Wilfrid 31
Lavell, Dr. M. 62, 187, 188, 189, 229
L'Ecole de Médecine et de Chirurgie de Montreal 99, 105
Lee, Hiram David 34
Lee, William 15
legislation 16-17, 18, 51, 53, 90, 216, 217, 218 (see also individual Acts)
Leitch, Dr. Archibald 84
Lemesurier, Dr. A.B. 247
Lemon, Dr. Benjamin Heaton 224, 225-26
licensing 10, 16, 17-18, 46, 166, 186, 193, 195, 196, 198, 220, 221, 223, 248
Liddell, Hart 209
"lodge practice" 204

London 27, 32, 34, 45, 92, 149, 152, 153, 175, 176, 200, 226, 228, 247, 249
Loudon, William 58, 172
Lount, Samuel 42
Low, George 18
lunatic asylums 52, 70, 181-82
Lynd, Dr. Ida 189
Lyons, Dr. William 17, 24

M

Macallum, A. Bruce 246
Macallum, Dr. Archibald Byron 245
Macara, John 53
MacAulay, James 13, 14, 24
MacAulay, Chief Justice John W. 45
MacAulay Town 13
MacCallum, Dr. J.B. 246
MacCallum, Dr. W.G. 246
MacDonald, Dr. J.D. 90
Macdonald, Dr. James 70
Macdonald, Sir John A. 25, 54, 63, 167, 209, 211
MacDonald, Dr. R. Ian 9
MacFarlane, Dr. A.J. 10
Machar, Rev. Dr. 210
Mack, Dr. Theophilus 176
MacKellcan, Dr. G.L. 90
Mackenzie, Dr. Andrew 45
Mackenzie, Major J.J. 236
Mackenzie, William Lyon 19, 39, 41, 42, 43, 44
Macklem, Rev. T.C.S. 218, 219
Mack's Hospital 179
MacMurchy, Dr. Helen 189
MacPhail, Sir Andrew 236, 242
Maitland, Sir Peregrine 29, 35, 36
malaria 31
Manion, Dr. R.J. 238
Marlow, Dr. Frederick William 249, 250
McCammon, Dr. James 229

McCaul, Dr. John 48, 52, 54
McCrae, Dr. John 242-43
McCullough, Dr. John Robert 226
McCully, Dr. Samuel Edward 227-28, 229
McEown, Dr. John 224
McGill, Dr. William 30, 198, 199
McGillivary, Dr. Charles F. 244-45
McInnis, Dr. Thomas Robert 31
McKay, Dr. Angus 216
McKellar, Peter 32
McKeown, Dr. Walter 236
McLean, Dr. Donald 212
McQueen, T.F. 28
measles 147, 160
Medical Act of Upper Canada, 1865 220, 223, 229
Medical Alumni Association of Victoria College 191, 192
Medical Defence Union 93
medical education 10, 11, 12, 15, 24, 25, 33, 34-7, 38, 46-7, 48, 50-1, 54, 55, 61, 62, 73-4, 94-106, 163-73, 169, 205, 209-19, 220-23, 244-45, 250
medical journals 85, 144, 145
medical practice 9, 15, 16, 17, 22, 27-32, 66-72, 191
Medical Register 224, 225, 226, 227, 229, 230
medical research 246, 247, 249, 250
medical schools 10, 12, 18, 19, 24-25, 34, 35-7, 46, 47, 48, 50-2, 73-82, 94-106, 163-73, 209-19, 220, 230, 245, 246
medical societies 32
medical students 50, 51, 52, 61, 67, 73, 74, 76, 80, 98, 99, 100, 143, 165, 187, 214
Melville, Dr. H. 56, 60
mental hospitals 182, 183, 184
mercury 23, 24, 147
Meredith, Sir William 216
Methodist church, 14, 49
microscopic observation of tissues 62
midwifery 16, 17, 18, 23, 84, 89, 203
military hospitals 235, 236, 237, 238, 239, 242
military medical service 231-43

military surgeons 11, 12, 13, 14, 27, 28, 68, 231, 232
Mitchel, Dr. James 42
Montgomery, John W. 67
Montreal General Hospital 70
Moodie, Susanna 30
Moore, Dr. Charles J. 213, 215
Moore, Charles S. 213
Moore, George 27
Moore, Dr. Vincent Howard 88
Morden, Dr. 88, 89
morphine 200, 249
Morrison, Dr. Thomas 43, 44, 56, 73
Muirhead, Dr. James 11, 14, 17
Mullin, Dr. J.A. 90
Mulock, Sir William 165, 168, 169, 171, 172, 201
Museum of Hygiene 161
Muskoka Cottage Sanatarium 157, 184
Muskoka Free Hospital for Consumptives 184
Muttlebury, Dr. James 151

N

Naismith, George C. 235, 242
National Research Council 245
Neilson, Colonel J.L.H. 234
Neish, Dr. James 85
Nelles, Mr. 101, 102, 103, 104
Nelson, Dr. Wolfred 45
Nevitt, Dr. R.B. 86, 189
New Guide to Health: or Botanic Family Physician 21, 22
Niagara-on-the-Lake (Newark) 11, 12, 15
Nichol's Hospital 179
Nicol, Professor 48
Niven, James 213
Nobel, Dr. Robert 244
Normal School 50
Northwest Rebellion 232, 233, 234
nurses 179

O

Odgen, Uzziel 85
Ogden, Dr. E.A. 85
Ogden, Dr. W.W. 51, 146-47

Oldright, Professor William 161
Oliver, Dr. Alfred S. 189, 232
Ontario College of Pharmacy 102, 199, 215
Ontario Hospital Association 185
Ontario Medical Act, 1869 186, 195, 196, 197, 198
Ontario Medical Association (O.M.A.) 90, 204, 205, 206, 207, 244, 249, 250
opium 26, 66, 91, 147, 200, 249
O'Reilly, Dr. Gerald 68, 177
Orton, Dr. G.T. 233
Oronhyatekha, Dr. 204
Oshawa 30, 31, 195
Osler, Sir William 163-64, 177, 207, 208, 221, 237, 246, 249
Ottawa (Bytown) 27, 28, 84, 149, 156, 175, 178, 199, 224, 229, 247

P

Park, Dr. George 73
Park Hospital 167
pasteurization 157
patent medicines 200, 201
Pearson, Lester B. 236
pediatric medicine 250
Pemwarden, Dr. J.M. 89
Perley, Sir George 240, 241
Peters, Dr. George Armstrong 247
pharmacy 198-201, 206, 215
Pharmacy Act, 1871 199, 200
Philbrick, Dr. Cornelius James 61
Plater, Dr. Edward 201
pneumonia 66, 68, 86, 160
politics — involvement of doctors 14, 15, 16, 18, 34, 35, 40, 41, 43, 44, 57, 67, 216
Poole, Dr. 96
postmortems 86, 88, 89
Post Office Act amendment 201
Poulett, Governor General Charles 47
Powell, Dr. Grant 17, 24, 49

"Practitioner" 195
Presbyterian church 25, 35, 68, 80, 209
Primrose, Dr. Alexander 216, 247
Proprietary and Patent Medicine Act 201
Provincial Act, 1839 46, 47
Provincial Asylum 182, 183
Provincial Board of Health 202
puerperal fever 248

Q

quackery 16, 18, 19, 20, 21, 22, 24, 72, 200, 201, 206, 220, 227, 228, 229, 230
Queen's Rangers 13, 14
Queen's University 77, 94, 187, 209, 210, 212, 213, 216; Faculty of Medicine 80, 209, 210, 211, 212-13, 232, 249

R

railways 202
Rankin, Dr. John Edward 28
Rattot, Dr. J.P. 248
Reade, Dr. G.H. 29
Rebellion of 1837-38 39, 41-5, 67, 84, 193, 248
Rees, Dr. William 182
Reformers 41, 43, 44, 45
regulation of medical practice 220, 223-30, 250
Reid, Dr. John 95, 97, 98
rheumatism 147, 176, 200, 222
Richards, Dr. Gordon 249
Richardson, James H. 52, 58
Richardson, Dr. J.W. 91, 101
Richardson, Professor 163
Richardson, Robert 27
Richardson, S.R. 102, 105
Rideau Canal 27-8
Ridley, George Neville 46
Robertson, Dr. Bruce 247
Robertson, Dr. D.E. 247

Rockwood Asylum 183
Rolph, Grace (née Haines) 73, 97
Rolph, Dr. John 25, 33-5, 37, 39, 40-4, 48, 55, 56, 57, 58, 61, 63, 67, 73, 74, 76, 77, 78, 79, 80, 81, 85, 94, 95, 96, 97, 98, 99, 101, 102, 151, 169, 170, 202, 208, 234
Rolph, Dr. John Widmer 101-02
Rolph, Dr. Thomas 68
Roseburgh, Dr. Abner 191
Ross, Dr. Alexander 158, 159, 160, 167, 172
Ross, Colonel A.E. 240
Rowntree, Dr. L.E. 246
Royal College of Physicians and Surgeons of Ontario 211, 212
Royal College of Surgeons 17, 18, 47, 198
Royal Medical College of Kingston 187
Rudolf, Dr. R.D. 205
Russell, Dr. Francis M. 61, 65, 74
Russell, Hon. Peter 14
Ryerson, Egerton 44, 49-50, 53, 234
Ryerson, Dr. George Sterling 234

S

Samaritan Hospital 74
Sampson, Dr. James 29, 152, 153, 209, 210, 211
sanatarium 184, 185
Sangster, Mr. 97
sanitation 155, 156, 157
sassafras 68
Saunders, Dr. J.J. 189
Saunders, W. 215-16
scarlatina 71, 72, 147, 160
Scarlett, Dr. E.P. 248
Schofield, James 28
Schofield, Dr. Peter 28, 92
scientific medicine 86, 143, 160, 164, 166, 168, 205, 216, 245, 246, 250
Scott, Dr. W.J. 30

Scott, Dr. Wallace 236
self-abuse 158-59, 250-51
Sheard, Dr. C. 219
Shortt, Elizabeth (née Smith) 187, 188, 190
Shumate, Dr. 69
Shuttleworth, E.B. 102, 148, 199
Simcoe, Governor John Graves 12, 14
Sims, Dr. 31
smallpox 14, 19, 22, 88, 147, 149, 157-58, 159, 160, 161, 168, 250
Soudan Campaign 234
Sovereen, Albert William 229-30
spa movement 176, 177
Sparham, Dr. Eric Benzel 87, 88, 89
specialists 206, 244
Starr, Dr. Clarence L. 247
state medicine 250
Stephenson, John A. 213
Stevenson, J.A. 216
Stewart, Dr. Alex 158
Stewart, James 28
Stewart, Dr. John 209, 210, 211
Stimson, Dr. Elam 27, 32, 150
Stowe, Dr. Augusta 187, 189, 190
Stowe, Dr. Emily Howard Jennings 186, 187, 189, 190
Stoyel, Thomas 14
Strachan, Bishop John 19-20, 25, 26, 35, 36, 40, 41, 48, 49, 53, 54, 55, 59, 60, 78, 151, 163, 175, 209
Stratford, Dr. Samuel John 46, 85
Strychnine Act, 1840 198
Sullivan, Prof. Henry 48
Sullivan, Dr. M. 189, 210, 212
"Summerhill" 211
Sumner, Dr. Cyrus 23, 27
Sunnybrook Hospital 9
Sutton, Dr. Arthur 248

T

Telfer, Dr. 76, 77
Telford, Walter 46

temperance 91, 92

Tempest, William 232

textbooks 221

Theller, Dr. Edward 45

Therapeutic and Electrical Institute 195

Thom, Dr. Alexander 68

Thomson, Samuel 20, 21, 22, 23, 192

Thomsonians 20-2, 23, 85, 176, 192, 230

Thornburn, James 90

Thorburn, Dr. 232

Tims, Dr. John A. 43

Tisdall, Dr. Fredrick 250

Tissot, Dr. S.A. 158, 159

tissue transplants 247

Toronto (York) 12-13, 14, 15, 26, 28, 31, 35, 36, 40, 41, 43, 45, 48, 49, 62, 65, 73, 77, 80, 149, 150, 151, 152, 154, 156, 157, 174, 175, 199, 203, 209, 210, 230, 233, 247, 248, 249

Toronto Chemists and Druggists Association 199

Toronto General Hospital 36, 37, 49, 51, 52, 57, 60, 62, 64, 74, 75, 76, 78, 86, 95, 99, 100-01, 102, 105, 175, 177-78, 179, 183, 184, 232, 247, 249

Toronto Hospital for Tuberculosis 185

Toronto Lunatic Asylum 44, 52

Toronto Orthopaedic Hospital 181

Toronto School of Medicine 50, 55, 56-7, 63, 65, 73-82, 95, 99, 100, 105, 164, 166, 167-68, 186, 189, 190, 207, 208, 232

Toronto Western Hospital 181

Toronto Women's Medical College 189, 190

Tozer, Dr. Charles 31

Trait, Dr. Lawson 216

treatments 14, 15, 17, 19, 20, 21, 22, 23, 24, 50, 66, 68, 69, 71, 78, 83-9, 98-9, 145, 146, 147, 148, 150, 152, 153, 154, 195, 204, 247, 248

Trinity College 50, 51, 63, 64, 65, 75, 76, 161, 163, 207, 209, 216, 217, 218

Trinity College, Faculty of Medicine 60, 61, 62, 63, 64, 65, 77, 79, 80, 163-64, 165, 166, 167, 168, 170, 216, 218-19, 227

Trout, Dr. Jennie Gowanlock 186, 187, 188, 189, 190, 195

Trudel, E.H. 99

Trull, Jessy 83, 84

tuberculosis 157, 159, 184, 185, 237

typhoid 146, 147, 154, 155, 156, 208

typhus 46, 67, 147, 154

U

United Empire Loyalists 11, 12, 19, 28

"University Question" 50

University of Toronto 55, 56, 57, 58, 59, 64, 65, 74, 75, 76, 161, 164, 165, 166, 167, 168, 169, 171, 172, 207, 216, 217, 218, 219, 245, 246

University of Toronto, Faculty of Medicine 50, 55, 56, 57, 61, 62, 63, 80, 217, 218, 219

University of Western Ontario 213, 214, 215

University of Western Ontario, Faculty of Medicine 213, 214, 216, 246, 249

unlicensed physicians 18, 20, 21, 31, 32, 83, 223, 224, 230

Upper Canada College 26, 36

Upper Canada Journal of Medicine Surgical and Physical Science 85

Upper Canada Medical Board 13, 15, 16, 17, 18, 24, 29, 31, 37, 38, 39, 46, 47, 48, 49, 52, 55, 57, 71, 75, 95, 156, 196, 220, 223

Upper Canada Medical Board examinations 16, 17, 18, 37, 38

Upper Canada Medical School 50, 56, 59, 60

V

vaccination 157-58, 159, 160
variolation 14, 19, 149
Victoria College 49, 76, 77, 79, 81, 82, 94-106, 186, 191, 216
Victoria Hospital 214, 215
Victorian Order of Nurses 190, 206
Voluntary Aid Hospitals 237, 238, 240

W

Wade, Dr. William R. 192, 202
Wafer, Dr. Francis Moses 232
Washington, Dr. Nelson 224, 225
Waugh, William 213
Weir, Dr. William 88
Wellesley Hospital 235, 247
White, Dr. J.E. 90
Widmer, Dr. Christopher 17, 24, 37, 39, 46, 49, 52, 75, 78, 152, 175, 231
Wilson, Sir Daniel 169, 170, 172
Wilson, Dr. F.W.A. 236
Wilson, Dr. John 44, 45
Wishart, Dr. John 189, 213
Women's College Hospital 190
Women's School of Medicine at Kingston 188, 189, 190
Wooder, Dr. 76
Woodstock Hospital for Epileptic Patients 249
Woolverton, Dr. John 71-2
Workman, Dr. Joseph 56, 58, 73, 74, 77, 90, 182, 248
World War One 235-43, 244, 247
Wright, Dr. Henry H. 42, 43, 56, 73, 76, 77, 95, 96, 99, 105, 171, 172

Y

Yates, Dr. Horatio 198, 209, 210, 211

Z

zinc 23, 24, 66